OLIVE PRODUCTION MANUAL

Second Edition

....

Technical Editors

G. STEVEN SIBBETT
LOUISE FERGUSON

Assistant Editors

JOANN L. COVIELLO
MARGARET LINDSTRAND

University of California
Agriculture and Natural Resources
Publication 3353
2005

To order or obtain ANR publications and other products, visit the ANR Communication Services online catalog at http://anrcatalog.ucanr.edu/ or phone 1-800-994-8849. Direct inquiries to

University of California
Agriculture and Natural Resources
Communication Services
2801 Second Street
Davis, CA 95618
Telephone 1-800-994-8849
E-mail: anrcatalog@ucanr.edu

Publication 3353

ISBN-13: 978-1-879906-14-3

Printed in Canada.

Library of Congress Control Number: 94-60033

UC PEER REVIEWED ✓ This publication has been anonymously peer reviewed for technical accuracy by University of California scientists and other qualified professionals. This review process was managed by ANR Associate Editors for Pomology, Viticulture, and Subtropical Horticulture, and for Pest Management.

Cover photographs by Jack Kelley Clark.
Olives courtesy of the California Olive Committee and Musco Family Olive Company.

PRECAUTIONS FOR USING PESTICIDES

Pesticides are poisonous and must be used with caution. READ THE LABEL CAREFULLY BEFORE OPENING A PESTICIDE CONTAINER. Follow all label precautions and directions, including requirements for protective equipment. Use a pesticide only on crops specified on the label. Apply pesticides at the rates specified on the label or at lower rates if suggested in this publication. In California, all agricultural uses of pesticides must be reported. Contact your county agricultural commissioner for details. Laws, regulations, and information concerning pesticides change frequently, so be sure the publication you are using is up to date.

Legal Responsibility. The user is legally responsible for any damage due to misuse of pesticides. Responsibility extends to effects caused by drift, runoff, or residues.

Transportation. Do not ship or carry pesticides together with foods or feeds in a way that allows contamination of the edible items. Never transport pesticides in a closed passenger vehicle or in a closed cab.

Storage. Keep pesticides in original containers until used. Store them in a locked cabinet, building, or fenced area where they are not accessible to children, unauthorized persons, pets, or livestock. DO NOT store pesticides with foods, feeds, fertilizers, or other materials that may become contaminated by the pesticides.

Container Disposal. Dispose of empty containers carefully. Never reuse them. Make sure empty containers are not accessible to children or animals. Never dispose of containers where they may contaminate water supplies or natural waterways. Consult your county agricultural commissioner for correct procedures for handling and disposal of large quantities of empty containers.

Protection of Nonpest Animals and Plants. Many pesticides are toxic to useful or desirable animals, including honey bees, natural enemies, fish, domestic animals, and birds. Crops and other plants may also be damaged by misapplied pesticides. Take precautions to protect nonpest species from direct exposure to pesticides and from contamination due to drift, runoff, or residues. Certain rodenticides may pose a special hazard to animals that eat poisoned rodents.

Posting Treated Fields. For some materials, reentry intervals are established to protect field workers. Keep workers out of the field for the required time after application and, when required by regulations, post the treated areas with signs indicating the safe reentry date.

Harvest Intervals. Some materials or rates cannot be used in certain crops within a specific time before harvest. Follow pesticide label instructions and allow the required time between application and harvest.

Permit Requirements. Many pesticides require a permit from the county agricultural commissioner before possession or use. When such materials are recommended in this publication, they are marked with an asterisk (*).

Processed Crops. Some processors will not accept a crop treated with certain chemicals. If your crop is going to a processor, be sure to check with the processor before applying a pesticide.

Crop Injury. Certain chemicals may cause injury to crops (phytotoxicity) under certain conditions. Always consult the label for limitations. Before applying any pesticide, take into account the stage of plant development, the soil type and condition, the temperature, moisture, and wind direction. Injury may also result from the use of incompatible materials.

Personal Safety. Follow label directions carefully. Avoid splashing, spilling, leaks, spray drift, and contamination of clothing. NEVER eat, smoke, drink, or chew while using pesticides. Provide for emergency medical care IN ADVANCE as required by regulation.

1.5m-pr-10/19-GHM/AS/VFG/CR/WS

Contents

1

History and Scope of the Olive Industry

JOSEPH H. CONNELL

ORIGIN AND HISTORY

The olive tree, *Olea europaea* L., valued for both its beauty and its fruit, has been a part of Mediterranean civilization since before recorded history. As early as 3000 B.C., Semitic peoples in Syria cultivated the olive and traded in its oil. Numerous biblical references to the olive, its cultivation, and use of its oil date it from 2000 B.C. Semitic influence spread olive cultivation northward into what is now Turkey and south into Egypt.

Three to four thousand years ago the Egyptians traded in olive oil and cured olives. Their dead were adorned with olive branches and preserved in part with olive oil. Cured olives were left in the tombs of the Pharaohs for food in the afterlife. From Egypt, olive culture spread west through North Africa to southern Spain.

The Minoan people came to ancient Crete from North Africa. Archeological excavations at the Palace of Knossos just outside Heraklion, Crete, revealed large pottery vessels (amphora) used to store wine and olive oil. Clay tablets documenting trade in olive oil dating from 1700 B.C. were also found. The Minoans were probably responsible for the spread of olive culture to the early Greeks and Romans. Around 900 B.C., Homer in the *Odyssey* referred frequently to the olive. In the fifth century B.C., Herodotus described Athens as a vast center of Greek olive culture. Olive oil was a profitable export of that time, as was the technology associated with olive culture and curing.

By the beginning of the fifth century B.C., the Romans were becoming familiar with the uses of olive products and with olive cultivation. They are credited with inventing the screw press method of extracting olive oil. Cato described several quality grades and uses for the oil in Roman society. The Roman methods for producing oil remained unchanged for the next two millennia, until the advent of the modern centrifuge. At the fall of the Roman Empire, olives were cultivated throughout the Mediterranean basin, and olive products were a principal item of commerce in the Middle East, North Africa, and as far west as Spain and Morocco.

Figure 1.1. Mission San Diego de Alcalá.

From the late Renaissance through the colonial period of the European powers, explorers and colonists brought olives to the New World. In 1560, olive cuttings were carried to Peru by Spanish explorers. In the early 1700s, Jesuits established missions in Mexico and Baja California; olives were among the few fruits that were grown in those early mission settlements. Franciscan padres journeying north from Mexico founded their first California mission at San Diego in 1769 (fig. 1.1). Olives were soon produced there, but not until a century later did a commercial industry become well established in California.

DISTRIBUTION AND PRODUCTION

In the Mediterranean basin, olive trees were thoroughly distributed by the Romans and later by the Arabs. Today, most of the world's olives are still produced in the Mediterranean region (table 1.1). The olive tree is best suited to areas with a Mediterranean climate: a long, hot growing season and a relatively cool winter with minimum temperatures above a lethal limit. The trees do not usually survive below about 10°F (–12°C), and most cultivars are injured at 15°F (–9°C). Commercial, olive-producing areas of the world are found between 30° and 45° north and south latitudes.

1

Table 1.1. Total oil and table olive production in the leading olive producing countries of the world.

Country	Oil production (1,000 tons)			Table olive production (1,000 tons)		
	2000–01	2001–02*	2-yr avg. world %	2000–01	2001–02*	2-yr avg. world %
Algeria	26.5	15.5	0.80	33.5	47.0	2.91
Argentina	4.0	10.0	0.27	30.0	47.0	2.78
Cyprus	5.5	6.5	0.23	8.5	9.5	0.65
Egypt	—	—	—	70.0	135.0	7.41
France	3.2	3.5	0.13	1.8	1.8	0.13
Greece	430.0	360.0	15.04	85.0	85.0	6.14
Israel	7.0	3.5	0.20	19.5	10.5	1.08
Italy	509.0	562.0	20.38	65.0	70.0	4.88
Jordan	27.0	15.0	0.80	24.0	13.0	1.34
Lebanon	6.0	5.0	0.21	7.0	5.5	0.45
Libya	4.0	7.0	0.21	2.5	2.5	0.18
Morocco	35.0	60.0	1.81	80.0	90.0	6.14
Palestine	20.0	18.0	0.72	8.0	7.0	0.54
Portugal	24.6	40.5	1.24	8.7	10.0	0.68
Spain	973.7	1,370.0	44.61	415.8	552.6	35.00
Syria	165.0	92.0	4.89	142.0	80.0	8.02
Tunisia	130.0	35.0	3.14	11.5	7.0	0.63
Turkey	175.0	65.0	4.57	224.0	75.0	10.80
USA (California)	0.5	0.5	0.02	60.0	125.0	6.68
All others	19.5	19.5	0.73	46.0	52.5	3.56
World Total	2,565.5	2,688.5	100.00	1,342.5	1,426.0	100.00

Source: Abassi 2002

Carried from its Mediterranean homeland by explorers and colonists, olive culture failed in England and the eastern United States due to inhospitable climates. A long dry season with low humidity is essential to minimize disease, and rainfall during bloom reduces fruit set. In tropical regions nearer the equator, olives grow vegetatively, but most cultivars do not set fruit due to insufficient winter chilling, which prevents flower formation. Olive production has been commercially successful in other Mediterranean climates around the world including parts of South America, South Africa, and Australia.

The most extensive olive cultivation is practiced in Spain, which produces nearly 45 percent of the world's olive oil and about 35 percent of the world's table olives. Italy, Greece, and Turkey are the other major olive producers. Together these four countries account for 85 percent of the olive oil and 57 percent of the table olives produced in the world (table 1.1). During the 1990s, numerous oil producers in California began to market small quantities of high quality extra virgin olive oil. The relatively small U.S. olive industry produces only .02 percent of the world's olive oil and 6.7 percent of the world's table olives.

CULTIVARS AND THEIR USES

In the Mediterranean basin, hundreds of cultivars have been selected over the centuries for their adaptation to various microclimates and soil types. Within each country, certain cultivars predominate in different producing districts. Some cultivars are best suited for oil production, others for table use, and still others are used either way depending on the relative prices of oil and table olives.

Some cultivars are common only locally, whereas others are found in several countries. Throughout the Mediterranean region there is considerable cultivar confusion: the same name may be given to similar but clearly different selections, and different names may be used for identical cultivars.

In Spain, major cultivars used for oil production include Picual, Cornicabra, Hojiblanca, Empeltre, Arbequina, and Lechin de Sevilla. Manzanilla, Manzanilla Cacereña, Hojiblanca, and Gordal Sevillana are the major cultivars processed for use as table olives. Most Spanish table olives are processed green-ripe. The manufacture of pitted stuffed olives is also a major component of the Spanish industry. In recent years, Spanish olives, processed using the California black ripe method, have made significant inroads into the U.S. domestic olive market (fig. 1.2).

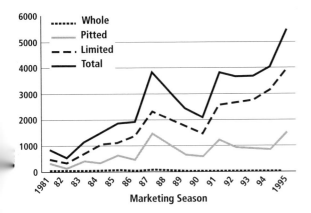

igure 1.2. Imported canned ripe olives and bulk olives
rocessed into canned ripe olives.

Italy has many cultivars used for oil production and
several that are commonly processed for table use.
Notable among the Italian oil cultivars are the Coratina,
Leccino, and Frantoio. Tondaiblea and Giarraffa are
used to produce black table olives, and Cerignola,
Ascolana Tenera, and Nocellara Etnea are varieties
known best as green table olives. Italian olives may be
salt brine cured, salt brine cured and packed in vinegar,
or dry salt cured, rubbed with oil, and packed in herbs.

In Greece, table olives are a prominent export crop.
Kalamata is a black olive that is brine cured and packed
in vinegar. Conseruolea is another black cultivar of
importance, and Chalkidikis is used both as a table
variety and as an oil olive. Agrinion is Greece's most
famous green olive cultivar. Koroneiki is the main oil
cultivar representing about 75 percent of Greece's oil
production.

Turkey is unique among the four major olive-producing countries in that its table olive production is
larger in tonnage than its production of olive oil (table
1.1). The cultivars Domat, Szmir, and Trilya are grown
both for oil and table olive use.

Throughout the Mediterranean region, olive cultivars are grown in a specific climate, for a specific use,
and with a method of processing in mind. Over the
centuries, the best use for each particular cultivar has
been highly developed. Cultivars adapted to humid
coastal areas, dry continental climates, frost-free mari-
time zones, and frosty uplands have all been selected.
Cultivars exist that thrive under a wide variety of soil
and nutritional conditions. Olives ideal for oil production, salt brine pickling, black processing, green processing, and dry salt curing are produced throughout
the region.

In contrast to the rest of the world, the California
ive industry relies largely on one product: the black-
olive. Other olive products are produced in rela-

tively small amounts. The California industry uses the
five cultivars Mission, Manzanillo, Sevillano, Ascolano,
and Barouni interchangeably.

CALIFORNIA HISTORY

The olive was brought to California in the late 1700s by
Franciscan padres who journeyed north from San Blas,
Mexico. Led by Father Junipero Serra and sent by Jose
de Galvez, the Franciscans established Mission San
Diego de Alcalá in 1769 (fig. 1.1). Within two decades,
olives were being grown at the mission. It is likely that
artisans who arrived at the mission around 1800 built
the first mills and screw presses for the production of
olive oil. Father Lasuen wrote in 1803 that Mission San
Diego de Alcalá had harvested olives and produced
some very good oil. This is the earliest record of oil production in California. Distributed from San Diego, olive
trees were soon producing at all missions along the
coast south of San Francisco.

Early explorers, such as George Vancouver in 1792
and Edwin Bryant and John Fremont in 1846, wrote of
seeing olive trees in California. Bryant noticed olive
trees growing at Mission San Luis Obispo, and Fremont
wrote that olives and other fruits grew luxuriantly
together in spring-fed valley gardens among the hills
south of San Diego.

In 1834, secularization of the missions led to the
decline of most of the mission orchards and gardens.
Olives in the mission orchards survived neglect,
drought, and browsing cattle for decades until 1855 to
1875 when early American pioneers began propagating
new trees using cuttings from the old mission orchards.

Considerable variation existed in early mission
olives, as both seedlings and rooted cuttings were used.
Olive pits found in adobe bricks from early California
mission buildings are of variable shape and size. The
Mission cultivar that eventually predominated from the
early plantings at San Diego may have originated
through vegetative propagation of superior trees from
an original mixed seedling source although this is
uncertain.

Statistics from the California State Agricultural
Society indicate that by 1855, 503 olive trees were
growing in the state. A renewed interest in olive oil production led to significant expansion of the industry
between 1870 and 1900. In 1872, Frank and Warren
Kimball secured olive cuttings from among the 347
trees remaining at Mission San Diego de Alcalá and
planted an orchard at their ranch in National City in
San Diego County. Ellwood Cooper of Santa Barbara
planted six olive orchards in different locations, the first

near Goleta in 1870. Edward E. Goodrich had an 80-acre (32-ha) orchard at his El Quito ranch near Los Gatos in Santa Clara County. All these early pioneers were involved in the production of olive oil. Aside from the early efforts in the missions, the first commercially produced olive oil in California probably came from the Camulos oil mill, established in 1871 in Ventura County.

John Wolfskill of Winters, George C. Roeding of Fresno, F. M. Hunt of Redlands, and John S. Calkins of Pomona were other early orchardists who experimented with olive trees. The old olive trees at Mission San Jose served as a source for many subsequent plantings in Northern California. In the mid-1890s, Warren Woodson, a land developer, established the Corning olive district by planting as many domestic olive trees as he could get. His plantings were supplemented with imported Spanish trees when the domestic supply fell short. Trees procured from Spain turned out to be the Sevillano cultivar, which was disappointing as an oil producer but later became valuable for its large, pickled fruit. About the same time, growers in Tulare County discovered that olives were well suited to their soils. Initially, Mission olives were used as windbreaks and as ornamentals, but after the black-ripe pickled olive became popular, planting increased. Lindsay became the leading olive-producing district in the state by the early 1900s.

Between 1850 and 1900, numerous olive cultivars from Mediterranean countries were introduced to California, primarily for the purpose of improving oil production. By 1885, California growers had learned to produce olive oil equal in quality to the best imported oils. With this success in oil production, the number of trees planted in the state went from 5,603 in 1876 to 539,568 by 1901. The heavy increase in production that followed led to lower prices, and growers found they could not compete with the less expensive European olive oil. Shortly thereafter, the industry shifted its emphasis to the production of pickled olives, the mainstay of the California industry ever since. The cultivars other than Mission that are important in the contemporary olive industry were all introduced into California during the expansion between 1875 and 1905.

PICKLED OLIVES

Before 1900, early olive producers experimented with processed olives as a sideline to their oil operations. Ellwood Cooper of Santa Barbara used a water cure process to remove the bitterness from the fruit and then packed the olives in a light brine. Frank Kimball of National City and A. D. Thacker of Pomona used a lye process to remove the bitterness, leached the lye out with water, and then packed the fruit in brine. Olives were also salt-cured and sometimes served in olive oil. Different producers using various processes pickled olives in four stages of ripeness: some were processed green, some with a reddish cast, some after turning black, and some after shriveling on the tree.

The various processing methods led to marketing problems since some products were clearly inferior. Eugene Hilgard's research at the University of California at Berkeley indicated that different varieties of olives should be processed separately (fig. 1.3). Work done at UC by Frederic Bioletti (fig. 1.4) and G. E. Colby in 1899 proved that when properly processed, large-fruited olives were palatable and nutritious. They demonstrated ripe olives could be preserved indefinitely in a weak brine when sufficiently heated and hermetically sealed in glass. Within a decade, Bioletti perfected a method of canning olives in tins, giving growers better control of product supply. His high-temperature, high-pressure retort method gained consumers' confidence, and the modern olive industry had its start.

One of the first to make use of the new methods was Freda Ehmann (fig. 1.5), founder in 1898 of the Ehmann Olive Company in Oroville. She contacted Professor Hilgard at UC Berkeley in 1897, requesting a recipe for processing ripe olives. She used his method for lye curing and shortly thereafter began to market her product in barrels, kegs, and glass jars. By 1905 Ehmann Olive Company had begun canning ripe olives. This mild ripe olive became the olive of choice in the United States.

Clifford C. Graber of Ontario, California began to process table olives as a hobby in the 1890s. His interest in olives continued to grow as he developed and built a practical size grader for olives, packed processed olives in kegs, and then began to can olives in 1910. The C. C. Graber Company devoted full time to the olive business in 1929 and still produces processed specialty olives today.

The new, superior method of canning and the encouraging economic outlook created another statewide planting boom between 1900 and 1920. The development of the major olive-producing districts in Oroville and Lindsay took place during that time. In 1916, Lindsay olive growers formed a cooperative processing plant to take advantage of Bioletti's new canning methods.

Meanwhile, in the Corning district it was discovered that processing Sevillano olives the same way as the Mission cultivar blistered the fruit. Fred G. Beresford of Corning and W. V. Cruess, professor of food technology at the University of California at Davis, developed

ew method of processing Sevillano olives that pre-
ented damage. As a result, growers in Corning began
grafting their groves over to the Sevillano cultivar in
1913. Today, the Corning area primarily grows the
Sevillano variety, although this may change as growers
graft over to still more desirable varieties.

Disaster struck in 1919 when 35 people died of bot-
ulism after eating improperly canned black olives;
demand for canned olives plummeted. It took 10 years
to convince consumers that with safe canning methods
and rigid inspection, canned olives were indeed safe.

Canning methods developed by the University of
California and carried to the marketplace by pioneer
canners like Freda Ehmann set the stage for widespread acceptance of the California black-ripe olive. By
1910, the foundation was laid for the California olive
industry. There were 26,000 acres (10,500 ha) in production by 1925, and the industry was stable at that
level for the next five decades. In the mid-1970s, an
expansion of olive acreage occurred in the southwest-
ern San Joaquin Valley due to the increased availability
of water from the newly completed California Water
Project. By the mid-1980s, Verticillium wilt and olive
knot on trunk injuries began to decimate this new
acreage. Just after reaching maturity, tree losses made
plantings uneconomical in this area and much of the
acreage was removed.

Figure 1.3. Eugene Woldemar Hilgard came to the University of California in 1874. He did early studies on processing olives by variety and size. (Bancroft Library, UC Berkeley)

Figure 1.4. Frederic Bioletti, UC professor, improved olive-processing methods and perfected a method of canning olives in tins. (Bancroft Library, UC Berkeley)

CURRENT PRODUCTION

Virtually all commercial olive acreage in the United
States is in California, with approximately 0.3 percent
of the world's olive trees. California produces roughly
6.7 percent of the world's table olives and 0.02 percent
of its olive oil. More than 99.5 percent of commercial
olive acreage in California is located in the interior valleys of central California although olive trees grow
throughout the state from San Diego County in the
south to Shasta County in the north (fig. 1.6 and table
1.2). Economic advantages such as suitable soils, water
availability, and low land prices resulted in the current
distribution and concentration of olive acreage in the
Central Valley. Conditions in Southern California and
the coastal area were less suitable for olive production
since those areas had no competitive yield advantage.
Since the 1920s, acreage has steadily declined there in
response to reduced profitability (fig. 1.7).

Within the Central Valley there are two major producing areas. In the northern Sacramento Valley, the
counties of Butte, Glenn, and Tehama have 38 percent
of the reported bearing acreage, and in the southern San
Joaquin Valley, the counties of Fresno, Kern, Madera,

Figure 1.5. Freda Ehmann of Oroville commercialized the black-ripe processing method that became the industry standard. (Butte County Historical Society)

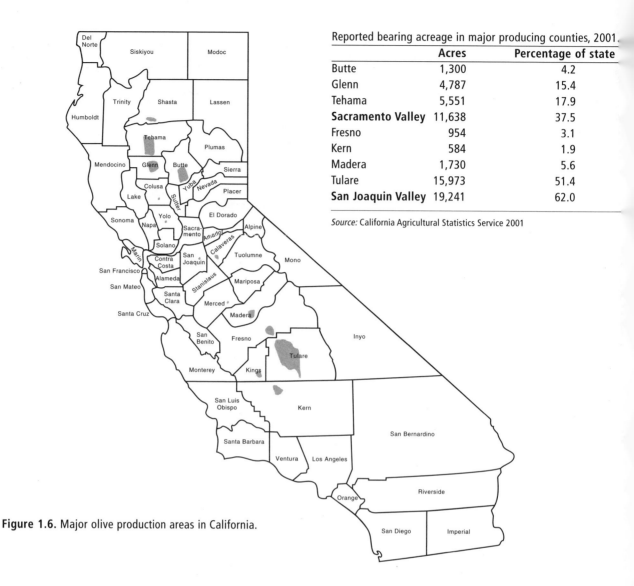

Reported bearing acreage in major producing counties, 2001.

	Acres	Percentage of state
Butte	1,300	4.2
Glenn	4,787	15.4
Tehama	5,551	17.9
Sacramento Valley	**11,638**	**37.5**
Fresno	954	3.1
Kern	584	1.9
Madera	1,730	5.6
Tulare	15,973	51.4
San Joaquin Valley	**19,241**	**62.0**

Source: California Agricultural Statistics Service 2001

Figure 1.6. Major olive production areas in California.

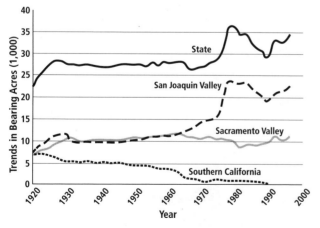

Figure 1.7. Bearing acreage of olive trees, statewide and by district, 1920 to 2000. (Johnston and Dean 1969; Foytik 1960; California Agricultural Statistics Service 1966, 1976, 1984–1992, 2001)

and Tulare have 62 percent of the acreage. Together, these seven counties had nearly 100 percent of the state's reported 2001 bearing acreage.

The Orland and Corning areas in Glenn and Tehama counties are noted for Sevillano production while the Oroville district in Butte County produces primarily Mission olives. Manzanillo is the major cultivar of the Lindsay area of Tulare County and on the West Side of Kern County.

Olive acreage in the Sacramento Valley has remained relatively stable for the past 70 years. Recent increases in bearing acres are the result of plantings in Glenn and Tehama counties since harvested acreage has declined recently in Butte County. Acreage in the San Joaquin Valley remained the same between 1925 and 1965. In the late 1960s and early 1970s, an accelerating increase in San Joaquin Valley acreage began as better-quality water became available from the state water project.

Table 1.2. Olive acreage in California by district and county, 1992.

District	County	Bearing acreage	Nonbearing acreage	Total
Sacramento Valley	Butte	2,755	41	2,796
	Colusa	58	38	96
	Glenn	1,934	1,033	2,967
	Sacramento	5	0	5
	Shasta	623	0	623
	Sutter	9	0	9
	Tehama	4,911	520	5,431
	Yolo	57	0	57
	Yuba	9	0	9
	Total	10,361	1,632	11,993
San Joaquin Valley	Calaveras	200	0	200
	Fresno	1,335	40	1,375
	Kern	2,187	41	2,228
	Kings	526	0	526
	Madera	1,696	80	1,776
	Merced	74	0	74
	San Joaquin	78	0	78
	Stanislaus	5	0	5
	Tulare	13,515	2,343	15,858
	Total	19,616	2,504	22,120
Southern California	Orange	1	0	1
	Riverside	37	0	37
	San Diego	36	0	36
	Total	74	0	74
All Others*		25	0	25

Source: California Agricultural Statistics Service 1992. (Although more recent data is unavailable, trends have remained constant.)
* Placer, Santa Clara, and Sonoma counties.

Thousands of acres of olives were planted on lands in western Kings and Kern counties that were previously planted to cotton. The soilborne fungal pathogen of cotton, Verticillium wilt, was common in many of these West Side soils. Tree losses due to Verticillium wilt and trunk shaker injuries infected with olive knot led to a decrease in San Joaquin Valley olive acreage (fig. 1.7). New plantings in Tulare and Glenn counties are responsible for the most recent increases in bearing acreage.

CULTIVARS

Between 1850 and 1950, more than 75 cultivars of olive were imported, primarily from countries surrounding the Mediterranean Sea. Some were oil varieties, but in the later years most were table olive varieties thought to

have potential in California. Although an extensive search was made for improved material, over the past 100 years four major varieties have come to account for 98 percent of the olive acreage in the state. Planting trends suggest that the predominance of the Manzanillo cultivar will continue in the future (fig. 1.8).

Although total olive acreage has not changed much in the past 50 years, the shift in varietal composition of the industry has been significant (fig. 1.9). The Mission cultivar was the most important olive in the state in 1936, accounting for 52 percent of the acreage. By 1996, Mission trees constituted just 5 percent of the bearing acreage. Manzanillo has steadily become more important since the 1930s and today accounts for more than 70 percent of the bearing acreage. Sevillano increased in importance until the late 1970s, when its popularity waned; yet it still accounted for 18 percent of bearing acreage in 1996. Ascolano has always been

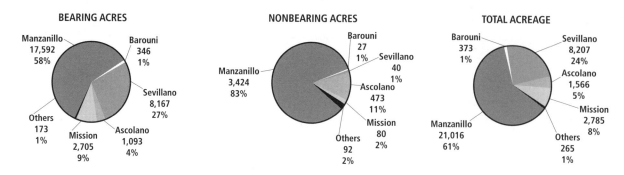

Figure 1.8. Olive acreage and planting trends, by variety, 1992. (California Agricultural Statistics Service 1992) (More recent data unavailable.)

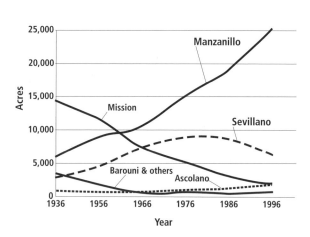

Figure 1.9. Trends in bearing acreage of California olive varieties, 1936 to 1996. (California Agricultural Statistics Service 1966–1996, California Olive Committee 1980–1996)

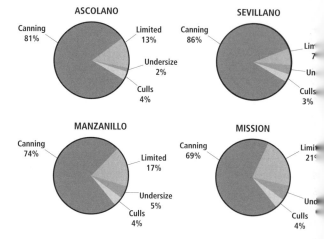

Figure 1.10. Average quality of California olive varieties, as delivered to handlers 1990–1991 through 1997. (California Olive Committee)

less important than the other three major cultivars since it bruises easily and is difficult to process without damage. In recent years there has been a small increase in Ascolano acreage, to about 5 percent of the bearing acreage. The Barouni cultivar has a small market as a fresh shipping fruit for home processing. It has not changed significantly in importance over the past 50 years. Barouni and other minor cultivars constitute about 2 percent of the bearing acreage. The shifts in cultivar composition were accomplished by topworking existing acreage and by replacing orchards of undesirable cultivars with more desirable cultivars. Average quality, measured by canning percentage, limited-use fruit, undersize fruit, and cull fruit varies by variety (fig. 1.10). Quality and resultant returns to the grower are also implicated in variety shifts over time.

In the first eight years of the 1990s, an average of 111,145 tons of fruit was delivered to olive handlers annually. In this period the annual crop ranged from a

low of 63,259 tons in 1991–1992 to a high of 163,024 tons in 1992–1993. On the average, over two-thirds of yearly production was from the Manzanillo cultivar, 20 percent from Sevillano, 6 percent from Ascolano, and 5 percent from Mission (fig. 1.11). The percentage of total production generated by each of the four major cultivars is representative of the cultivars' bearing acreage.

FRUIT USES

Canning

The California olive industry is based almost entirely on the production of canned ripe olives. Generally, about 90 percent of the state's olive crop is canned. Canning packs include ripe (whole or pitted); green-ripe (whole or pitted); and sliced, chopped, wedged, and broken (all

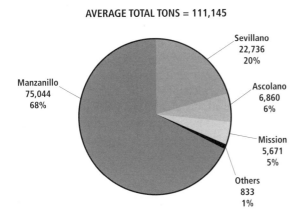

AVERAGE TOTAL TONS = 111,145

Manzanillo
75,044
68%

Sevillano
22,736
20%

Ascolano
6,860
6%

Mission
5,671
5%

Others
833
1%

Figure 1.11. Average yield (tons) of California olives by variety, 1990 through 1997. (California Olive Committee)

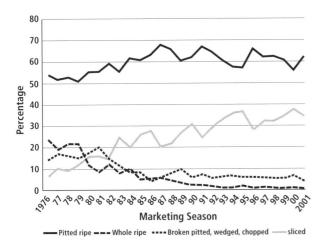

Figure 1.12. Trends in pack type of canned ripe olives in California, 1976–77 through 2001–02. (California Olive Committee)

pitted). The largest-volume canned product is pitted ripe olives, followed by sliced olives (fig. 1.12). The pack of pitted ripe olives increased by roughly 20 percent, and the sliced olive pack increased approximately five fold from 1976 through 2001. Over this time, packs of whole-ripe, green-ripe, broken-pitted, wedged, and chopped all decreased. During this 26-year period the whole-ripe pack dropped from 24 percent of the canned pack to less than 1 percent. Broken-pitted, wedged, and chopped olives dropped to one-third of their former levels, compared with 26 years earlier (fig. 1.12). The green-ripe olive pack declined to insignificance during this same period. These trends are the result of changing market demands for canned ripe olives.

Olives that are too small for canning, culls, and those damaged by frost, are diverted to oil production. Due to low grower returns, olive oil production in California has been almost entirely a salvage operation. Spain and Italy ship olive oil to the United States more cheaply than California can produce it. Land and labor costs in the United States are generally too high for the industry to produce olives solely for oil production unless a high-priced specialty product can be marketed and sold through a vertically integrated organization or unless labor costs are reduced through mechanical harvest. In recent years, there has been renewed interest in the production of specialty olive oil from specific European oil varieties. Chapter 23 discusses this in more detail.

A limited amount of specialty olive products such as Spanish green-processed, Greek or Sicilian style, and salt-brined are also produced in California, but their production is not a significant factor in the California industry. A very small portion of the Barouni olive crop is sold fresh and shipped to eastern markets in the United States for home processing.

Five basic processes used to produce olives for table use are discussed in detail in chapter 22. Each effectively leaches the bitter principle from the olive to produce an edible product. The standard method in California is lye curing, which produces the popular black-ripe olive. All California olive canneries use this method. The other four methods are used to produce a small volume of specialty olives in California but are of major importance in other parts of the world. Oil-cured olives are soaked for one to a few months in olive oil. Water-cured olives have the bitterness removed by simple leaching. They are soaked in water, rinsed, and soaked again for a period of months. Olives that are brine-cured are soaked in a salt-brine solution for one or more months. Dry-cured olives are packed in salt for one or more months, then rubbed with olive oil. Olives cured by these last four methods have a stronger flavor than the mild, black-ripe olive that is the standard in the United States.

Producing Oil

Of the four major cultivars grown in California, the Mission is the best for oil production since 21.8 percent of its fresh weight in winter is oil. Manzanillo has 20.3 percent oil and is also used for olive oil production. Sevillano (14.4 percent oil) and Ascolano (18.8 percent oil) are too low in oil content to be grown specifically for oil production so for these varieties, only cull fruit from the table olive industry can be processed for profitable oil extraction.

The highest-quality oil is produced by crushing the fruit, mixing the paste to promote the formation of larger oil droplets, and pressing or horizontal centrifuging the paste to separate the oil and water from the pomace. The olive juice (oil and water) can be decanted to allow the oil to float to the top, or, modern processors may use vertical centrifuges to remove the water. The oil is then filtered and ready to bottle. This virgin olive oil, as defined by the International Olive Oil Council, comes from the fruit in the first pressing of the olives and is immediately suitable for human consumption. Extra virgin olive oil is virgin oil that meets a higher standard for stability and flavor characteristics. Additional methods are discussed in detail in chapter 23.

Another process used to make olive oil in California from culled table fruit involves crushing the fruit and mixing it to form larger droplets of oil, followed by horizontal centrifuging to extract the oil, pomace, and water. This oil meets virgin standards but not extra virgin because of bad flavors from rotten, moldy, or brined olives. To correct this, the oil is refined using a heating and vacuum suction technique to remove volatiles. This produces clear, tasteless oil that is mixed with extra virgin oil and sold as extra virgin oil.

A final method is an industrial chemical refining process using solvent extraction to recover the olive oil. While this method is not currently used in California, it is used in Europe to recover oil from dried olive pomace. The dry meal is exposed to solvent extraction, and the solvent and oil go through a refining tower. The solvent is recovered, and the oil is further refined and deodorized into a clear tasteless liquid called pomace oil. Pomace oil is often blended with a small amount of virgin oil to restore some flavor. Oil yield using this refining process is greater but is of lesser quality. In the past, when California olive oil production was a marginally economical salvage operation, much of the oil produced was pomace oil.

In recent years, the upscale U.S. consumer has begun to value virgin oil for its flavor and nutritional qualities. It is vegetable oil—without cholesterol—and is monounsaturated. The market for virgin oil is likely to continue to grow among health-conscious people in the United States. Renewed consumer interest in extra vir-

gin oil recently created a renaissance in growing olive oil cultivars in California. The California Olive Oil Council was formed by new oil producers to improve quality and develop market identity. It now certifies the production of top quality extra virgin table oil.

As its value is recognized, the olive and its products will likely take a more significant place in the U.S. diet. The olive, important in commerce from the dawn of Western Civilization, will undoubtedly continue to occupy a unique position for both producers and consumers far into the future.

REFERENCES

Abassi, F., ed. 2002. The world olive oil market, the world table olive market. Olivae 10(92): 22–27.

California Agricultural Statistics Service. 1966, 1976, 1984–1992, 2001. California fruit and nut acreage reports.

California Olive Committee. 1980–81 to 2001–2002. California olive industry annual reports.

Doutsias, G. T. 1988. The production of table olives as an alternative to the production of olive oil. Olivae 5(20): 9–11.

Economic and Table Olive Committees. 1988. 57th session of the International Olive Oil Council. Olivae 5(20): 5–7.

Foytik, J. 1960. California olive industry: Trends and outlook. Calif. Agric. Ext. Serv. Circ. 492.

Johnston, W. E., and G. W. Dean. 1969. California crop trends: Yields, acreages, and production areas. Calif. Agric. Ext. Serv. Circ. 551.

Nuckton, C. F., and W. E. Johnston. 1985. California tree fruits, grapes, and nuts: Location of acreage and trends in acreage, yields, and production, 1946–1983. Giannini Foundation Information Series 85-1

2

California Table Olives: Marketing, Imports, and the Federal Marketing Order

JANET E. NELSON

PROCESSED OLIVE MARKETING

The dominant product of California's olive industry is canned, black-ripe olives. This style accounts for 80 to 85 percent of the California fresh olives grown in the state. Other products are olive oil, Sicilian, Greek, green, tree-ripened, and other styles of processed table olives.

Figure 2.1 shows the total market for canned, black-ripe olives in the United States over the past few years, and the proportion filled by domestic and import sources. The total U. S. market has grown from 170.9 million pounds in 1988 to 236.8 million pounds in 2000 with imports averaging about 21 percent of the total.

Along with growth in the total market, a shift in the outlets and product mix has also affected the ripe olive industry. In 1988, the food service market, restaurants, and other noncommercial mass feeders accounted for 4.3 million cases of ripe olive sales, and retail sales through stores accounted for 6.5 million cases. By 2000, the respective sales were 5.2 million cases and 9.1 million cases. The slower growth in food service is due to the impact of imported sliced olives in No. 10 cans. Imports from Spain and Morocco continue to sell into the food service trade at prices considerably below

the domestic products, putting pressure on canners to reduce grower prices in order to compete.

The product mix has changed over the past 20 years, as shown in figure 2.2, with a dramatic decline in sales of whole fruit and growth in sales of pitted and sliced olives. During this period of time canners invested in new pitting and slicing machines; the expanding pizza market was gained and then largely lost to low-price imports; and new outlets were developed for frozen and acidified olive products. Finally, as sales of whole olives declined, retail stores discontinued slower-moving items. The discontinued items were not replaced with additional sizes of pitted olives, and as a result the olive industry lost valuable retail shelf space.

Another factor affecting canners' costs is the fluctuating crop size of limited-size olives (figure 2.3). Limited-size olives are those with pit-to-flesh ratios too large to be acceptable as whole or pitted olives; their use is therefore limited to sliced, chopped, or wedged styles. Growers have historically received lower prices for limited-size olives than for canning-size olives. The increased demand for sliced olives has prompted canners to slice canning-size olives to meet demand. Consequently, grower prices for the smallest canning size have decreased in recent years.

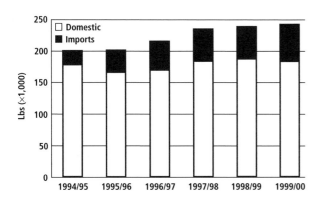

Figure 2.1. Consumption of canned black-ripe olives, 1994 to 2000.

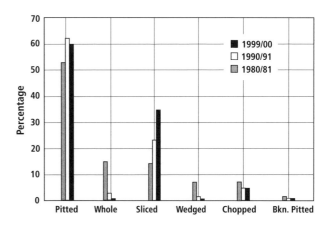

Figure 2.2. Comparison of sales of domestic ripe olive styles, 1980 to 2000.

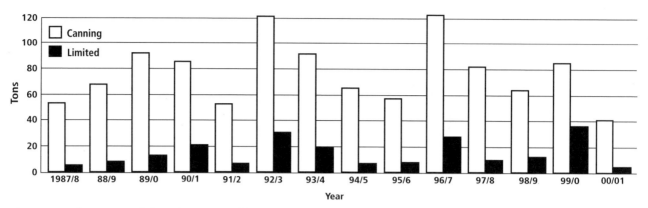

Figure 2.3. Olive tonnage delivered to regulated handlers.

IMPORTS

In 1981 the total California olive crop was only 43,000 tons. When California canners could not meet the demand for sliced olives, food service customers began to purchase imported product.

Canned ripe olives were imported to supply approximately 30 percent of the U.S. market at the end of 2000 (fig. 2.1). Before 1982, imports of California-style canned ripe olives were almost nonexistent. The market for Spanish-style green olives, olive oil, and specialty olives is dominated by imports. Some California-grown olives are used for these products, but with the exception of olive oil, the market for these items has not been growing. The rise in new food preparation methods has caused olive oil sales to increase. There has been an upsurge in interest in high-end California olive oil. Small acreages of oil varieties, imported from Europe, are being planted in the state.

As noted above, imports of canned ripe olives became a factor after the small 1981 harvest when large food service customers began to order canned product from Spain and later from Morocco. As figure 2.1 shows, imports have become a significant factor in this market. Most of these imported olives are sliced, pitted, and wedged styles.

Initially many of the imports were of the Hojiblanca variety, which is grown primarily for oil. This olive has a strong flavor and a tough skin, two points against its acceptance as a direct replacement for the California product. However, Spanish processors have improved their quality, and varieties with a milder flavor are now being imported. For example, Spain has planted many new acres of the Manzanillo variety. At least two state-of-the-art canned ripe olive plants opened in Spain in 1998.

Olive imports can affect domestic growers in two ways. First, the domestic growers lose market share to the imported product. If these losses continue, growers and canners may no longer be able to sell all of the product produced in California.

Second, the lower prices of imported sliced olives for the food service trade hurt domestic product sales. The price difference between California and imported sliced olives can be as much as $5 to $8 per case. California canners have had to reduce their selling prices to be competitive, and that has reduced their profit margins. This could cause grower prices to decline and reduce growers' returns.

MARKETING AND IMPORT SUMMARY

The marketing of canned ripe olives will continue to evolve as tastes and eating habits change. Olives are considered a nonessential food item, and retail sales are affected by impulse buying and feature prices. In the food service area, price and availability will continue to be major factors as imported product competes with California product in the U. S. market.

THE OLIVE MARKETING ORDER

California olive growers and ripe olive canners have had a Federal Marketing Order in place since 1965. The Marketing Order, approved by grower vote, establishes a California Olive Committee (COC) consisting of eight growers elected from four olive-producing districts and eight representatives designated by California canneries.

The COC can recommend regulations to the U. S. Department of Agriculture to provide for third-party inspection and size grading of fresh olives delivered to canners. The olive industry prefers a federal marketing order rather than a state order because minimum quality and size requirements established by the COC apply not only to domestic production, but also to imported, canned black-ripe olives. All actions taken by the COC must be approved by the U. S. Department of Agriculture before they can be implemented, but, when approved, the COC's rules and regulations carry the authority of federal law.

Through assessments collected per ton of olives received at the cannery, the COC supports University of California crop research projects, both basic and production-oriented, dealing with all aspects of olive production and processing. In the past 5 years, the COC has expended well over $1 million in research and development of new mechanical harvesters for olives. The first production harvesters were in the field in 2001. The discovery of an olive fly in California in 1998 created the need for research into management of this pest. The COC now helps coordinate the efforts of the California Department of Food and Agriculture, county agricultural commissioners, researchers, and others.

The California Olive Committee has always had a generic marketing program designed to increase awareness and consumption of black-ripe olives from California. Current specific goals include developing and promulgating new uses for olives, communicating the nutritional benefits of the product, and pursuing a strategy to create a high-quality image for California ripe olives in the food service industry to differentiate the California product from imports. A number of different strategies have been utilized to achieve these goals over the years, including magazine advertising for consumers and the food service industry, distribution of recipes and nutritional information to newspaper and magazine editors, promotional programs for food service operators, and various other efforts. History, nutrition, recipes, and other information can be obtained from the industry website at www.CalOlive.org.

Total COC budgets vary depending on crop size and industry needs. For example, the total COC budget in 1980 was $1.5 million with 3 percent spent on crop research and 89 percent on marketing. In 2001, the total budget was $1.3 million with 30 percent spent on research and 44 percent on marketing.

REFERENCES

California Olive Committee. 1980–81 to 2000–2001. California olive industry annual reports.

3

Botany of the Olive

GEORGE C. MARTIN AND G. STEVEN SIBBETT

Olive is a member of the Oleaceae family, which contains the genera *Fraxinus* (ash), *Forsythia* (golden bell), *Forestiera* (*F. neomexicana*, the California wild olive), *Ligustrum* (privet), *Olea* (olive), and *Syringa* (lilac). Commercial olives belong to the species *Olea europaea* L., one of about 20 species of *Olea* found in tropical and subtropical regions of the world. Only *Olea europaea* L. produces edible fruit.

GENERAL DESCRIPTION

Olive is a long-lived evergreen tree; some specimens have been reported to live for more than 1,000 years. Although the wood *resists* decay very well, heart wood can decompose, resulting in hollow tree trunks. When the top of the tree is killed by mechanical damage or environmental extremes, new growth arises from the root system. Whether propagated by seed or cuttings, the root system is generally shallow, penetrating only 3 or 4 feet even in deep soils. However, lateral spread can be considerable with reports of roots found 49 feet (15 m) from old tree trunks. The aboveground portion of the olive tree is recognizable by its dense assembly of limbs, short internodes, and compact nature of the foliage (fig. 3.1). Light does not readily penetrate into an olive tree unless the tree is well managed and pruned to open light channels toward the trunk. If unpruned, olives develop multiple branches with cascading limbs that are pendulous and flexible, swaying with the slightest breeze. In pruned, well-attended trees the annual growth can be vigorous. There, shoots represent the fruiting wood for the following year's crop. If light is not allowed to penetrate the tree, growth and fruiting will be restricted to the outer shell of the tree. In some cultivars the shoot growth is pendulous while in others the growth is quite upright. The branches are able to carry large populations of fruit on terminal twigs.

Olive leaves are thick, leathery, and oppositely arranged. Each leaf reaches its final size within 2 weeks.

Leaves live for a 2 to 3 year period. Leaves have stomata on their lower surfaces only. Stomata are nestled in peltate trichomes that restrict water loss and make the olive relatively resistant to drought (fig. 3.2). Some multi-cellular hairs are present on the underside of the leaf surface. Olive leaves usually abscise in the spring like other evergreens. Yellow leaves in the spring signal the abscission process, but yellow leaves may also reveal other physiological and pathological problems discussed elsewhere in this book.

INFLORESCENCE

Flower bud inflorescences are borne in the axil of most leaves. The bud is usually formed on the current season's

Figure 3.1. Mature olive tree.

Figure 3.2. Surface structure of olive leaf showing peltate trichomes. Notice how the trichomes overlap. (Source: K. Pinney and V. S. Polito)

taining four lobes. The two stamens are opposite on either side of the two-loculed ovary that bears a short style and capitate stigma. Two types of flowers are present each season: perfect flowers, containing stamen and pistil (fig. 3.5), and staminate flowers, containing aborted or degenerated pistils and functional stamens. The proportion of perfect and staminate flowers varies with inflorescence, cultivar, and year. Large commercial crops occur when 1 or 2 perfect flowers are present among the 15 to 30 flowers per inflorescence. For some cultivars, including Barouni, more staminate flowers than pistillate flowers are present.

The perfect flower is evidenced by its large pistil, which nearly fills the space within the floral tube (fig. 3.5). The pistil is green when immature and deep green when open at full bloom. Staminate flower pistils are tiny, barely rising above the floral tube base. The style

growth and begins visible growth the next season. Buds may remain dormant for more than a year and then begin growth, forming mostly vegetative shoots but can, although rarely, produce viable inflorescences with flowers a season later than expected. When each leaf axil maintains a developing inflorescence, there are hundreds of flowers per twig (fig. 3.3). Each inflorescence contains between 15 and 30 flowers, depending on developmental processes for that year and the cultivar (fig. 3.4).

Figure 3.4. Olive inflorescence prior to opening of all flowers. Actual size is approximately 1¼ inch (3 cm) long.

FLOWER

The flowers borne on the inflorescence are small, yellow-white, and inconspicuous. Each contains a short, four-segmented calyx and a short-tubed corolla con-

Figure 3.3. Olive inflorescence and open flowers on 1-year-old twig.

Figure 3.5. Perfect flower, showing stamen and pistil.

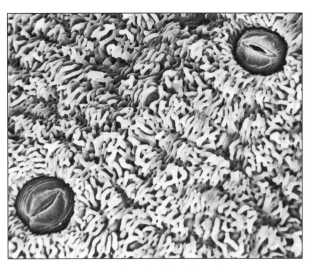

Figure 3.6. Young olive fruit (pistil) surface showing stomata and wax. (*Source:* K. Pinney and V. S. Polito)

is small and brown, greenish white, or white, and the stigma is large and plumose as it is in a functioning pistil (fig. 3.5).

The reasons for flower and young fruit abscission are not well known. However, pistil abortion is often involved. Stress from lack of water and nutrients during floral development can lead to pistil abortion and large proportions of staminate flowers. Also, excessive populations of flowers or leaf loss up to a month before full bloom contribute to pistil abortion.

Ultramicroscopic and histochemical evidence shows that flower buds begin forming by November. By about 8 weeks before full bloom, flower formation is visible under low-power microscopic examination. During the next 8 weeks, flower development is rapid. Full bloom in California occurs during May; blooming in the southern areas of the state generally takes place 1 to 2 weeks earlier than in the northern areas. The viable pistil has two carpels, each containing two ovules, but only one is fertilized and develops. Thus, only one carpel containing one seed is present in the fruit.

FRUIT

The olive fruit is a drupe, botanically similar to almond, apricot, cherry, nectarine, peach, and plum. The olive fruit consists of carpel, and the wall of the ovary has both fleshy and dry portions. The skin (exocarp) is free of hairs and contains stomata (fig. 3.6). The flesh (mesocarp) is the tissue eaten, and the pit (endocarp) encloses the seed. Fruit shape and size, pit size, and surface morphology vary greatly among cultivars.

SEED

The seed undergoes most of its development starting in July and ending in about September (fig. 3.7). The fruit is horticulturally mature in September or October (ready for the California black-ripe or green-ripe process), and physiologically mature in January or February. The seed is horticulturally mature by October, and if harvested and stratified or detergent washed at that time, it will achieve maximum germination. When the fruit is physiologically mature by January, seed germination is greatly reduced.

The mature seed is covered with a thin coat that covers the starch-filled endosperm. The latter surrounds the tapering, flat, leaflike cotyledons, short radicle (root), and plumule (stem). Seed size and absolute shape vary greatly by cultivar.

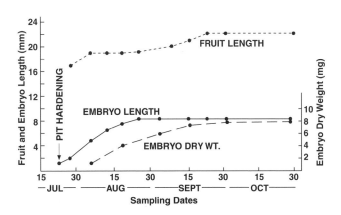

Figure 3.7. Seasonal growth curves for olive fruit and embryo.

4

Olive Cultivars and Propagation

ELLEN G. SUTTER

Of the many known cultivars of *Olea europaea*, only five are used commercially in California: Manzanillo, Sevillano, Mission, Ascolano, and Barouni. The fruitless cultivar, Swan Hill, is used as an ornamental tree. Factors determining selection of cultivars include suitability for processing, size of fruit, climatic limitations, and disease resistance. Tables 4.1 and 4.2 summarize the characteristics and harvest periods of these cultivars.

Table 4.1. Characteristics of major olive cultivars grown in California for fruit

Cultivar	Mean fresh weight per fruit (grams)	Flesh-to-pit ratio	Oil content (percent of fruit)	Main uses
Ascolano	9.0	8.2:1	18.8	black-ripe, green-ripe
Barouni	7.4	6.8:1	16.5	fresh, black-ripe
Manzanillo	4.8	8.2:1	20.3	black-ripe, green-ripe, Spanish-green, oil
Mission	4.1	6.5:1	21.8	black-ripe, green-ripe, oil
Sevillano	13.5	7.3:1	14.4	black-ripe, green-ripe, Spanish-green

Table 4.2. Harvest periods of major olive cultivars in California

Cultivar	Sept.	Oct.	Nov.	Dec.
Ascolano	●●●●●●●●●●●			
Manzanillo	●●●●●			
Sevillano		●●●●●●●●●●●●		
Barouni			●●●●●●●●	
Mission		●●●●●●●●●●●●●		

CULTIVARS

Manzanillo

The Manzanillo cultivar was introduced into California from Spain in about 1875. It is the most popular cultivar used for canning in California and the most widely planted. Its popularity is due to its high percentage of desired fruit sizes, ranging from medium to extra large.

Physical Characteristics. Manzanillo has a low-spreading growth habit, reaching about 15 to 30 feet (5 to 9 m) in height at maturity. Fruit are oval, uniform in size and shape, and are borne singly. Average fruit weight is 4.8 grams; the majority of fruit range in weight from 4.0 to 5.5 grams. Flesh-to-pit ratio after canning is 8.2:1. Manzanillo trees are commonly propagated by rooted stem cuttings.

Climatic Adaptation. Manzanillo is grown mostly in Tulare, Kings, and Fresno counties in the southern San Joaquin Valley, where it produces high yields. Manzanillo has had limited usage in Tehama and Butte counties in Northern California because it is not tolerant of cold winter temperatures. An additional problem with growing Manzanillo in cold winter environments is that freeze damage exacerbates olive knot.

Bearing, Harvest, and Uses. Although the fruit matures in October or early November, Manzanillo fruit is harvested in mid-October to avoid injury during early frosts. Fruit is processed mostly as black-ripe and green-ripe olives. Some fruit is used to produce fermented Spanish-style green olives. Oil content in fruit in winter averages approximately 20.3 percent of fresh weight, making the Manzanillo fruit suitable for oil extraction.

Diseases and Pests. Manzanillo is very susceptible to olive knot (*Pseudomonas savastanoi*) and Verticillium wilt (*Verticillium dahliae*). Its susceptibility to black scale is similar to that of other olive cultivars.

Shotberry, a physiological disorder resulting in parthenocarpic fruit set with subsequent arrested fruit growth, also affects Manzanillo.

Sevillano

Sevillano, the second most popular variety of olive, was introduced into the United States from Spain in 1885.

Physical Characteristics. Sevillano trees have a spreading growth habit. Growth can be quite variable; trees reach a height of 25 to 35 feet (8 to 11 m) at maturity. The height of Sevillano trees can be trained to stay lower, making them relatively easy to harvest by hand. Sevillano fruit is the largest of the cultivars grown in California, with an average weight of 13.5 grams; flesh-to-pit ratio averages 7.3:1. The fruit grows singly on peduncles and varies in shape from plump and ovate to elongated oval. Sevillano is difficult to root from cuttings; consequently, it is produced commercially by grafting. The predominant method of propagation is to graft shoots onto 1-year-old Manzanillo rooted cuttings. The variations in size seen in mature Sevillano trees may be due to use of seedling rootstocks.

Climatic Adaptation. Sevillano is planted mostly in the Corning area of Tehama County in Northern California, but small plantings have been established in Butte and Tulare counties. It is somewhat resistant to cold damage. Sevillano is also used as a pollinizer for Manzanillo, particularly where temperatures may reach or exceed 95°F (35°C) during pollination.

Bearing, Harvest, and Uses. Bearing is variable in Sevillano. In addition to normal yearly alternate bearing, it reportedly may have a few off years followed by one year with a heavy crop. The fruit mature relatively late and are harvested in October. The main disadvantage of Sevillano is that the fruit are difficult to process; they bruise easily, and split pits can be a problem. Sevillano fruit must be harvested at an earlier stage than other cultivars for acceptable processing results. Sevillano is used mostly as a canned ripe olive or as fermented Spanish-style olives. Its low oil content (averaging 14 percent in winter) precludes its use for oil extraction.

Diseases and Pests. Sevillano is resistant to peacock spot fungus (*Spilocea oleaginea*), but it is susceptible to olive knot (*Pseudomonas savastanoi*). It is also affected by several physiological disorders, including soft nose (which causes the fruit to darken at the apex and to shrivel), split-pit (which causes the pit to split into two parts), and shotberry.

Mission

Mission was originally introduced into the United States by way of Mexico in 1769.

Physical Characteristics. Mission trees grow tall and upright, often reaching 40 to 50 feet (12 to 15 m) at maturity. They must be topped to make hand harvesting practical. The fruit are relatively small, averaging only 4.1 grams. Mission has the lowest flesh-to-pit ratio (6.5:1) of any commercial cultivar. Fruit are borne singly or in clusters and are broad-oval to oval-elongated in shape. Mission is propagated commercially by rooted cuttings.

Climatic Adaptation. Mission is the most cold resistant of all commercial cultivars in California and consequently is the preferred cultivar in colder districts, such as the Sacramento Valley. Trees have been known to survive 8°F (–13°C). Many Mission trees in the southern San Joaquin Valley have been topworked to cultivars with less cold hardiness and more favorable fruit characteristics.

Bearing, Harvest, and Uses. Mission bearing patterns are somewhat erratic with both alternate-bearing and consistent annual crops have been reported. Mission is the latest-maturing variety in California; harvest often starts in late October and continues through November. Harvest dates depend on fruit use. Mission olives can be picked when green for Spanish-green processing; when the fruit develops some red coloration, they can be used for ripe olive processing. Because the fruit mature late in the season, early fall frost can damage them, making them useless for pickling. Mission olives are primarily used for pickling but can be used for oil extraction because of their high oil content (21.8 percent). When used to produce oil, they are harvested from mid-December to late February.

Diseases and Pests. Mission is very susceptible to peacock spot and also develops olive knot. Its susceptibility to scale insects is similar to that of other cultivars.

Ascolano

Ascolano originated in Italy and was introduced into California in about 1885.

Physical Characteristics. The Ascolano tree has a naturally rounded shape and grows to 20 or 30 feet (6 to 9 m) at maturity. Fruit grows singly or in clusters. Ascolano is characterized by large fruit with a soft texture. The fruit is very tender and difficult to pick without bruising. The shape of the fruit varies from round to oval, and most range in size from 9.8 to 11.1 grams. The greatest advantage of Ascolano is that it has a very high flesh-to-pit ratio (8.2:1).

Climatic Adaptation. Ascolano makes up approximately 3 percent of California's total acreage. Most plantings are in the San Joaquin Valley, particularly in Kings and Tulare counties. Ascolano is resistant to cold injury and grows well in all olive-producing areas of California.

Bearing, Harvest, and Uses. Ascolano bears regularly when trees are young, but develops alternate bearing at maturity. The fruit matures early and is picked from mid-September to early October, earliest of all commercial cultivars. The main disadvantage of Ascolano is that its fruit bruises easily during harvest. Ascolano fruit is used as canned ripe olives. The Spanish green-pickling process shrivels the fruit. The average oil content of Ascolano olives is 18.8 percent.

Diseases and Pests. Ascolano is fairly resistant to both peacock spot and olive knot. Ascolano is considered somewhat more susceptible to olive knot than Mission, but is more resistant than Manzanillo, Sevillano, and Barouni. Ascolano shows some resistance to Verticillium wilt.

Barouni

Barouni was introduced into California from Tunisia in 1905. It was planted more extensively in the early 1920s, but there have been no recent plantings.

Physical Characteristics. Barouni trees are relatively small, reaching 15 to 25 feet (5 to 8 m) at maturity, with spreading tops. Their natural growth habit makes the fruit easy to harvest by hand. The fruit is large and borne singly on peduncles. Fruit shape ranges from oval to oval-elongated. Barouni has a low flesh-to-pit ratio, averaging approximately 6.8:1.

Climatic Adaptation. Barouni is grown mostly in Butte County, and Tulare County has some small acreage. The trees show resistance to cold damage.

Bearing, Harvest, and Uses. A major advantage of Barouni is that it exhibits regular, dependable bearing. Fruit is harvested from mid-October to early November. Barouni olives are usually sold fresh for home processing since they process poorly as a commercial canned product. The small amount of fruit that is processed commercially is used for black-ripe table olives. Barouni olives have a low oil content (16.5 percent) and are not used for oil extraction.

Diseases and Pests. Barouni is susceptible to olive knot and somewhat resistant to peacock spot. Barouni is thought to be more resistant to peacock spot than Mission, but less resistant than Sevillano, Manzanillo, and Ascolano.

Oblonga

Oblonga is used only as rootstock. When used as a rootstock for Manzanillo, it produces smaller trees than own-rooted Manzanillo trees from cuttings. Oblonga can carry Verticillium wilt without showing symptoms of the disease. The fungus continues to proliferate in the rootstock, and when it reaches the scion, the scion dies. Oblonga is widely used as a rootstock for Swan Hill in Arizona.

Allegra

Allegra has potential as a *Verticillium*-resistant rootstock. It is reportedly also resistant to nematodes. Allegra does not dwarf Manzanillo as does Oblonga.

Swan Hill

Swan Hill was introduced into the United States from Australia by H. T. Hartmann in 1961 and was patented in the United States by the University of California. It has some Verticillium wilt resistance, which would be useful if it could be propagated as a rootstock. Swan Hill has not been commercially successful as a rootstock because it is extremely difficult to root from cuttings. It produces predominantly staminate flowers and thus sets very few fruit, making it desirable as an ornamental tree. It has been used as an ornamental in Arizona. Although research reports indicate that 80 to 90 percent of subapical cuttings taken in July or August could be rooted, these results are difficult to repeat on a commercial scale. Some nursery workers have reported less than 10 percent rooting. When propagated commercially as an ornamental, Swan Hill is often grafted onto an Oblonga rootstock.

PROPAGATION OF OLIVE TREES

Olive trees may be propagated sexually by seed or vegetatively by cuttings, grafting, or budding. There are several reasons why seed propagation is used mostly for breeding and rootstock production rather than for the fruit-bearing part of the tree. Olive trees do not come true from seed; moreover, seedlings retain juvenile characteristics for long periods, and may not reach full production for as long as 10 years. Production of the fruit-bearing part of the tree by vegetative means results in clonal material that has greater uniformity in critical factors, such as time of harvest, size of fruit, shape of trees, and oil content of the fruit, than could be achieved with seed propagation.

Propagation by Seed

The olive pit consists of the seed together with the stony endocarp (the hard covering surrounding the seed itself). In botanical terms, the endocarp, being derived from the ovary, is not part of the seed, whereas seeds are derived from the ovule. Olive seeds germinate slowly, taking 1 to 6 months or longer. Germination is also unreliable, ranging from 5 to 90 percent, depending on the cultivar. These variations are due to incompletely satisfied internal dormancy requirements, which may involve inhibitors in the embryo or inner seed coat. Slow and unreliable germination is also attributed to mechanical dormancy, the inability of the embryo to penetrate the endocarp.

For seed production, the fruit should be harvested when ripe, but before turning black. This period extends from late September to mid-November, depending on the cultivar. The pit is removed from the flesh of the fruit with a seed-cleaning machine.

Pits can be planted directly, but germination is slow and uneven. Pregermination treatments are designed to overcome both mechanical and internal dormancy. Mechanical or chemical scarification is used to treat mechanical dormancy. In scarification, the endocarp can be cracked mechanically or clipped at the radicle end, with care taken not to damage the embryo. Clipping just the cotyledonary end of the endocarp does not improve germination. Pits may also be scarified by soaking them in concentrated sulfuric acid. The acid chars the outside of the seed and results in softening of the endocarp. The length of time for soaking in the acid depends on the thickness of the endocarp; typical soaking times for Manzanillo are between 24 and 30 hours. The only way to determine the proper amount of soaking is by testing several time periods and then germinating the seeds. The acid bath is followed by 1 to 2 hours of water rinsing to ensure that all acid is removed.

The pits can be planted directly after the endocarp treatments. Pits should be planted at a depth approximately two to three times their diameter. Seeds planted outdoors in December do not germinate until the following spring. Pits can also be planted in pots or in a seedbed in a greenhouse maintained at a 70° to 75°F (21° to 24°C) daytime temperature. Germination may take up to 3 months. It is critical that the seeds not dry out after germination begins.

Germination is quicker and more uniform when treatments to overcome internal dormancy are carried out in addition to scarification. The most successful of these treatments on a commercial scale is stratification, also known as moist chilling. Pits are scarified as described above and then soaked in water at room temperature for 24 hours. The pits are mixed with moist sand or vermiculite and then placed in the dark in a controlled environment. The temperature is kept at 55°F (13°C) for 30 days. Stratification is thought to reduce abscisic acid (which inhibits germination) within the embryo or seed coat. After stratification, pits can be planted outdoors if the weather is suitable; severe weather can cause losses. Pits can be planted in a greenhouse maintained at a 70° to 80°F (21° to 27°C) daytime temperature. Bottom heat is necessary. Germination should occur within 1 month using this method. Transplanting seedlings from the greenhouse to the nursery should include steps to harden the seedlings, such as shade provided by a lathhouse. Adequate irrigation and fertilization through drip or hand watering are recommended to ensure continued rapid growth. It is most important to maintain appropriate nitrogen levels to ensure proper vegetative growth.

Propagation by Cuttings

Rooting shoot cuttings is the major method of propagating olive trees in California and in other major olive-producing areas, such as Spain and Italy. Cultivars vary widely in their ability to produce roots on cuttings. Rooting percentages range from 20 to 30 percent in Sevillano to 95 to 98 percent in Manzanillo, Nevadillo, or Picual. Similar variability is seen in Mission, Barouni, and Ascolano. Kalamata roots very poorly, less than 10 percent if at all. Success in rooting cuttings depends on the cultivar, the type of wood used, and the season in which cuttings are made. Cuttings can be made from hardwood or leafy stems, suckers, ovuli, or truncheons.

Hardwood Cuttings. Hardwood cuttings are made from 3- to 4-year-old wood, ranging from 1 to 3 inches (3 to 8 cm) in diameter. Wood for cuttings is gathered in late January or early February. All leaves are removed and the wood is cut into sections 8 to 12 inches (21 to 31 cm) long. It is preferable that the bottom cut be made below a node. The base of the cutting is soaked in a water solution of 10 to 20 parts per million indolebutyric acid (IBA) for 24 hours. Cuttings should be planted with correct polarity (that is, with the basal end of the cutting in soil) in flats with a mixture of perlite and vermiculite (1:2 or 1:3 v:v) and kept moist in a greenhouse at 70° to 75°F (21° to 24°C) until roots start to form. Rooting may take as long as 3 months. Rooted cuttings can be transplanted to pots or planted directly in the nursery. They should be buried one-half to three-fourths of their length. Rooted cuttings should be protected from excessive sunlight and water stress for 2 to 3 weeks after transplanting and should be hardened gradually.

Another method for handling hardwood cuttings is to treat them with IBA as described earlier. Then place them, with correct polarity, in a box, and cover them completely with moist sawdust. After storage for approximately 30 days at 60° to 70°F (16° to 21°C), they can be planted in pots or flats in the greenhouse or taken directly to the field or nursery with the same precautions previously described.

Hardwood cuttings may have less reliable rooting than smaller, leafy-stem cuttings. Use of hardwood cuttings involves removing fruiting wood, which can significantly affect fruit production if many cuttings are made from one tree.

Leafy-Stem Cuttings. Propagation by leafy cuttings was made possible by the use of intermittent mist, a technology introduced by Hudson Hartmann in the 1950s. This method reduces transpiration and leaf temperature and increases relative humidity, enabling cuttings to remain turgid throughout root induction. Leafy cuttings are prepared using 1- to 2-year-old wood from vigorous shoots. Cuttings should be approximately ¼ inch (7 mm) in diameter (fig. 4.1). Larger diameter wood, up to 3½ inches (9 cm), can also be used. Wood is collected either in spring (April and May) or in late summer (July and August). The succulent, terminal portion of the shoot is discarded. The stem is trimmed to 4 to 5 inches (10 to 12 cm) long, with a slant cut on the top and straight cut on the bottom to mark the correct polarity.

The bottom cut is made just below a node. If the bottom cut is too far below the node, the cutting will not root. Leaves are removed from all but the top 1 inch (2.5 cm) of the cuttings and the base is dipped for 5 seconds into a 50 percent alcohol solution of 4,000 parts per million IBA. Prepared root-inducing products that contain IBA and talc may also be used. The base of the cutting is dipped briefly into water and then into the powder.

The basal end of the cutting is inserted 2 inches (5 cm) into the rooting medium. The medium used for root induction must be porous and drain well yet retain some moisture. Perlite and vermiculite are generally used, in a ratio of 2:1 or 3:1 (v:v) although all perlite may be used instead of a mixture. The cuttings are then placed in a greenhouse at 70° to 75°F (21° to 24°C) daytime temperature under intermittent mist. Bottom heat at 70°F (21°C) is required to maintain the temperature in the medium because evaporation of water can lead to significant cooling. Alternatively, the cuttings can be placed in a closed frame in which the relative humidity is kept high (fig. 4.2). Bottom heat is not necessary as the closed frame results in adequate temperatures of air and rooting medium. Cuttings take 8 to 12 weeks to form roots regardless of the method used.

Cuttings that are started in late summer are kept in a greenhouse all winter. They would not survive if moved outdoors in September or October as they would be insufficiently hardened to survive winter. They are moved to individual pots under lath in early spring. Growth is often slow for a period after roots form. New trees are trained in containers to a single stem about 2 feet (61 cm) long with three main scaffolds rising from the top of the single stem.

Figure 4.1. Leafy cuttings of olive prepared for sticking.

Figure 4.2. Leafy cuttings of olive in a propagation bench.

The trees are ready to be sold in July after the winter in which the cuttings were rooted. They are usually not planted the first year but are kept in the nursery until the following March because early spring is a far better time than July to plant trees. Thus, although a complete plant can be obtained in 12 months, it is actually about 18 to 20 months from the time cuttings are taken to the time trees are planted.

Another schedule for producing trees from rooted cuttings was implemented in the early 1990s. Cuttings are taken in February from shoots grown the previous year (1-year-old wood) that measure approximately ³/₈ inch (10 mm) in diameter. The thin, terminal section is discarded and the leafy stem cuttings are treated with IBA as described above. The cuttings are placed under fog in a greenhouse. Bottom heat is maintained at 56°F (13°C), which is somewhat warmer than the outside temperature at that time of year. If the temperature of either the air or rooting mix is too high, the buds break and the cuttings do not root. After the cuttings root they are potted in 1-gallon cans and kept in a greenhouse at 86°F (30°C) in high relative humidity. These conditions promote growth of shoots and roots without the cessation of growth that occurs in cuttings taken in July. The advantage of this method is that trees can be planted in March, 1 year after cuttings are taken.

Suckers. Suckers are shoots that originate on roots or basal parts of trunks of older trees. When suckers are separated from the tree with part of the root attached, they can produce a tree ready to be planted in the orchard in 1 year. Suckers are cut back to about 18 inches (46 cm) tall and planted in the nursery together with the root section, which should be about 3 inches (8 cm) in diameter. Alternatively, suckers can be removed from the tree without any root portion and be treated as a leafy stem cutting as described previously. As suckers retain some juvenile characteristics, they are often easier to root than stem cuttings taken from higher in the tree. One disadvantage of this method is that juvenile characteristics often make the tree develop and come into production more slowly than trees grown by cuttings and grafting or budding. It is also crucial that the suckers used have grown from the scion rather than the rootstock of grafted trees.

Ovuli. Ovuli are protuberances composed of meristematic tissue that form at the base of older olive trees. Ovuli can be induced to form shoots and roots by removing them from the mother tree and covering them with soil to exclude light. Propagation from ovuli is practiced mostly in North Africa. The relative scarcity of ovuli and the damage done to the mother tree when removing them limit their use for propagation.

Budding and Grafting

Uses and compatibility. Seedlings or rooted cuttings may be used as rootstocks to propagate cultivars that are difficult to root as cuttings. Rootstocks may also be used when special characteristics, such as Verticillium wilt resistance and dwarfing, are desired. There appears to be no incompatibility among most cultivars of *Olea europaea*.

Incompatibility has been reported when *Olea europaea* has been grafted onto other species of *Olea*, such as *O. ferruginea* and *O. chrysophylla*, or onto other members of the Oleaceae, such as *Syringae*, *Fraxinus*, and *Forestiera*. Grafting within cultivars of *Olea europaea* can affect vigor. In studies by Hartmann, own-rooted Mission and Manzanillo trees were more vigorous than trees produced by grafting these cultivars onto rootstocks, regardless of which of 12 rootstocks was used. Own-rooted Sevillano, however, was less vigorous than trees produced by grafting Sevillano scions onto vigorously growing rootstocks, such as Mission and Manzanillo. The cultivars Oblonga and Allegra appear to dwarf Manzanillo somewhat but have no effect on Sevillano, Ascolano, or Mission. Use of seedling rootstocks is thought to impart variability to the tree.

General Technique. Both seedlings and rooted cuttings can be budded and grafted. Seedlings are produced as described above and are budded or grafted when 1 year old, at which time they are approximately ¼ to ½ inch (7 to 13 mm) in diameter. Rooted cuttings are budded or grafted 1 year after the cutting is taken. Rooted cuttings should also be ¼ to ½ inch (7 to 13 mm) in diameter. Thus, cuttings are rooted the first year and then budded at the beginning of the second year. The trees must be nursery grown during the second year before they are ready for planting. Because it is advisable to plant in spring rather than in summer, budded or grafted trees are held in the nursery until the following spring (beginning of the third year) before planting. It takes an additional year to produce a tree that is grafted or budded onto a rooted cutting compared with a tree produced on its own roots from a cutting. Rooted cuttings of Manzanillo are often used as rootstock for difficult-to-root cultivars, such as Sevillano, whose seeds are difficult to germinate and whose seedling rootstocks are thought to impart variability to the complete tree.

Budding. For budding propagation, the T-bud (also known as the shield bud) is most often used. The rootstock is budded in March or April when the bark is slipping. The bark of the stock must be slipping for T-budding. A cut in the shape of a "T" is cut into the bark of the scion at the point where the graft is going to be, generally 2 to 10 inches (5 to 26 cm) above the ground. A "shield" is cut from the scion starting at about ½ inch

(13 mm) below the bud, slicing under the bud to about 1 inch (2.5 cm) beyond the top of the bud. The shield should be quite thin but thick enough to have some rigidity. The top of the shield is cut off horizontally. The bud is inserted into the "T" cut starting at the top under the flaps. It is pushed down until the top of the shield and the horizontal cut of the "T" match. The bud is wrapped with a budding rubber to hold it in place and to keep the union from drying out. No waxing is required. The budding rubber will deteriorate over time and fall off. The stock is cut back to the new bud 2 to 3 weeks after budding to stimulate growth of the bud. Additional details of T-budding are available in Hartmann et al. (1997).

Grafting. Grafting is done on 1-year-old seedlings or on 1-year-old plants produced from cuttings. Nursery workers prefer grafting to budding because of the relative ease of preparation and the added insurance of success as several buds are present on grafted scionwood. Grafts do not require the bark of the stock to be slipping and thus can be made when the stock is dormant during late winter as well as in spring and early fall. The greatest success appears to be in February or March with the growth of shoots in spring. Either V-grafts (saddle grafts) or side grafts are used. V-grafts have become more popular because they are relatively easy and quick to perform and have a high rate of success.

Grafting is also used in topworking, to change the cultivars of an established tree or an entire orchard. Bark grafting is commonly used and is best done between early March and late April because it requires the bark to be slipping. Three well-spaced, primary scaffolds from 4 to 6 inches (10 to 15 cm) in diameter are selected and are cut back close to the trunk of the tree. Several nurse branches are left on the tree until the graft has made sufficient growth. This may take up to 2 years.

Scionwood should be 1-year-old wood, ¼ to ½ inch (7 to 13 mm) in diameter. It should be cut into sections containing two nodes above the point of grafting. Two to three scions are inserted on each limb. All exposed surfaces should be covered with grafting wax or a similar compound immediately after grafting. Painting the graft union, scions, and trunks of the trees with white latex paint or a commercially available whitewash compound reduces the temperature of the wood and prevents sunburn. Aftercare includes removal of suckers from below the graft union, prudent fertilization and irrigation, and gradual removal of the nurse branches after 1 or 2 years. Only one of each set of grafts on any limb is retained.

REFERENCES

Crisosto, C., and E. G. Sutter. 1985a. Improving Manzanillo olive seed germination. Hort. Sci. 20:100–102.

Crisosto, C., and E. G. Sutter. 1985b. Role of the endocarp in Manzanillo olive seed germination. J. Amer. Soc. Hort. Sci. 110:50–52.

Hartmann, H. T. 1967. Swan Hill: A new ornamental fruitless olive for California. Calif. Agric. 21:4–5.

Hartmann, H. T., D. E. Kester, F. T. Davies, and R.T. Geneve. 1997. Plant propagation: Principles and practices, 6th ed. Englewood Cliffs, NJ: Prentice Hall.

Hartmann, H. T., and F. Loreti. 1965. Seasonal variation in rooting leafy olive cuttings under mist. Proc. Amer. Soc. Hort. Sci. 87:194–198.

Hartmann, H. T., K. W. Opitz, and J. A. Beutel. 1980. Olive production in California. Berkeley: Univ. Calif. Div. Agric. Sci., Leaf. 2474.

Hartmann, H. T., and P. Papaioannou. 1951. Olive varieties in California. Berkeley: Calif. Agric. Exp. Stn. Bull. 720.

Hartmann, H. T., and J. E. Whisler. 1970. Some rootstock and interstock influences in the (Olea europaea L.) cv. Sevillano. J. Amer. Soc. Hort. Sci. 100:670–674.

Lagarda, A., G. C. Martin, and D. E. Kester. 1983. Influence of environment, seed tissue, and seed maturity on Manzanillo olive seed germination. Hort. Sci. 18:868–869.

Lee, C. I., H. C. Kohl, and J. L. Paul. 1983. Propagation of Swan Hill fruitless olive by leafy cuttings. Plant Propagator 29:11–13.

Loreti, F., and H. T. Hartmann. 1964. Propagation of olive trees by rooting leafy cuttings under mist. Proc. Amer. Soc. Hort. Sci. 85:257–264.

Nussbaum, J. J., and A. T. Leiser. 1972. Rooting cuttings of Swan Hill fruitless olive. Calif. Agric. 26:10–12.

5

Site Selection and Preparation, Tree Spacing and Design, Planting, and Initial Training

G. STEVEN SIBBETT AND JOSEPH OSGOOD

A mature olive orchard must produce moderate crops of large fruit annually in order to be profitable. Because new olive orchards are expensive to develop, it is equally important that they reach economic bearing as soon as possible after planting. Economic bearing is considered the point at which the income from a crop exceeds its harvesting costs. To make this happen, yields must increase quickly during an orchard's premature years. Proper planning that includes site selection, preparation, orchard design and tree spacing, planting, and initial training is critical to attaining this objective.

SELECTING A SITE

The orchard site strongly affects its capacity to produce. Prospective growers must give considerable attention to the local climate, physical and chemical qualities of the soil, and amount and quality of water that will be available to the trees.

Climatic Considerations

The best olive production and quality occur in areas with mild winters and long, warm, dry summers to mature the fruit. Olives are subtropical trees, sensitive to hard freezing temperatures. The small wood and branches are injured, often killed, by temperatures below 22°F (–6°C). Minor freeze injury to fruit wood causes openings that are easily invaded by the olive knot bacterium, which kills the injured area. Large limbs and whole trees can be killed if temperatures fall below 15°F (–9°C). Cultivars differ in their sensitivity to freeze damage; the vegetative growth of Manzanillo is more sensitive to freezing than Mission, Sevillano, and Ascolano. Olive fruit is also injured by freezing temperatures during the growing and maturation period. Districts having a high probability of frost before harvest should be avoided. Winter temperatures fluctuating between 35° and 65°F (2° and 18°C) are ideal, supplying the winter chilling that many olive cultivars need for subsequent flower development.

Flower bud development, pollination, and ultimate fruit set are influenced by climatic conditions. Prolonged cold (<55°F [13°C]) and wet weather during the bloom development period results in fewer perfect flowers and more staminate flowers than normal (see chapter 8: Flowering, Pollination, Fruiting, Alternate Bearing, and Abscission). The same conditions hinder pollination and thus reduce fruit set. Conversely, hot, dry conditions during bloom shorten the receptive period and desiccate the flowers.

Areas where summer rainfall is common should also be avoided. Epidemics of fungal and bacterial diseases can injure trees and reduce their productivity. Additional management expense is required for disease control in such areas.

Soil

Although olive trees adapt to a wide variety of soils, production is best where the trees can develop roots without chemical or physical restriction. The soil's physical and chemical condition is critical to olive production.

Physical Soil Condition. The physical condition of a soil describes its texture, depth, and stratification. Olives prefer unstratified, moderately fine textured soils, including sandy loam, loam, silt loam, clay loam, and silty clay loam. Such soils provide aeration for root growth, are quite permeable, and have adequate water holding capacity. Sandier soils do not have good nutrient or water holding capacity, and heavier clays often do not have adequate aeration for root growth. These soils are difficult to manage for maximum production.

Olive trees are shallow rooted and do not require very deep soils to produce well. Soils with an unstratified profile of 4 feet (1.2 m) are suitable for olive. Stratified soils, either cemented hardpan or varying soil textures within the described profile, impede water movement resulting in saturated layers that damage olive roots.

Soil Chemistry. Olives tolerate soils of varying chemical quality. Although trees grow or produce on moderately acid soils (pH 5.0–7.0), basic soils (pH <8.5) are most productive. Olive trees tolerate relatively high levels of boron (2 ppm) and chloride (10–15 meq/l) in soils. Sodic soils that cannot be reclaimed should be avoided since their poor structure prevents water penetration and drainage, creating saturated soil conditions that kill olive roots.

Water

Olive trees require about 3 acre-feet per acre (3,699 m^3/.04 ha) of water per year to be productive. Although olives are drought tolerant, California orchards require supplemental irrigation during the growing season to satisfy the trees' water requirements and to produce optimal crops. Adequate water must be available throughout the season for tree growth and maximum production (see chapter 10: Olive Irrigation Management).

Olive trees tolerate water that is relatively high in boron, up to 3 ppm. However, irrigation water that is high in nitrogen promotes excessive vegetative growth that hinders fruit production. Excess sodium in supplemental water accumulates in the soil, causing sodic soil conditions and water penetration problems. Water analysis can be a valuable tool in selecting a site and in managing an orchard. The most valuable chemical measurements of a water sample include acidity or alkalinity (pH), electrical conductivity (EC_w), sodium (Na^+), bicarbonate (HBO_3^-), sodium absorption ratio (SAR), chloride (Cl^-), boron (B^+), and nitrate nitrogen (NO_3-N).

PREPARING A SITE

Proper site preparation is essential to the ultimate profitability of an olive orchard. Preparation includes ensuring uniform water application to the trees by leveling the land or selecting appropriate irrigation systems, deep tillage to destroy cemented, compacted, or layers of differing soil textures that impede water movement in the soil profile, fumigation to destroy plant parasitic nematodes (for example, root lesion, citrus, and root knot nematodes), and installation of the irrigation system. Site preparation is completed before the orchard is planted. The best time to prepare the site is before rains begin in fall of the year before spring planting.

Leveling

Maximum production occurs when all of the trees are uniformly supplied with water. How much to level or grade the land to promote this uniform water supply

depends on the original terrain and the cost of moving earth versus the cost of an irrigation system designed for rolling or sloping land.

If an orchard is to be flood or furrow irrigated, leveling the land for uniform water application to all trees is recommended. For all but quite sandy soils, the orchard floor should be leveled flat. It is better to shorten irrigation runs than to level to grade as a way of facilitating water movement over long distances. The latter practice often results in overly wet ends with less water available to the middle portion of the row. If flood or furrow irrigation is to be used on sandy soils where it is difficult to move water, leveling to a slight grade (.05 to .10 ft per 100 ft [1.5 to 3 cm per 30.5 m] of irrigation run) is recommended.

Some sites have rolling or sloping terrain, where leveling would incur either excessive cost or environmental damage. For such sites, using sprinkler or low-volume irrigation is more cost effective than leveling.

Deep Tillage

Once the land has been leveled, the next step is deep tillage. This process, involving rippers, moldboard plows, slip plows, and so on (fig 5.1), breaks compacted, cemented, or textural layers that impede water movement within the soil profile; olive trees are killed when saturated soil conditions in the root zone result from poor drainage. Soils with 4 feet (1.2 m) of uninterrupted profile do not usually require deep tillage. A backhoe should be used to examine the soil profile in several representative areas of the field to determine the method of deep tillage, if any, that is required.

Ripping, pulling a 3- to 5-foot (0.9- to 1.5-m) shank through the soil profile with a track-layer tractor, breaks up cemented, hardpan layers. Once these layers are shattered, they do not recement during the life of the orchard. Ripping should be done both in and between the proposed tree rows.

Slip and moldboard plows are used to invert the soil profile where the blade is placed. This practice is usually more costly, since it usually requires more power than ripping, but it is effective if the soil layers are compacted or textural; ripping does not work where textural or compacted strata exist because they cannot be broken like cemented (hardpan) layers. A backhoe can be used to excavate individual tree sites, but the local flowerpot effect may eventually impede water drainage. Ripping or slip plowing is usually done in the proposed tree row.

Fumigation

After leveling and deep tillage, fumigation destroys parasitic nematodes (root lesion, citrus, root knot, and so

Figure 5.1. Equipment used to modify the soil profile: (A) ripper, (B) moldboard plow, (C) slip plow.

on) and eliminates weeds. Any nematode or weed problem should be assessed carefully before planting to determine whether fumigation is necessary.

Fumigation is an expensive practice and must be done correctly to be effective. It is essential that the soil be prepared and at the proper temperature and moisture conditions for treatment. Manufacturers of fumigants and commercial applicators supply directions for proper soil preparation.

Selecting and Installing the Irrigation System

The irrigation system should be selected and installed before the olive grove is planted. All irrigation systems can deliver the proper amount of water to the trees if they are used in the circumstances for which they are designed.

System selection is based on its initial cost, its maintenance, the terrain to be irrigated, and the cost and availability of water. Low-volume systems—drip, mister/fogger, mini-sprinkler, and fan jet—are expensive but efficient and well adapted to sloping land. They apply small, precise amounts of water (usually 1 to 15 gal [3.7 to 55.5 L] per hour) to localized areas around the trees when terrain cannot be economically leveled to the degree necessary for less expensive systems. Low-volume irrigation is also useful when water is costly and must be used most efficiently and when automation is desired. Sprinkler systems are expensive but useful on sloping terrain. Sprinklers apply more water per hour than low-volume systems and are suitable where runoff does not occur. Sprinklers can be permanently set in the orchard or on movable hoses or pipelines. Movable systems have less initial expense, but their use is labor intensive. Furthermore, movable systems operate every day, so some part of the orchard is wet on any given day, hindering access for other cultural work. Pipeline systems and open-ditch systems usually cost the least and are quite effective if water is inexpensive and abundant and the orchard floor is flat to ensure uniform distribution.

The irrigation system should be installed before planting. The best time to install the system is after pre-plant preparation. Once the trees are planted it is more difficult to install an irrigation system.

TREE SPACING

Optimal olive orchard designs involve planting trees for optimal use of space and maximizing cultural efficiency. Maximum production from the young and mature orchard is a result of effective orchard design. The following considerations are important in designing a new olive orchard.

Sunlight

The olive tree bears fruit on 1-year-old wood found on its outer periphery in the presence of adequate sunlight (color plate 5.1). Olive shoots do not flower and do not produce fruit in full shade. If shoots become shaded, production decreases. A mature orchard is considered at optimal bearing potential when trees are spaced and managed at the greatest density that still lets them intercept enough sunlight for annual productive shoot growth on the tree's periphery.

New olive orchards must produce economic crops as soon as possible. How soon an orchard reaches economic bearing depends on tree density. Before trees reach full size and utilize all allotted space and sunlight, per-acre production is directly related to the number of producing trees. Olive orchards are therefore commonly planted at high densities to use the sunlight most efficiently and reach maximum production quickly. Such high-density planting assumes that either some trees are removed as they grow crowded or that the planting is managed to confine each tree or row to an allotted space. Tree-to-tree competition for water and nutrients increases with tree density, but competition alone does not restrict tree size sufficiently. It is still necessary to remove trees or to use intense row management techniques.

Tree Size and Soil Type

Cultivar and soil type largely determine a tree's ultimate size, which must be considered when spacing trees. Sevillano, Mission, and Ascolano cultivars are vigorous and grow to a large size. Manzanillo is a moderately sized, spreading tree and requires much less space than other cultivars. All cultivars develop their maximum size on fertile, well-drained soils. Trees on marginal soils do not grow as large. Larger-growing olive cultivars on good soils require approximately 40 feet (12 m) between trunks if trees are to be farmed as individual production units; Manzanillo requires only a 30-foot (9-m) spacing. Closer in-row spacing can be used if the tree row is managed as the production unit.

Harvest Method

If trees are to be hand harvested, considerable flexibility in tree spacing is available. However, when a mechanized harvest is anticipated, ease of access to trees by large equipment must be ensured. Row spacing decisions must consider equipment access.

DESIGNING THE OLIVE ORCHARD

There are several appropriate orchard designs for olives. In all cases, the design must (1) provide maximum sunlight exposure to the planned number of trees both initially and when they reach full size, and (2) allow for efficient orchard equipment operation.

When determining tree configuration within the orchard, the first decision that must be made is what the productive unit will ultimately be, the individual tree or the row. Where individual trees are to be the productive unit, these are spaced in a design that ensures light to the entire productive tree canopy. Temporary trees, alternate trees that are removed as the orchard crowds, can be included in these designs. When the tree row is to be used as the productive unit, a hedgerow configuration is used.

Individual Trees As the Production Unit

Filler Trees. The first decision to be made before selecting a design is whether or not filler trees are to be used to increase tree density and early production. The choice depends on the grower's goals. Filler trees increase (and usually double) tree density during the first 6 to 10 years. Such a high-density orchard begins production sooner and reaches higher levels than an orchard with standard spacing during the same period. However, the greater number of trees per acre translates into higher development and managerial costs. Also, any cultural practice done on a per-tree basis (such as training, pruning, and fertilizing) results in higher per-acre production costs. Finally, removing filler trees once the orchard becomes too crowded is expensive.

Filler trees are usually placed between permanent trees that are set 30 to 40 feet (9 to 12 m) apart in a square design. Two designs are well suited for filler trees: hedgerow and offset square/diamond.

Square. The square pattern is the most popular design and is used by most olive orchardists. Trees are equally spaced within and between rows so that a line drawn from one tree to its closest neighbor in the next row forms a right angle to the rows (fig. 5.2). With a square design, trees are usually spaced at distances of 20 to 35 feet (6 to 11 m). The square is popular because it is easy to lay out and orchard operations can be carried out in both directions. Filler trees are often included in an orchard designed as a square by placing them half way between the permanent trees down the row. Such trees are in place to improve the early productivity of the orchard. These must be removed later to avoid crowding and shading the permanent trees.

Offset Square. This system is similar to the square design except that trees in adjacent rows are offset (fig. 5.3). At a given permanent tree spacing, the square and offset square designs have an equal number of trees per acre.

This design is less popular than the square. It is more difficult to lay out, and unless farmed on the diagonal, the rows are closer.

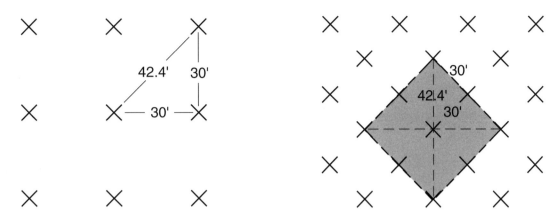

Figure 5.2. Tree spacing: square pattern.

Figure 5.3. Tree spacing: offset square pattern.

Hexagonal or Equilateral Triangle. The hexagonal/equilateral triangle design is similar to the offset square except that distances between trees in any direction are equal, so that lines drawn between three trees produce an equilateral triangle (fig. 5.4). This system cannot be used with filler trees. However, it is the most efficient in use of both sunlight and land and allows 17.5 percent per acre (43.2 percent/ha) more trees than the square or offset square at any given spacing.

Quincunx. In the quincunx design, the permanent trees are set in a square pattern with a filler tree in the center of each square (fig. 5.5). Filler trees can be left in the orchard longer in a quincunx planting before shade interferes with permanent tree production.

   The main disadvantage of the quincunx design is that initially there are twice as many tree rows as will be in the permanent planting, so establishment and operating costs are proportionally higher. The rows of filler trees may need separate irrigation lines, adding to orchard development costs. Access with equipment is more difficult, and more middles must be driven to perform cultural practices. Unplanted drive rows should be left every 6 to 10 rows to allow access for harvest equipment.

Tree Rows As the Production Unit

Hedgerow or Rectangle. The hedgerow or rectangle design places trees closer within rows than between rows (fig. 5.6). This is a permanent system, and trees are spaced 10 to 20 feet (3 to 6 m) apart down the row. With this system, the tree is no longer the productive unit but is merely a component of a tree row that is managed to produce olives. Harvest and pruning operations are usually mechanized so row spacing must allow easy access by equipment. Row direction is a very significant factor in hedgerow olive plantings. Hedgerow or rectangular configured orchards must be laid out with north-south rows to use sunlight most effectively.

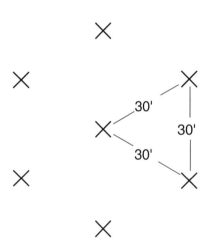

Figure 5.4. Tree spacing: hexagonal pattern.

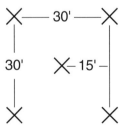

Figure 5.5. Tree spacing: quincunx pattern.

Figure 5.6. Tree spacing: hedgerow/rectangular pattern.

Figure 5.7. Nursery trees ready for sale.

36 to 48 inches (91 to 122 cm) long at the nursery (fig. 5.7). These trees are planted with the soil intact around the root system.

Canned or balled trees can be planted throughout the year, since the soil is intact around the roots. The best time to plant in the interior valley olive districts, however, is in March or April at the start of the growing season, when the threat of frost is past. Plantings made in the hot midsummer are more difficult to establish, and growth is mediocre the first year. Nursery trees planted in September and October can be severely damaged by a freeze, so it is recommended that nursery stock be held over and protected until the next March or April. Districts with more moderate climates have more flexibility in planting date.

Pollinizer Placement

Pollinizer varieties are used in large blocks or isolated locations to enhance pollination for optimal production of olives (see chapter 8: Flowering, Pollination, Fruiting, Alternate Bearing, and Abscission). Research has shown that the most effective dissemination of wind-blown pollen occurs within a 100-foot (30-m) radius of the pollinizer. Pollinizer trees or rows should be spaced every 200 feet (61 m) in a new orchard. Olive varieties differ in ultimate tree size, and row or tree spacing may need to be adjusted accordingly for pollinizer placement.

PLANTING AND TRAINING OLIVE TREES

Planting

Canned Trees. Olive nursery trees are commonly sold as canned or balled stock. Trees are rooted for 2 to 3 months in beds then transplanted to 1-gallon cans, burlap, or plastic tubes and grown for 12 to 18 months in the nursery. They are usually trained to a single trunk

Bare-Root Trees. Olive trees are occasionally available as bare-root trees. Bare-root trees are produced by rooting directly in the nursery row, growing the trees for at least 2 years, then digging them up during late winter for direct orchard planting. Ideally, bare-root trees are trained to one trunk, but more often they come with several low shoots near ground level. All but one should be removed at planting time.

Bare-root trees are dug in mid to late winter for orchard planting in January, February, or March, before the onset of new growth. In heavy soils, planting should be delayed to avoid root damage from saturated soil. Bare-root trees must have their roots kept moist at all times once dug from the nursery. If planting is delayed, bare-root trees must be heeled in moist soil to prevent root desiccation.

Truncheons. Some growers plant large portions of olive branches, called truncheons. These pieces are 3 to 4 inches (8 to 10 cm) in diameter, approximately 12 inches (31 cm) long, and are planted horizontally several inches deep in late winter. Numerous shoots develop from truncheons, making them difficult to train in a conventional manner. Erratic survival, slower initial development, and multiple shoot growth are disadvantages of this type of planting stock when compared to conventional nursery stock.

Digging Holes and Planting the Trees. The hole for new olive trees should be large enough to accommodate the root system and, if trees are canned or balled, the accompanying soil. Take care not to glaze the sides of the tree hole during digging as this limits lateral root growth and water movement. Once the tree hole is dug, chop at the sides with a shovel to destroy any glazing before planting. The tree's roots should not be crammed into the hole, and the tree should not be planted deeper than in the can or nursery.

When planting the new olive tree, prune off any broken roots and long roots that do not easily fit into the tree hole. Once the tree is placed at the desired depth, refill with soil, tamping firmly until the hole is filled. At this point, the tree should be very difficult to pull up by hand.

Immediately after planting, wet the soil around the tree thoroughly. Adequate moisture should be maintained around the tree during the growing season, but take care not to overwater. Olive trees are sensitive to saturated soils. Once the tree is established, proper weed control and light nitrogen applications (1 oz [28 g] of actual nitrogen per tree) ensures good growth throughout the season.

Sunburn, Weed Killer, and Animal Protection. Trunks of newly planted trees sunburn readily and can be damaged by animals and weed killer if left exposed. Protective paper or foil wrappers 18 inches (46 cm) tall provide adequate protection. As the trunk grows, the wrappers must be removed to prevent the ties from girdling the trunk. Painted-on whitening agents such as interior, water-based white latex paint prevent sunburn, but do not protect trees from contact weed killers or animal damage.

Training

There are two training objectives during the first 3 years of olive orchard development. The first is to develop a strong, well-spaced framework of uncongested scaffold branches to support heavy crops and facilitate shaker attachment for mechanical harvest. The second is to bring the new olive trees into bearing as soon as possible. Initial training and pruning during these 3 years are largely responsible for reaching these objectives simultaneously. Therefore, while pruning should be sufficient to direct the tree's growth, it should also be kept to a minimum to promote early production.

After Planting. Once the tree is planted, only shoots below a 30-inch (76-cm) height should be removed, and the leader should be pinched at 36 to 40 inches (91 to 102 cm) to stimulate lateral growth. If lateral shoots above 30 inches (76 cm) have begun growth on the tree in the nursery, no pinching of the terminal is necessary.

First Summer. Early in the growing season, select three to five lateral-growing, upright shoots to be the scaffold branches. Space the scaffolds around the trunk, leaving sufficient distance between them to allow eventual shaker access if that method of harvest is planned. A vertical separation of 1 to 2 inches (2.5 to 5 cm) between scaffolds is necessary to provide strength in attachment to the trunk. Remove any other vigorous shoots on the trunk while they are quite small to direct growth into the selected scaffolds. Avoid selecting scaffolds late in the growing season since large cuts delay production.

Training and pruning olive trees should be avoided during dormancy. Such pruning usually requires heavier cutting, which adversely affects production and renders the new tree more susceptible to freezing injury because protective branches are removed.

Second and Third Growing Seasons. The only training and pruning suggested for the second and third growing seasons serves to continue directing tree growth into the framework branches. Usually all that is required is the early removal of suckers, waterspouts, and excessively low-hanging shoots. Excessive cutting should be avoided because it delays the onset of bearing. Once bearing begins, ideally in the third growing season, a secondary scaffold system of two to three branches per primary scaffold can be selected and developed. Heavy cutting should be avoided until moderate bearing begins (fig. 5.8).

Figure 5.8. With little pruning, this 4-year-old tree is trained for maximum cropping.

6

Carbohydrate and Nitrogen Assimilation

WILLIAM H. KRUEGER

Sixteen elements are considered essential for plant growth and development. Two of those, carbon and oxygen, come from the air. The others are provided by the soil. In order of magnitude required by the plant, they are carbon, hydrogen, oxygen, nitrogen, phosphorus, potassium, sulfur, calcium, magnesium, iron, manganese, copper, boron, zinc, molybdenum, and chloride. The first nine are referred to as macronutrients because they are required in large quantities; the remaining seven are known as micronutrients because they are required in minute quantities.

Carbon in combination with hydrogen, oxygen, nitrogen, phosphorus, and sulfur enables living organisms to store and transfer energy via chemical binding and transformation. Only green plants and some bacteria have the ability to convert inorganic substances to organic (carbon-containing) compounds by photosynthesis. In this process (fig.6.1), energy from the sun is trapped in green pigments (chlorophyll) and used to convert carbon dioxide and water into simple carbohydrates, giving off oxygen in the process. Carbohydrates are carbon-containing compounds that contain hydrogen and oxygen at a ratio of 2:1. These products are known as photosynthates.

In the reverse process, respiration, these carbohydrates are broken down to carbon dioxide and water, and energy, is released. Respiration is basic to all plant and animal life and, unlike photosynthesis, can occur without light or chlorophyll.

PHOTOSYNTHESIS

In photosynthesis, six molecules of carbon dioxide combine with six molecules of water to form one molecule of glucose and six molecules of oxygen. Glucose is transformed into other simple sugars such as fructose, sucrose, and a sugar alcohol known as mannitol. Mannitol is thought to be the main translocated sugar in olives and is also an important storage product. Glucose serves as a building block for other carbohydrates such as starch, cellulose, hemicellulose, pectins, and gums.

Carbon dioxide (CO_2), which makes up about 0.03 percent of the Earth's atmosphere, diffuses into the olive leaf through stomata, specialized pores located on the leaf undersurface. Water is distributed by the plant's vascular system. In addition to allowing for the entry of carbon dioxide into the leaf, the stomata allow for the loss of water vapor into the atmosphere through transpiration. The opening of the stomata is actively regulated to allow just enough carbon dioxide into the leaf for photosynthesis to continue. If water is in short supply, the stomata close to reduce water loss and photosynthesis is reduced.

Carbon dioxide is absorbed by chlorophyll-containing cells and photosynthesized during daylight hours into water-soluble carbohydrates.

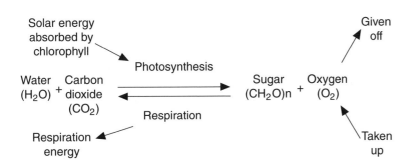

Figure 6.1. The use of solar radiant energy to convert carbon dioxide and water into energy-rich sugars and oxygen is called photosynthesis. In the reverse reaction, respiration, sugar is broken down by living cells into carbon dioxide and water, releasing chemical energy.

Factors Influencing Photosynthesis

Light Interception. Any tissue containing chlorophyll is capable of photosynthesis. Leaves are the primary units of photosynthesis in olives. An olive leaf exposed to full sun can only use a portion of the light for photosynthesis. It becomes light saturated, reaching its maximum photosynthetic rate, at approximately 30 percent full sun. Only leaves on the outer edge of the canopy are ever exposed to full sun, and these only for a portion of the day as the sun crosses the sky. Therefore, for most of the day, photosynthesis in most of the leaves is not light saturated. Light becomes even more limiting inside the tree canopy. Because the product of photosynthesis is used in fruit development, light management to maximize photosynthesis is an important part of maximizing yields.

The total leaf area of a tree divided by the land area the tree occupies is called the Leaf Area Index (LAI) and is one criterion for land productivity. Optimal LAI occurs when all leaves can contribute to the carbon gain in the plant. Because light intensity and leaf area are critical to maximum photosynthesis, plant spacing, row orientation, and pruning and training are important considerations in starting a new orchard. Increasing plant density and minimizing pruning can result in high early yields. As trees become crowded, LAI increases, but the efficiency of photosynthesis declines unless the canopy is pruned to manage light distribution. Pruning costs in high density plantings may become excessive.

Temperature. Photosynthesis is optimal in olives at temperatures between 59° and 86°F (15° to 30°C). During California summers, low-temperature inhibition of photosynthesis is rare, but photosynthesis may often be reduced by excessive heat.

Carbon Dioxide Concentration. Carbon dioxide concentration in the Earth's atmosphere rarely varies enough to affect photosynthesis. However, carbon dioxide must enter the leaf to be utilized, and anything that reduces diffusion into the leaf reduces photosynthesis.

Nutrient Supply. Every molecule of chlorophyll contains four nitrogen atoms and one magnesium atom. Phosphorus plays a vital role in energy transfer and metabolism. Iron, manganese, molybdenum, and zinc regulate enzyme activity. Deficiencies in one or more of these elements result in chlorosis and limit photosynthesis. Additionally, any deficiency in a nutrient such as nitrogen that reduces leaf growth also reduces photosynthesis.

Water Supply. Water stress limits photosynthesis by directly affecting the photochemical processes involved or by causing stomata to close, which limits carbon dioxide availability. In a typical olive leaf with good sun exposure on a summer day, the stomatal opening increases as light intensity increases, reaching its maximum by midmorning. Afternoon temperatures may be excessive, and stomata may narrow or close to prevent water loss.

Translocation and Storage of Photosynthates

Many of the photosynthates produced in olive leaves are stored in the leaf as mannitol, and some are translocated out for use or storage in other plant parts. Mature leaves, which remain on the tree for up to 3 years, are the main source of photosynthates. Growing shoot and root tips and developing fruit utilize these photosynthates and are referred to as sinks. Half-expanded leaves are highly efficient photosynthetically but need to retain much of their photosynthates for growth; thus, they are both source and sink. The concept of source-sink relationships is used to describe the internal competition for photosynthate within the plant.

During years of heavy crops, developing fruit has a high demand for photosynthate. Consequently, vegetative growth is reduced. Additionally, previously deposited storage products are mobilized into developing fruit.

Photosynthates move from leaves through the phloem to twigs and limbs. In limbs, phloem tissue is found on the inner side of bark and consists primarily of specialized pipe-like structures called sieve tubes that transport organic substances to developing root and shoot tips and to newly forming cells (the cambium) that add girth to trunk and roots.

The xylem is made up largely of vascular bundles and mainly serves to conduct water and nutrients absorbed from the soil solution to the leaves. In stems, trunk, and roots, the xylem tissue is the wood. As the tree grows each year, the new xylem adds another ring to the trunk. Dissolved elements usually remain in the leaf cells while the water evaporates from leaf surfaces or passes through the stomata.

RESPIRATION

Respiration is the reverse of photosynthesis: the photosynthates are broken down using oxygen, to yield chemical energy and carbon dioxide (fig. 6.1). This energy is used for carrying on metabolism in other parts of the plant.

Respiration can be divided into two types: maintenance and growth. Maintenance respiration goes on continually and is necessary to keep tissue healthy and functioning efficiently as metabolically active compounds, such as enzymes, are continually broken down and rebuilt. Maintenance respiration takes place at a lower rate during winter than in summer. Growth respiration occurs when new tissues are developing as photosynthates are converted into products required by the plant to build new tissue.

Factors Influencing Respiration

Temperature. Respiration is catalyzed by enzymes that are temperature sensitive. In the temperature range of 50°F (10°C) to 86°F (30°C) the respiration rate doubles for each 18°F (10°C) increase in temperature. Near-freezing temperatures change the fluidity of the protein and the water, and the reaction rate slows. At temperatures greater than 104°F (40°C), the enzymes can be denatured so the reaction slows.

Oxygen. Oxygen is generally not limiting in aboveground parts; however, in heavy or waterlogged soils it can be limiting in the roots. This can reduce respiration and limit root growth and nutrient uptake.

Soluble Carbohydrates. In a healthy olive tree, mannitol and other sugars are produced in the leaf and exported to all parts of the tree. They are converted to glucose at their destination and used in respiration or stored as reserve food in the form of starch, sugars, or sugar alcohol (manitol). Factors that inhibit photosynthesis thus limit carbohydrates supplied to the cells and reduce respiration.

Internal Factors. Changes in the physiological state of the plant tissues, such as leaf age or growth cycles, affect respiration rates. Plant tissues are less active during winter, so respiration rates are lower. Hormones are thought to regulate the physiological state of plant tissue, and therefore indirectly affect respiration rates.

CARBON ECONOMY OF THE TREE

The carbon economy of an olive tree as discussed to this point is summarized in figure 6.2. Carbon in the form of CO_2 is taken up during photosynthesis and converted to carbohydrates, which are transported to various parts of the plant. These serve as energy sources for maintenance and growth respiration or as building blocks in new plant parts. Carbon is lost in three ways: crop harvest, pruning and leaf loss, and losses to pests and diseases.

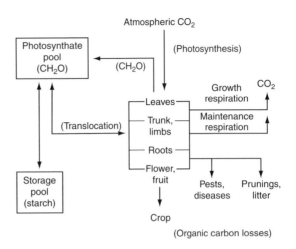

Figure 6.2. Diagram of an olive tree's carbon economy.

NITROGEN CYCLE IN ORCHARDS

Nitrogen is the element most often deficient in the soil solution and the one on which most fertilizer programs are based. The Earth's atmosphere is 78 percent nitrogen. Atmospheric nitrogen is not readily available for use by plants and must first be converted to various organic and inorganic forms common in soils. This conversion process is known as nitrogen fixation. While some fixation occurs in the atmosphere due to photochemical reactions and lightning discharges, the bulk of it occurs in the soil and is accomplished by a variety of soil-dwelling microorganisms. They convert atmospheric nitrogen to proteinaceous material and ammonium ion (NH_4^+). This fixed nitrogen finds its way into the organic fraction of the soil and is retained in semistable form. Nitrogen mineralization (the breakdown and release of nitrogen in soil organic matter) and its reabsorption by plants and return to the soil in residues make up the continuous process known as the nitrogen cycle (fig. 6.3). In an olive orchard where nitrogen is removed in the crop and prunings, it is necessary to return nitrogen through fertilizer in order to maintain high yields.

Soils generally contain no more than 1 percent nitrogen, of which only 2 to 10 percent is water soluble. Stored nitrogen in organic matter becomes available through mineralization (fig. 6.3). The first step in mineralization is the formation of amino (NH_2) compounds through enzymatic hydrolysis of proteins. These amino compounds are either utilized by microorganisms or rapidly transformed to ammonia (NH_4^+) by ammonification. The ammonia ion can be absorbed by plants or microorganisms, or it can be held as an exchangeable ion by soil particles.

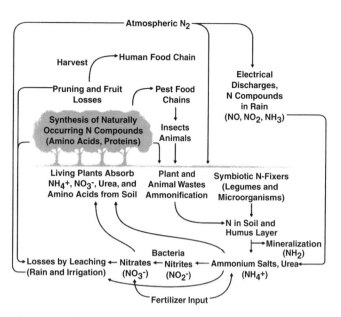

Figure 6.3. The nitrogen cycle.

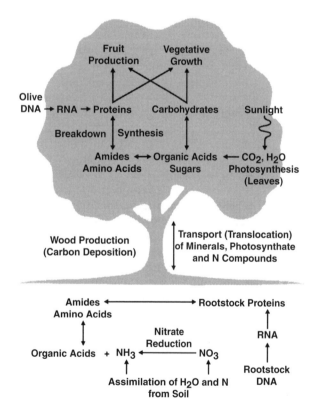

Figure 6.4. Nitrate reduction and related processes for the formation of organic nitrogenous compounds during vegetative and productive development of the olive tree.

The ammonia ion is usually rapidly converted, first to nitrite (NO_2^-) by a group of bacteria known as Nitrosomas. Nitrite is then converted to nitrate (NO_3^-) by the Nitrobacter group of bacteria. Normally, t he conversion to nitrate is more rapid than the conversion to nitrite, and nitrite does not build up in the soil. Nitrate is the most common form of nitrogen that is absorbed and utilized by olives.

Nitrates and ammonia are removed from the soil solution and used by the olive tree along with carbohydrates to produce amino acids and, in turn, proteins. When the leaves fall or the plants die or are eaten by nematodes, insects, or animals, the nitrogen is eventually returned to the soil.

Nitrogen can be lost from the soil through crop removal, pruning, denitrification, volatilization, runoff, and leaching to groundwater. In denitrification, nitrate is reduced to volatile oxides of nitrogen and elemental nitrogen by microorganisms. This loss is greatest under low soil oxygen and abundant nitrate conditions.

NITROGEN UPTAKE AND ASSIMILATION

The nitrate taken up from the soil is reduced to the ammonia ion in root cells, which reacts immediately with organic acids and respiration by-products to form various nitrogenous compounds (fig. 6.4). The simplest of these are amino acids, the building blocks for protein.

Some of the amino acids are converted to proteins by the growing roots, and some are transported to aerial plant parts, mostly through the xylem. A portion of the nitrogenous component is absorbed by cells in the cambium of the trunk and scaffold limbs, to be assimilated by the newly dividing cells that add to the girth of the tree. As these cells mature, their contents are redissolved and carried upward to newer tissues. Cells in mature vessels lose their endwalls and thus become very efficient at transporting water and solutes. This accounts for the presence of nitrogenous compounds in sap.

Dissolved substances not absorbed in transit are carried to growing shoot tips where they are assimilated into various structures. The kinds and amounts of different nitrogen compounds assimilated by tissues depend on their physiological age and factors such as plant age and light exposure. Cultural practices may affect assimilation patterns inasmuch as they affect stress in the plant and light distribution within the canopy.

7
Root Physiology and Rootstock Characteristics

JOSEPH H. CONNELL AND PETER B. CATLIN

Tree root systems are difficult to study as the examination itself usually alters them profoundly. Thus, the extent and quality of information about roots in their natural environment are subject to considerable uncertainty. The olive root system adds further complexity because of its extent, bulk, and perennial nature, with carryover effects from season to season. Fortunately, research has revealed a general similarity in behavior among woody perennial plants, so that reasonable interpretations and projections are possible.

Until a problem affecting roots becomes severe enough to limit shoot growth or production, the underground part of the tree is often taken for granted. The tree's aboveground and underground parts depend intimately on each other; thus, an appreciation of what is, or should be, occurring in the roots is fundamental to understanding the tree.

ROOT SYSTEMS AND COMPONENTS

Roots and root systems consist of a number of components. A framework consisting of relatively few large roots extends both laterally and vertically (fig. 7.1). From this root framework there are branching and rebranching laterals of decreasing diameter. This branched network terminates with the tips of recently formed fine roots. Root systems are shorter vertically and more spreading than the aboveground growth, a profile especially common in species that are adapted to arid or semiarid conditions. Olives are commonly planted on shallow soils, and roots are frequently restricted to the top 3 to 4 feet (0.9 to 1.2 m); even in deeper soils they tend to remain shallow rooted. As with other orchard species, olives generally have approximately 70 percent of their roots in the top 2 feet (0.6 m) of soil.

Figure 7.1. Form of root system expected for a mature olive tree.

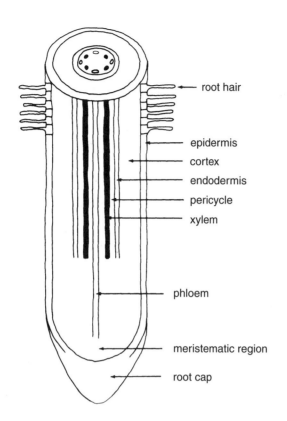

Figure 7.2. Diagram of an actively growing root tip including the internal tissues.

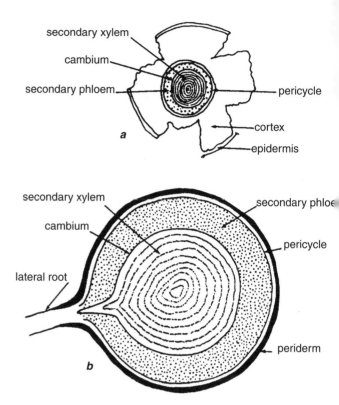

Figure 7.3. Cross-section diagrams of roots with secondary development: (a) early stage and (b) advanced stage.

Branching or lateral root formation does not fit a regular pattern, and roots are not uniformly distributed in the soil. Root systems remain in balance with the shoots, but this balance changes with age and can be altered by cultural management. Tree root systems are considerably lighter than aboveground portions on a weight basis.

Root systems consist of at least two different types of roots, those that are short-lived and those that develop secondary enlargement. The form and tissues of recently formed roots, including the root tip, are shown in figure 7.2. New roots may become highly branched with laterals arising from cell division and differentiation originating in the pericycle. Elongating and recently matured new roots may persist for varying lengths of time, but these are usually short-lived, frequently lasting only several weeks.

In some new roots, a vascular cambium forms and secondary development or enlargement occurs. Cell division in the cambium produces new xylem (wood) toward the inside and new phloem (bark) toward the outside (fig. 7.3a). As this occurs, tissues external to the pericycle collapse, are sloughed off, and decay. Another change is the formation of periderm and suberization. Periderm (fig. 7.3b) is analogous to the corky outer bark of stems. Suberin, a complex mixture of fatty substances, resins, and tannins, is deposited in association with cell walls of the outer periderm. Death of outer periderm cells and suberin account for the dark external color of older roots. As the diameter of large framework roots increases, there is a greater proportion of xylem in relation to the exterior tissues that are gradually sloughed off (fig. 7.3b).

There is some variation in the fine roots that occur in woody perennial plants. In one type, the cortex and associated tissues are lost, surfaces become suberized and turn brown, but little if any secondary thickening occurs. In other instances roots become brown, but the cortex remains. Both types persist as fine brown roots, 2 millimeters or less in diameter, for up to several seasons. These small roots probably account for more than 80 percent of the total length of the root system. Outer cells appear to be suberized.

ROOT FUNCTIONS

Roots provide five primary functions: anchorage, absorption of water, absorption of nutrients, synthesis, and storage of chemicals. How well they carry out these functions has much to do with the growth and production of the aboveground part of the tree. Root function can depend on the type of rootstock, the scion variety, the soil environment, and especially cultural management practices.

Anchorage

Good anchorage results when root systems are deep and spreading. Such systems are more likely to develop when the tree is vigorous and growing in loamy soils 3 to 4 feet (0.9 to 1.2 m) deep. Deep, spreading root systems are difficult to realize in shallow soils or in soils with restrictions to root growth such as sand layers, clay pans, high or fluctuating water tables, or very fine texture.

Anchorage characteristics can differ with rootstock and cultivar. Olive trees propagated by grafting onto seedlings develop better anchorage only when grown directly in the orchard from the beginning, and then, only for their first few years. When olives are propagated as rooted cuttings, poor anchorage of young olive trees is rare compared with problems associated with other cutting-propagated tree species.

Absorption of Water and Nutrients

Trees with deep and spreading root systems are best suited for performing the two most commonly recognized functions: absorption of water and absorption of mineral nutrients. Such root systems have the best potential for exploiting the soil profile. Absorption of water and absorption of nutrients are different physiological processes. Uptake of water depends on physical forces in the soil and within the plant. Selective and active absorption of nutrients requires expenditure of respiratory energy and the existence of cells and tissues characteristic of the root tip region.

Absorption of water and nutrients was once thought to occur mainly, or even exclusively, in the root tip region. The efficiency and rate of absorption appear greatest near the root tip, but there is increasing evidence that other parts of roots participate in uptake. Uptake of water and nutrients has been demonstrated by both secondarily thickened and fine, "browned" roots. It is uncertain whether suberization in these roots causes selective absorption of nutrients or increased resistance to water movement. The very small-diameter brown roots appear capable of contributing significantly to total absorption because of their extensive length and surface.

Synthesis of Chemicals

The fourth root function, one frequently overlooked, is conversion or synthesis. Each year a considerable amount of nitrogen is lost from the tree in the crop, leaves, and prunings; this nitrogen must be replenished.

Nitrogen absorbed from the soil as nitrate is reduced by root enzymes to the ammonium form. Carbohydrate from the leaves is converted to organic acids that, combined with ammonium, form amino acids and amides—the basic units of protein and the forms in which nitrogen is transported to the shoot.

Two types of hormones, gibberellins and cytokinins, are formed in the apical portions of roots and move to the aboveground portion of the tree, mainly via the xylem. They are involved in controlling vegetative and reproductive growth. Reduced hormone supply due to root problems is one cause (among many) of small leaves and lack of vigor. Experimental restriction of roots, preventing new root formation, has been shown to reduce shoot growth.

Another hormone, ethylene, can arise in roots and, at low levels, stimulates root growth and branching. With root damage or various other stresses, high levels of ethylene may form, inhibiting root growth, and, if transported to shoots, causing senescence and abscission of leaves. Still another growth substance, abscisic acid, is synthesized in the root cap and when transported to leaves can affect stomatal behavior.

Storage of Chemicals

The fifth function of roots is the storage of carbon and nitrogen. Carbon is stored as starch and soluble carbohydrate, which provide metabolic intermediates, respirable substrate for energy production, and the basic structural units for root growth. Nitrogen is stored mainly as amino acids and protein. Part of the nitrogen absorbed, especially in late summer and autumn, is retained for later use. Accumulation of suitable reserves at this time is particularly important for development of olive flower buds and resumption of growth the following spring.

Storage, as well as other root functions, depends on the supply of photosynthetic products from leaves. Any condition or cultural practice that adversely affects photosynthesis is potentially harmful to root performance. Downward translocation of sucrose and mannitol from leaves in the phloem cannot be unduly restricted or all root processes will be affected. Under optimal conditions, about half of the photosynthate produced by leaves is transported to belowground tissues. Roughly half of this is consumed, principally in growth and respiration, and the remainder is stored for use when supplies from shoots are low.

ROOT GROWTH AND ACTIVITY

Root growth is essential for optimal tree performance. Olive trees can remain alive with limited root growth, but tree size and production can be severely limited. Smaller trees on very fine-textured, wet soils are examples of this. Waterlogging that occurs at a time of active growth can kill the trees since active roots must have oxygen.

Increases in diameter of large roots and laterals provide the framework, anchorage, and storage capacity. Enlargement of major laterals is regular and rapid in young trees. In mature trees secondary thickening of individual roots (fig. 7.3) may stop for several years but then resume.

Formation, extension, and branching of small-diameter laterals is of major importance as these include the root tip (fig. 7.2). Recently formed fine roots are white and are often referred to as new roots, white roots, or feeder roots. As noted, absorption and synthesis are major activities with fine roots. With many plants, root hairs—lateral extensions of epidermal cells—exist just behind the root apex. Root hairs greatly increase the absorbing surface.

New white roots can vary from a few millimeters to more than 60 centimeters (24 in) long and are usually 2 millimeters or less in diameter. Most live from 1 to several weeks and are later replaced by new white roots, provided soil or plant conditions are not limiting. Before dying naturally, new white roots become suberized and brown, this change progressing from base to tip. In contrast, browning that progresses from the tip toward basal portions indicates damage from soil, environmental, or pathogenic causes.

Not all new roots die. A few undergo secondary thickening and become part of the perennial root framework. Others, persisting as fine brown roots, have been described previously. Although these fine brown roots provide considerable length and surface and some absorptive capacity, it is uncertain whether they fulfill storage or extensive synthetic functions.

Effects of Shoot Pruning on Root Growth

Pruning, if severe enough to stimulate vigorous shoot growth, tends to suppress root growth in spring. This is likely because of retention of photosynthate in above-ground parts of the tree. Except where pruning is drastic, as with "dehorning," greater root growth later in the season would be expected.

Root Activity. In other publications, the term *root activity* often means uptake of water and nutrients. In this publication, root activity includes synthesis and storage of chemicals as well as root growth. This is because these functions are interrelated; deficiencies in one or more affect others and, ultimately, the performance of the tree canopy. The most important component is root growth because this provides the potential for realizing other functions.

SOIL ENVIRONMENTAL EFFECTS ON ROOTS

Nematodes, bacteria, and fungal pathogens are important components of the root-soil environment. These are discussed in detail in the section on pest management. Water relations and irrigation are also treated in detail elsewhere. Because of the importance of soil moisture—too little or too much—this subject is treated here from the standpoint of its effects on roots. It is also a variable that can be controlled in arid, irrigated areas like California.

Not Enough Moisture

Readily available moisture is necessary for optimal root activity. Roots do not grow through dry soil, and their exploration for available resources is limited under these conditions. Uptake of water and nutrients becomes more difficult with reduced available moisture. Movement of nutrients to roots is slower with low soil moisture. For this reason, potassium deficiency can sometimes be corrected by improving irrigation practices. Insufficient moisture or a partially dry soil profile can suppress root activity and reduce vegetative and reproductive growth in spring. Synthetic functions of roots (and, thus, supplies to the shoots) are reduced with restricted root growth. Increasing soil strength (mechanical resistance to penetration) as soil water content decreases markedly inhibits root growth.

Too Much Moisture

Under certain conditions, too much water in the soil can be more damaging than too little. Olives are very sensitive to water excess and subsequent lack of oxygen. Air is displaced from the pore spaces of the soil when they fill with water; thus, the supply of oxygen to roots is removed. This can occur with flooding, seepage, perched or fluctuating water tables, or even irrigation. Excessive soil moisture is also a strong influence on soil pathogens (root and crown rots), but discussion here is restricted to the direct effects on oxygen requirements of roots.

Terminals of new roots can be killed in 1 to 4 days in a saturated soil. Such short periods of waterlogging may inhibit shoot growth, as well. As saturation is prolonged, damage to roots becomes greater and can lead to chlorosis and leaf abscission. In extreme cases, entire root systems can be killed. The effects of waterlogging proceed faster as soil temperatures increase. Survival in water-saturated soils during winter results from a combination of low soil temperature, low respiration rate, and few active roots.

There is greater danger of damage to roots from excessive moisture with fine-textured or compacted soils because reentry of oxygen is slower after saturation. Deficient aeration is partly responsible for shallower root systems and smaller trees in fine-textured soils, even without excessive water. A fluctuating water table can have more serious effects than a static one because of periodic encroachment on active roots.

Olive is sensitive to excessive soil moisture. Little experimental work has been done, but response of olive would be expected to be more sensitive than plum and some apple rootstocks. As with other plants, differences could exist among different seedling types, own-rooted cultivars, and grafted trees. However, no specific California observations concerning trees grafted on seedling rootstocks or cultivars functioning as rootstocks can be cited.

Effects of Salt

Excessive salt, always a potential problem in irrigated agriculture, is of increasing concern in some parts of California. High levels of sodium, chloride, and sometimes sulfate in the soil or irrigation water can cause these ions to accumulate in the tree and ultimately cause toxic reactions (specific ion toxicity) in leaves. Leaf symptoms begin with chlorosis at their edges, then necrosis, and later leaf abscission. Symptoms become more prevalent late in the season. Fruit drop can also occur. Concentrations in leaves are considered injurious at greater than .5 percent chloride or .2 percent sodium on a dry weight basis.

Specific ion toxicity is only one way in which salinity can adversely affect olives and other tree crops. Effects of total salts on water relations (osmotic effects) can also be significant. In a soil solution, more water than salt is absorbed; thus, salt concentration in the soil increases, and greater force is required to extract additional water. As a result, water stress is more likely to occur.

Grower concern centers mainly on leaf toxicity symptoms; if these are absent, the potential for adverse effects is often ignored. However, reduced shoot and root growth and lower fat content in fruit due to salinity have been reported without the appearance of leaf symptoms.

Olive is considered moderately tolerant of salinity. It can withstand levels of salt that would cause extensive damage or death of deciduous tree fruit and nut crops. Certain cultivars of olive are more tolerant of salinity than others; responses may also differ depending on the rootstock. Unfortunately, the relative responses among cultivars and rootstocks grown in California are not known.

In North Africa, various olive cultivars have been found to differ in their degree of tolerance to high salinity; in some, root growth and stem elongation are reduced, but in other cultivars these parameters are not affected. A recent study (Marin, Benlloch, and Fernandez-Escobar 1995) in Spain found that the important cultivars Picual and Lechin de Sevilla, along with another five cultivars not so widely grown, displayed great salinity tolerance when grown with water containing elevated sodium chloride. Field studies to confirm the salinity tolerance of these cultivars and to assay their performance as rootstocks must still be conducted. Compared with other species, olive translocates less salt to its leaves and retains more in its roots. This difference is a possible explanation for olive's salt tolerance. The uptake and transport of salt to the shoots is a rootstock-related phenomenon.

Effects of Mycorrhizae

Mycorrhizae are beneficial fungi that commingle with roots. In woody perennial plants, mycorrhizae can have a positive effect on growth. Some mycorrhizal fungi penetrate the root; others are mainly on the root surface. This association can provide increased surface as well as specific absorptive capacities, especially for phosphorus or zinc.

Plant species differ considerably in their dependence on mycorrhizal fungi, and specific information on olive is not available. Positive responses have usually been associated with conditions of low fertility; in fact, regimes of regular, high fertilization suppress mycorrhizae. Mycorrhizal fungi occur naturally in most soils, but these may be of questionable importance given the intensive cultural practices being employed in fertile soils in California. Mycorrhizal inoculations have sometimes shown beneficial effects in nursery or replant situations after fumigation.

ROOTSTOCKS

Historically, olives have been grown from cuttings as own-rooted plants. In the early California olive industry, ease of propagation was the primary reason a rootstock was used. Easily grown seedlings were budded or grafted to the desired variety. Potentially variable tree performance was not a major consideration when early California orchardists chose to propagate olive trees by grafting on seedling rootstocks.

Since olive is most often propagated on its own roots, experience with rootstocks is often confined to situations where cultivars existed as own-rooted trees but later became rootstocks when the orchard was top worked to a different selection. This occurred in California when oil cultivars or undesirable table olives were grafted over to cultivars preferred for canning and table use. In Spain, cultivars successful under adverse conditions such as resistance to drought, calcareous soil, wet soil, cold winters, and Verticillium wilt are currently being evaluated for their potential as rootstocks. Field studies to confirm these evaluations and to assay their performance as rootstocks for the main varieties are in development. Previous scion-rootstock relationship trials have shown that the same rootstock may induce more or less productivity and size, depending on the tried scion (Caballero and del Rio 1990); so, additional field studies must still be conducted.

Today, easily rooted cultivars like Manzanillo and Mission are often grown on their own roots. Those difficult to root, like Sevillano, are almost always grafted. In years past, grafting on seedling rootstocks was practiced largely to aid propagation. Seedlings of all varieties vary in size and vigor as each plant is genetically unique, differing slightly from every other plant. Much of the irregular tree performance observed in California olive orchards could result from the variable influence of seedling rootstocks. In the propagating of seedling rootstocks, small-fruited olive varieties such as Mission or Redding Picholine were often selected as stock because their seeds generally germinate faster and in higher percentages than do those of large-fruited varieties. Today, rooting cuttings is preferred in olive propagation. It may take 2 years longer to produce a tree by growing seedlings than by using rooted cuttings.

Rootstock Influences

There is no ideal rootstock for olive. The influence of a rootstock on the vigor and performance of one variety cannot necessarily be expected to be the same for another scion variety. Rootstock selections and effects must be considered for each rootstock-scion combination. In recent Spanish trials, rootstocks affected the fruiting surface of the tree and the trunk cross sectional area of some of the grafted varieties. Olive-fruit weight was also affected, as was yield and oil production. However, results varied with the varieties used as rootstocks and scions, thus confirming that there is not a unique model in olive scion-rootstock relationships. (Caballero and del Rio 1997)

H. T. Hartmann (1958b) measured rootstock effects on a variety of parameters in several long-term rootstock trials conducted in Lindsay, Winters, and Corning, California. A wide range of rootstock material was examined, with three prominent varieties— Mission, Manzanillo, and Sevillano—used in various rootstock-scion combinations.

Tree Size and Yield. One of the principal rootstock influences on the scion variety observed in these trials was vigor. The significant yield differences measured generally reflected differences in tree size. When grown from cuttings on their own roots, Mission and Manzanillo were more vigorous and yielded more fruit than when they were grafted on any other rootstock. Sevillano on its own roots was only intermediate in size but showed greater vigor when grown on Mission or Redding Picholine seedling rootstocks or on Oblonga clonal stock.

Fruit Characteristics. Rootstocks that produced satisfactory scion growth generally showed slight differences in their effects on fruit characteristics. Manzanillo and Sevillano fruit were slightly larger from trees on their own roots than from trees on other rootstocks. Mission fruit has shown little size variation among scions on the various rootstocks. The same variety relationships are observed regarding flesh-to-pit ratios.

Fruit shape is affected to some extent by rootstock. Own-rooted Manzanillo and Sevillano trees produced fruit that was no different in shape from that on other rootstocks. Mission, however, produced fruit with a slightly greater length-to-width ratio on its own roots compared with fruit from trees on other root stocks.

Production of split-pit fruit appears to be strongly influenced by rootstock in the case of Sevillano. Own-rooted Sevillano had as much as 30 percent split-pit fruit; Sevillano on Mission seedling rootstock exhibited about 6 percent split-pits. The influence of rootstock on split-pit in other varieties has not been documented.

Maturity. Evaluation of Mission, Manzanillo, and Sevillano scions grafted onto rootstocks producing acceptable scion growth showed no consistent relationship between rootstock and rate of fruit maturity. Soft nose, an undesirable softening and darkening of the mesocarp at the distal end of the fruit, has been observed when Sevillano was grafted onto Mission seedling rootstock. That combination resulted in 13 percent soft nose; Sevillano on its own roots averaged about 3 percent soft nose.

Mineral Nutrition. In California, mineral nutrient levels in olive leaf tissue show no consistent relationship relative to rootstock. Across the range of rootstocks tested by Hartmann (1958b), all leaf nutrient levels were within the range usually found in olive leaves in well-maintained orchards. In Spain, some olive cultivars recognized as adapted to soils high in lime continue to produce vigorous growth even under such poor soil conditions. These calcareous soils produce iron chlorosis in varieties that are less tolerant to the high lime conditions. Rapid evaluation of cultivars tolerant to low iron has been aided by hydroponic cultivation with low iron concentrations in the solution. So far, Cornicabra, Hojiblanca, and Nevadillo Negro are among the most tolerant, while Arbequina and Manzanilla de Sevilla are among the most susceptible to iron deficiency. Varieties identified as good performers on calcareous soil are being tested as rootstocks for cultivars that are less tolerant.

Dwarfing Effects. Size-controlling rootstocks have a place in olive production, much as they do with other fruit crops. Reducing tree size, while maintaining or enhancing fruitfulness and lowering harvesting costs, is a desirable objective. However, some production problems can accompany dwarfing or size control. With fruit production on 1-year-old shoots, some balance needs to exist between provision of sufficient shoot growth for adequate fruiting versus restriction of shoot growth to obtain dwarfing effects. Extreme dwarfing effects are often unsatisfactory. As with other characteristics discussed, dwarfing and invigoration vary with the rootstock-scion combination. Several combinations that impart dwarfing to the scion have been observed:

• Ascolano seedling rootstocks have a rather uniformly dwarfing influence on scions of Mission, Sevillano, and most notably on Manzanillo.

• Oblonga rootstock has a pronounced dwarfing effect on Manzanillo and somewhat less on Mission, but it invigorates Sevillano.

• Sevillano grown on its own roots makes a smaller tree but one that is acceptable if planted at higher density.

• Redding Picholine rootstock severely dwarfs Manzanillo, making growth unacceptable. It dwarfs Mission somewhat, but greatly invigorates Sevillano.

• Genetically dwarfed interstocks tested by Hartmann produced satisfactory graft unions and were compatible with both Mission and Sevillano (Hartmann and Whisler 1970). They have not been used commercially.

Italian research produced a mix of tree sizes depending on the specific rootstock, ranging from small bushes to larger trees. The table cultivar Giarraffa was evaluated on ten clonal dwarfing rootstocks. One rootstock, FS 17, produced shorter trees with smaller trunk circumference and lower vigor. The dwarfing of this stock was not related to internode length. Yield on a canopy size basis was maintained suggesting that the reduced vigor of FS 17 could permit higher planting densities and potentially higher total yields. (Fontanazza et al. 1996)

The potential advantages offered by dwarfing rootstocks have not been exploited in olive although appropriate rootstock material for certain cultivars seems to be available in either known varieties or as new materi-

al coming from breeding. Reduced growth of olive cultivars could be very useful for developing an intensive system of olive tree growing. However, since the same rootstocks affect different varieties differently, the main varieties must be evaluated by grafting to every intended dwarfing selection. This is required to ascertain whether the rootstock would pass the supposed dwarfing ability on to the scions and to check its effects on other desirable varietal features.

Disease Susceptibility. Several cultivars have shown some tolerance to Verticillium wilt when grown on their own roots. These include Oblonga, Frantoio, Empeltre, Allegra, and Ascolano. When used as rootstocks for other cultivars, this tolerance has not generally protected the scions.

Historical Rootstock Selections

As indicated earlier, ease of propagation has been the primary consideration in choice of rootstock. Certain stocks were selected for their invigorating characteristics or disease resistance. Some plantings of varieties have existed as own-rooted trees but later became rootstocks when the orchard was top worked to a different cultivar. These situations have all occurred in the past and are outlined in the following discussion of common and specialty olive rootstocks.

Mission. Early Mission orchards were grown as own-rooted trees propagated by cuttings or planted as seedling orchards and grafted. The 200-year history of Mission in California has led to several strains of the variety. Depending on the source, Mission seedling rootstocks can be quite variable, and this may account for variation in commercial orchards on Mission seedling rootstock. Fruit is generally borne singly, is slightly oblique in shape, and matures in mid- to late October (fig. 7.4).

Sevillano was commonly grafted to Mission seedling stock in the past. As the California olive industry developed, many older clonal Mission orchards were top worked to the Manzanillo or Sevillano varieties. At one time, about 20 percent of the Corning and Tulare County olive districts were Mission. Most of these orchards have since been top worked, resulting in Manzanillo or Sevillano orchards on Mission rootstock.

Redding Picholine. This variety was imported from France in 1872 by B. B. Redding and was originally thought to be a large pickling variety. It turned out to be a small-fruited seedling and not the true French Picholine (fig. 7.5). Although a vigorous tree, it was unacceptable for pickling and oil production due to its

Figure 7.4. Bearing habit of Mission.

Figure 7.5. Bearing habit of Redding Picholine.

small fruit size. For many years it was used as a root-stock for other varieties such as Sevillano and Mission. Redding Picholine roots very readily from cuttings, and its small oval seeds germinate easily when the tip end is clipped, resulting in a high rooting percentage. The small oval fruit are borne in clusters and mature to a velvet black color in late September to early October.

Nevadillo. F. Pohndorff imported this variety from Spain about 1885. It became an established variety in California and was generally used for oil extraction. Fruit is oval, slightly oblique, and pointed. It somewhat resembles the Mission but is generally longer in propor-tion to its diameter. The pit is small, curved, and gener-ally pointed at both ends. Fruit often forms in clusters and matures to a velvet black color in October (fig. 7.6).

As the oil market declined in the early 1900s, this variety was often top worked to more desirable pickling varieties. Considerable acreage existed in the Corning district; hence, current Sevillano orchards in that area may be found growing on this rootstock. For the same reason, Mission in the Oroville area and Manzanillo in Tulare County can be found on this stock.

Oblonga. The history of this variety is uncertain, but a supposedly volunteer seedling in the Earl Malott orchard near Corning, California, in 1940 was the pro-genitor of Oblonga tested in experiments at the University of California, Davis. The tree was noted for its rapid growth and large size. Sevillano scions grafted onto this rootstock developed into large, heavy-produc-ing trees. Oblonga has a dwarfing effect on Manzanillo. Mission and Ascolano on Oblonga have not shown dwarfing.

Figure 7.6. Bearing habit of Nevadillo.

H. T. Hartmann's field trial in Tulare County showed that the Oblonga stock prevented the movement of the Verticillium wilt fungus (*Verticillium dahliae* Kleb.) from the soil into the susceptible Sevillano scion top (Hartmann, Schnathorst, and Whisler 1971). While other rootstocks with Sevillano scions succumbed to Verticillium wilt, none of the 10 Sevillano-Oblonga trees showed Verticillium wilt symptoms for 16 years in a heavily infested orchard. In repeated tests, Oblonga has shown tolerance but not immunity to Verticillium wilt. Other cultivars grafted onto Oblonga died as Verticillium wilt was transported to the scion.

Oblonga must be clonally propagated to maintain these characteristics. Small, leafy Oblonga cuttings can be readily propagated under intermittent mist when cutting bases are dipped in rooting hormones.

Allegra and Ascolano. Allegra and Ascolano are other cultivars that, when grown on their own roots, have shown some tolerance to Verticillium wilt. Wilt-susceptible scions grafted on these rootstocks and exposed to infested soil contract Verticillium wilt and die. This suggests that although the cultivars are tolerant, when used as a rootstock, the pathogen is transmitted through the stock and graft to the susceptible scion.

Effects of these rootstocks on the top growth of commercial cultivars have not been thoroughly tested. There is some evidence that Allegra has a dwarfing influence on Manzanillo.

Other Rootstocks

Several other types of seedling rootstocks have been tested over the years. These have mostly been other species of olive, and no advantages have been revealed.

Grafting *Olea europaea* on seedlings of *Olea ferruginea*, *Olea verrucosa*, and *Olea chrysophylla* has not provided good results. Trees may show overgrowth at the graft union, have delayed fruit maturity, produce excessive numbers of shotberry fruit, and may develop large numbers of yellow leaves and ultimately die of incompatibility.

Sevillano on *Olea chrysophylla* seems to produce normal, healthy trees with adequate crops, but Mission and Manzanillo on this stock display clear incompatibility.

In rootstock trials, seedlings of California wild olive, *Forestiera neomexicana*, proved to be unsuccessful as rootstocks for Mission, Sevillano, and Manzanillo. Severe dwarfing, fruit quality problems, and incompatibility occurred. (Hartmann 1958b, Hartmann and Whisler 1970)

Olive cultivars have also been grafted on ash (*Fraxinus*) and on lilac (*Syringae*). Although the plants lived for several years, they displayed little new growth and eventually died.

REFERENCES

Barranco, D. 1999. Varieties and rootstocks. In D. Barranco, R. Fernandez-Escobar, and L. Rallo, eds., El cultivo del olivo, 3rd ed. Spain: University of Cordoba.

Caballero, J. M., and C. del Rio. 1990. Rootstock influence on productivity parameters of two olive cultivars. Abstracts of the 23rd International Horticultural Congress: 1763. Florence, Italy.

———. 1997. Relaciones reciprocas patron-injerto en olivo. Fruticultura profesional 88 (Especial Olivicultura II):6–13.

El-Gazzar, A. M., E. M. El-Azab, and M. Shehata. 1979. Effect of irrigation with fractions of sea water and drainage water on growth and mineral composition of young grapes, guavas, oranges, and olives. Alex. J. Agric. Res. 27(1):207–219.

Fontanazza, G., F. Bartolozzi, P. Rocchi, G. Vergari, and M. Patumi. Circa 1996. Observations on olive cv. Giarraffa grafted on different clonal rootstocks. Report of Insito di Ricerche Sulla Olivicultura, Perugia, Italy.

Hartmann, H. T. 1958a. Rootstock effect on olive. Calif. Agr. 12(9):13–14.

———. 1958b. Rootstock effects in olive. Proc. Amer. Soc. Hort. Sci. 72:242–251.

Hartmann, H. T., and J. E. Whisler. 1970. Some rootstock and interstock influences in the olive (*Olea europaea* L.) cv. Sevillano. J. Amer. Soc. Hort. Sci. 95(5):562–565.

Hartmann, H. T., W. C. Schnathorst, and J. Whisler. 1971. Oblonga… a clonal olive rootstock resistant to verticillium wilt. Calif. Agr. 25(6):12–15.

Marin, L., M. Benlloch, and R. Fernandez-Escobar. 1995. Screening of olive cultivars for salt tolerance. Scientia Horticulturae 64:113–116.

Therios, I. N., and N. D. Misopolinos. 1988. Genotypic response to sodium chloride salinity of four major olive cultivars (*Olea europaea* L.). Plant and Soil 106:105–111.

Wickson, E. J. 1926. The California fruits and how to grow them. 10th Ed. San Francisco: Pacific Rural Press.

8

Flowering, Pollination, Fruiting, Alternate Bearing, and Abscission

GEORGE C. MARTIN, LOUISE FERGUSON, AND G. STEVEN SIBBETT

FLOWERING

Flowering involves three developmental events: induction (the conversion of vegetative buds to inflorescence buds), initiation of flowers, and differentiation of the floral parts. The precise timing of each of these events is not completely clear at the present time, but some research indicates that the physiological process leading to spring flowering starts as early as the preceding summer. The vegetative bud present in the axil of each leaf begins developmental changes that result in a vegetative shoot or an inflorescence containing flowers. In summer, environmental factors interact with a tree's physiology to start the induction process. Once induction is underway, floral initiation occurs by November, followed by the formation of flower parts. Eventually, these can be seen with a microscope. Thus, olive differs from most fruit trees, which have a relatively short induction-to-initiation cycle. Induction in olive may occur as early as July or about 6 weeks after full bloom whereas the differentiation of flowers is not easily seen until 8 months later in February.

Floral Induction and Initiation

Well-managed, pest-free trees with moderate crops are most likely to flower and fruit each year. During the growing season, orchard managers are both culturing the current crop and influencing the formation of the following year's crop. The vegetative bud in the axil of each leaf competes with shoot and fruit growth for raw materials to start floral induction and subsequently initiation.

Effects of Stress. The floral developmental process depends on good nutrition, but there are many factors that can inhibit flower development. Nitrogen is usually the major element required for olive, and proper nitrogen management is a necessity. Excess nitrogen can increase flower set in some situations and indirectly decrease it in others. For example, pruning large limbs and then applying too much nitrogen leads to excessive localized vegetative growth, which decreases cropping.

Pruning to open trees for better light distribution benefits floral development. Moisture availability is crucial. In droughts, the internal water supply favors leaves over developing fruit and floral buds. Stress caused by pest infestations similarly takes essential materials away from developing fruit and floral buds.

Effects of Temperature. In winter, temperature greatly influences the continuing development of flowers among California olive cultivars; they are unfruitful unless exposed to a minimum of cold. In experiments at the University of California, Davis, half of a group of young, bearing Mission trees growing in large containers were kept in a warm greenhouse all winter; the other half remained outdoors. The greenhouse trees failed to bloom or fruit; the outdoor trees bloomed and fruited normally. When a single branch on a greenhouse tree was exposed to winter cold through an opening in the greenhouse wall, it bloomed and fruited normally. Likewise, a single branch on an outdoor tree extended into a warm greenhouse failed to bloom although the rest of the tree bloomed heavily. (Hartmann and Porlingus 1957)

Some olive cultivars, such as those grown in Crete, southern Greece, Egypt, Israel, and Tunisia, bloom and fruit heavily with very little winter chilling; those originating in Italy, Spain, and California require substantial chilling for good fruiting.

In experiments with cultivars grown in California (Hartmann 1953), optimal flowering occurred when the temperature fluctuated daily between a minimum of 35° to 40°F (2° to 4°C) and a maximum of 60° to 65°F (16° to 18°C). Trees held at a constant temperature of 55°F (13°C) also bloomed profusely but had poor pistillate flower formation. If temperatures did not rise above 45°F (7°C) or fall below 60°F (16°C), trees did not bloom. At 55°F (13°C), both chilling and warmth are sufficient for flowering but not for complete flower development. In contrast to flower buds, vegetative buds of olive seem to have little if any dormancy, growing whenever the temperatures are much above about 70°F (21°C). In addition to winter chilling, inflorescence formation requires leaves to be present on the fruiting shoots. Therefore, it is important to prevent defoliation. The occasional occurrence of hot, dry winds during the blooming period has been associated with reduced fruit set. Winds and heat increase the amount of natural abscission.

Prolonged, abnormally cold weather during April and May, when olive flower buds are developing rapidly, can have a detrimental effect on subsequent flowering, pollination, and fruit set. Such weather occurred in California in the spring of 1967, delaying bloom by several weeks and leading to flower abnormalities and a

crop of only 14,000 tons, the lightest in modern California history. In California, fruit that is on the tree by July 1, as a rule, continues on to maturity.

Floral Differentiation

Differentiation takes place between late February and May blooming when the formation of each flower part occurs in the inflorescence. Flower parts form from the outside in: the sepals first and the pistil last (fig. 8.1; also, see chapter 3: Botany of the Olive). Olive has two types of flowers: perfect flowers, which have both stamens and

Figure 8.1. Staminate (A, C) and perfect (B, D) flowers. C shows an aborted pistil in a staminate flower; D shows a normally developed pistil in a perfect flower.

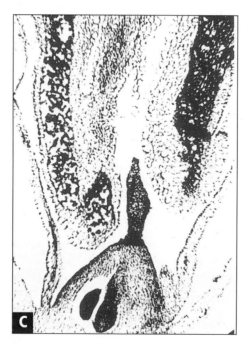
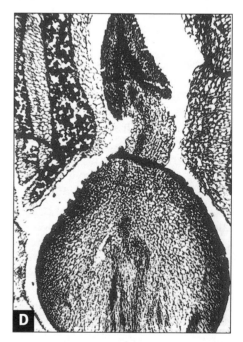

pistils, and staminate flowers, which lack pistils. Staminate flowers form when flowers have initiated a pistil, but the pistil aborts during the late stages of differentiation. The 8- to 10-week period of differentiation before bloom in May is the critical period for perfect flower development. Stress during those weeks can ruin an otherwise good flower population. As mentioned previously, stressed flowers compete poorly with leaves for available water. Lack of water during flower differentiation results in partially developed flowers with malfunctioning or absent pistils (see the staminate flowers in fig. 8.1). This occurs more frequently than expected and is only evident upon close examination of the flowers. In some seasons, orchards have been observed in which practically every flower was staminate. As mentioned elsewhere, it is best to start the growing season with a moist soil profile. Once vegetative growth and fruit growth start, and warm weather occurs, the irrigation capacity of most growers is not sufficient to replenish a depleted soil profile.

Girdling. Several experiments have shown that girdling the tree (removing a quarter-inch strip of bark around the limb or trunk) in mid-February can increase the proportion of perfect flowers and subsequent fruit set. Apparently, girdling leads to retention of carbohydrates above the girdle. Nevertheless, girdling is not recommended in California because olive knot can enter the girdle site. This practice can successfully influence cropping in countries like Israel where olive knot is not present, but long-term use may be detrimental to root growth.

In orchards infected with olive knot it is likely that the bacteria will become established in girdling cuts unless they are immediately covered with hot grafting wax, then a Bordeaux-mixture paste, and finally an asphalt-emulsion grafting compound. Bordeaux paste applied directly to the girdling cut causes considerable injury to the tissues and is not advised. Girdling tools should be disinfected between trees to prevent the spread of bacteria.

Full Bloom

At full bloom flowers are delicately poised for pollination, the critical event discussed next. Some 500,000 flowers are present in a mature tree; a commercial crop of 3 tons per acre (6.8 metric t/ha) or more can be achieved when 1 or 2 percent of these flowers remain as developing fruit. By 14 days after full bloom, most of the flowers destined to abscise have done so. By that time, about 494,000 flowers have abscised from a tree that started with 500,000 flowers.

In some years, a tree may not have sufficient perfect flowers to produce a satisfactory crop despite heavy bloom because the flowers produced are primarily staminate (male or pollen bearing). The relative proportion of

perfect to staminate flowers varies greatly among inflorescences, branches, trees, cultivars, and seasons, but is generally small. There are no commercial production practices that enhance the percentage of perfect flowers except for girdling in late winter, which is not recommended in California for reasons discussed previously.

POLLINATION

Olives are andromonecious: the same tree bears perfect and imperfect flowers. Flowers are borne axially along the shoot in inflorescences called panicles (fig. 8.2). The panicles of Barouni, Manzanillo, Mission, and Sevillano carry an average of 12 to 18 flowers; Ascolano averages 20 flowers. Perfect flowers, those with both pistillate (female) and staminate (male) parts, normally consist of a small calyx, four petals, two stamens and filaments supporting large pollen-bearing anthers, and a plump green pistil with a short thick style and a large

Figure 8.2. Manzanillo olive shoot showing inflorescences.

stigma (fig. 8.1B). Figure 3.5 in chapter 3 shows a perfect flower with the parts indicated. Perfect flowers are borne apically in an inflorescence. Within the typical triple-flower inflorescence, the middle flower is generally perfect. Imperfect flowers are staminate (pollen bearing or male), with the pistil either lacking or rudimentary (fig. 8.1A). Flowers with abortive anthers also occur and are common in Sevillano.

Self Pollination and Cross-Pollination

Olive pollination occurs by self-pollination or by cross-pollination. The former requires no agent although bees and wind may serve as agents. Wind is the primary agent of cross-pollination. Bees are not universally present in sufficient numbers or sufficiently attracted to olive flowers to be a factor in pollination. If present, bees can improve set, but they have never been shown to be necessary for cross-pollination.

In self-pollination, the pollen simply falls from anther to pistil in the same flower. The anthers of most perfect flowers are close enough to the stigma so that, at dehiscence, pollen falls upon the stigma easily. Wind or bees could also affect self-pollination simply by disturbing blossoms. In some flowers the filaments are flattened, spreading the anthers away from the stigma. Among California cultivars Ascolano is the most likely to have flowers with spreading anthers. In these flowers, dehiscence does not ensure automatic pollination, and wind or bees must be the agents of self-pollination. Cross-pollination is the transfer of pollen from one flower to the stigma of another.

Commercially grown California olive cultivars can be either self-compatible (able to regularly set commercial crops with their own pollen) or partially to largely self-incompatible, only setting regular commercial crops in those years when conditions, such as climate for bloom development and fruit set, are optimal. For example, Manzanillo has been shown to behave like a self-incompatible cultivar, requiring cross-pollination from a foreign olive pollen source for optimal fruit set. For California cultivars in general, most experiments have shown improved fruit set when a foreign pollen source was available. Inclusion of pollinating cultivars at intervals of no more than 200 feet (61 m) is recommended for commercial plantings, especially when environmental conditions for fruit set (for example, hot and dry or abnormally cool conditions during bloom) regularly occur.

Not all combinations of cross-pollination improve fruit set. Ascolano and Mission pollen do not improve fruit set in Manzanillo trees. Conversely, Mission pollinated by Manzanillo show the poorest fruit set of the five pollen cultivars. Sevillano has shown cross incompatibility when pollinated with Barouni pollen.

Successful Pollination

Once pollen lands on the stigma, the pollen grains germinate. The inner wall expands through one pore into a tube, and the grain's cytoplasm contents move into it. This pollen tube, enclosed by an extension of the inner pollen wall, conveys the male germ cells (sperm) to the female germ cell (egg). Over the span of about 1 week, the tube moves between the cells on the stigma's surface and grows through the pistillate flower tissues until it reaches the egg cell in the embryo sac. When a pollen tube arrives, it releases its two sperm cells; one fuses with the egg. The product of this fusion is a single-celled zygote. Within 10 days the zygote divides into two cells, an event that starts the complex development leading to formation of the embryo that is contained in the seed. Fruit set depends on embryo growth, thus, without successful pollination and fertilization, fruit set does not occur and the flower is lost.

Successful pollination requires the pollen grain to germinate and its pollen tube to grow fast enough to reach a still viable embryo sac. Cool temperatures that result in slow pollen tube growth can decrease fruit set. In such cases the tube either fails to reach the embryo sac or grows too slowly to reach the embryo sac before it degenerates. Excessive temperatures during bloom (>95°F [>35°C]), especially when accompanied by dry, windy conditions, often reduce fruit set. It is thought such conditions desiccate and shorten the receptivity period of the flower parts.

FRUITING

Fruit Set

The objective of pollination is fruit set. This term is vague but refers to flowers that are pollinated and fertilized and that develop into fruit that remains on the tree until harvest. Research shows that the major factor in reducing fruit set may not be pistil abortion but rather the intense competition among the perfect flowers of an inflorescence. Usually only one fruit is retained per inflorescence, and the winner cannot be determined in advance. There remains a great deal to be learned about fruit set for olive and all other crops. For no evident reason, some orchards fail to set crops for 2 consecutive years, perhaps due to extreme environmental conditions. Other orchards may produce large crops for 2 or 3 years before having a small crop. The latter situation must arise from the coincidence of several environmental and physiological factors.

Cultivars vary, but most fruit abscission occurs soon

after full bloom, and final fruit set nearly always occurs within 6 weeks of full bloom. Further fruit abscission can result from pest infestation and environmental extremes. When trees have an inflorescence at nearly every leaf axil, a successful crop is produced with 1 to 2 percent fruit set; when there is a small population of inflorescences, a successful crop may require 10 percent fruit set.

Shotberries. Occurring randomly and for reasons not clearly understood, shotberries (parthenocarpic fruit) may be seen in clusters on each inflorescence (fig. 8.3). When shotberries occur, the inter-fruit competition for raw materials differs from that of normal olive fruit. Shotberries mature much earlier than normal fruit and may be more prevalent when conditions favor a second consecutive year with a large crop.

Factors That Reduce Fruit Set. Fruit set results from the interaction of olive tree physiology with the environment. Several tree factors that can reduce fruit set are known. The absence of viable pollen results in no crop, as parthenocarpic olives are useless. Incompatible pollinating cultivars, as mentioned earlier, also result in no fertilization. Fortunately, there are numerous compatible combinations for olive. In many situations olives are self-compatible, but Manzanillo has special problems. In most years and areas of the world Manzanillo pollinates itself successfully. In hot weather during bloom, however, Manzanillo pollen grows slowly, resulting in no fertilization. The unfertilized ovary is viable for a very short period after full bloom.

Numerous environmental or management factors can influence fruit set; proper nitrogen management is the most important. Except for special local problems, nitrogen is the only nutrient supplement required annually. Fruit thinning, in combination with judicious pruning, helps manage better fruit allocation throughout the tree. Some localities by virtue of the microclimate—local temperature, moisture, and wind—have better fruit set than others. High winds consistently reduce fruit set. Pest and disease management is extremely important as without control the additional stress always reduces fruit set.

Fruit Growth

Olive fruit growth occurs in a typical sigmoid fashion (fig. 3.7 in chapter 3). The importance of the last period of fruit growth in October must be clearly understood. Research shows that profit and loss pivot around fruit growth, as the premium value for California black-ripe or green-ripe processing is reached in mid-October (fig. 20.1 in chapter 20). These data show that harvesting too early or too late costs orchardists hundreds of dol-

Figure 8.3. Clusters of shotberries on right.

lars per acre. Delaying harvest results in heavier, more valuable fruit but can also lead to losses due to black fruit and frost damage. For oil olives, the value based on oil continues to increase into January.

The endocarp (pit) enlarges to full size and hardens by 6 weeks after full bloom. At that time the endosperm begins to solidify and embryo development takes place, leading to embryo maturity by September. The mesocarp (flesh) and exocarp (skin) continue their gradual growth as shown in figure 3.7 in chapter 3. The environmental and management factors important for fruit set also optimize fruit growth. Fruit begins changing from a green color to yellow-white (straw) and accumulates anthocyanin from the distal or base end. This purple to black color eventually bleeds into the mesocarp, signaling fruit that is overmature for the California black-ripe or green-ripe processing. As has been reported for most other fruit crops, trees with few fruit mature their crops earlier than trees with many fruit.

ALTERNATE BEARING

Olive, along with numerous other fruit trees, including apple, pear, mango, orange, pistachio, and pecan, produces a large crop one year followed by a small, noncommercial crop the following year. The evidence shows that large crops reduce carbohydrate levels; however, when placed in growth chambers with high light, favorable temperature, and high CO_2 from November through February, olive trees increase starch reserves five times over controls but still fail to increase inflorescence development on either previously bearing or nonbearing trees (Hackett and Hartmann 1964). These data indicate that whatever their other roles are, a shortage of carbohydrates or starch from November through February may not be the direct cause of alternate bearing in olive.

Any cultural practices that diminish olive tree vigor (such as lack of nutrients, water, or leaving a large crop on the tree until December) add to the burden and extent of alternate bearing. Environmental extremes and lack of pest control also push trees toward alternate bearing.

Experiments have shown that the presence of seed in fruit may have some influence on alternate bearing (Stutte and Martin 1986). When seeds are killed by 6 weeks after full bloom, branches produce large populations of seedless fruit. These shoots contain viable inflorescences the following year. In shoots with similar populations of seeded fruit, few or no inflorescences are produced in the subsequent year. The question remains: How can growers make practical use of this information?

The best technique for avoiding, or at least modifying, alternate bearing is to use naphthaleneacetic acid (NAA) to decrease the fruit population during the cropping year, as described in chapter 14: Olive Fruit Thinning. Pruning is not as effective as fruit thinning in overcoming alternate bearing because leaves as well as fruit are removed. No fertilizer practice has been demonstrated to decrease alternate bearing.

ABSCISSION

Old leaves abscise in April in a natural process that causes no problems. Leaves that abscise at flower bud sites during the growing season are, however, a great problem as this decreases flower quality and fruit production. Good management maintains good foliage. Infestation by pests and lack of nitrogen or water can induce leaf abscission. Leaf abscission among younger leaves usually results in outbreaks of olive knot and diploidea.

REFERFENCES

Hackett, W. P., and H. T. Hartmann. 1964. Inflorescence formation in the olive as influenced by low temperature, photoperiod, and leaf area. Botanical Gazette 126:65–72.

Hartmann, H. T. 1953. Effect of winter chilling on fruitfulness and vegetative growth in the olive. Proc. Amer. Soc. Hort. Sci. 62:184–190.

Hartmann, H. T., and I. Porlingus. 1957. Effect of different amounts of winter chilling on fruitfulness of several olive varieties. Botanical Gazette vol. 19, no. 2.

Stutte, G. W., and G. C. Martin. 1986. Effect of killing the seed on return bloom of olive. Scientia Hortic. 29:107–113.

9
Pruning Mature Bearing Olive Trees

G. STEVEN SIBBETT

Bearing olive trees are pruned to complement other cultural practices in producing annual crops of large fruit. Pruning, in conjunction with fruit thinning, irrigation, fertilization, and pest control, is a valuable contribution to an olive orchard's annual productivity. This chapter discusses pruning bearing trees to produce annual crops of high-quality olives.

To understand pruning in olive production, it is important to understand the olive's fruit-bearing habit and the effect pruning has on tree growth.

FRUITING HABIT

Olives are produced on 1-year-old shoots in the presence of sunlight. Thus, production is mainly confined to a shell of new, well-lighted shoots 2 to 3 feet (60 to 90 cm) thick on the tree's periphery (Fig. 9.1). Few fruit are produced in the shaded interior or within dense clumps of shoots.

Figure 9.1. Productive outer "shell" of an olive tree.

The most productive olive shoots are 8 to 12 inches (20 to 30 cm) long. Short or excessively vigorous shoots are often unfruitful. An important objective of pruning is to stimulate and develop an annual complement of moderately vigorous, well-lighted shoots on the tree periphery to produce the subsequent year's crop.

Pruning decreases the number of current-season shoots but stimulates subsequent shoot growth for cropping. Pruning also reduces insect and disease development by eliminating the dense, brushy conditions conducive to their growth. Well-pruned trees have thin canopies that allow better penetration of spray materials.

Light is also essential to fruit quality and oil content. Fruit produced in well-lighted conditions are larger and higher in oil content than those produced in low to modest light conditions.

THE EFFECTS OF PRUNING ON TREE GROWTH

Pruning is a dwarfing practice. It physically removes stored carbohydrates while also removing potential carbohydrate-producing leaf surface. Reduction in leaf surface causes reduced root growth as food materials become more limiting. Unpruned trees grow larger in total leaf area than pruned trees.

Pruning induces new growth close to the cut primarily by increasing the amount of nitrogen available to each remaining growing point. A few cuts on large-diameter wood cause excessive localized growth of shoots. Well-distributed cuts on small-diameter wood spread the stimulus over the entire tree. Heading cuts generally stimulate more buds to grow than thinning cuts (fig. 9.2). This is because cutting the apexes of shoots or branches removes natural growth-control hormones that prevent lateral shoots from developing on unpruned branches. Understanding how pruning influences tree growth is essential to maintaining optimal olive production.

Figure 9.2. Thinning (left) and heading (right) cuts.

WHEN TO PRUNE

Prune mature olive trees in spring and summer, once winter rains have passed. Pruning then provides the opportunity to manage production at minimum risk of disease infection and insect attack.

PRUNING TO MANAGE PRODUCTION

Pruning in spring or early summer during bloom and young fruit development can help manage crop size. If bloom or fruit set is light, pruning can be confined to nonproductive parts of the tree, preserving as much bloom and potential crop as possible. In years of heavy bloom, pruning can be more severe without excessive crop removal. Pruning to thin heavy crops does not result in larger fruit; fruit size is largely determined locally on branches by an adequate leaf-to-fruit ratio, and pruning that removes entire shoots, both leaves and fruit, does not change this ratio.

PRUNING TO MANAGE DISEASE AND PESTS

Olive Knot

Olive knot disease is caused by a bacterium dispersed throughout the tree in moisture, commonly rainfall. The bacterium only infects the tree through openings such as leaf scars, pruning wounds, or cracks caused by freezing temperatures. Pruning before or during the wet season unnecessarily opens wounds for olive knot invasion. Also, pruning during winter thins out the tree's canopy, making it vulnerable to freezing temperatures and subsequent bark injury. Pruning in spring and summer, once rains and freezing temperatures have past, avoids these problems and can be used to cut away established olive knots, which supply inoculum for future infection. In areas where spring rains are common, fresh pruning wounds have been shown to be exceptionally susceptible to olive knot infection. Here, chemical protection should be applied (see chap. 17: Diseases of Olive) and pruning should be further delayed until rains have passed.

Black Scale

The black scale insect prefers dense shade. It is sensitive to heat and light and does not survive well with exposure. Pruning to thin the tree canopy before warm summer temperatures arrive effectively minimizes this pest without using insecticides.

OTHER OBJECTIVES OF PRUNING

The main objective of pruning is to manipulate tree growth to produce maximum crops of large fruit annually. Olive trees are also pruned for other reasons.

Maximizing Sunlight Exposure

Production is confined to the well-lighted periphery of the tree. The pruning strategy should include developing a tree with a lobular shape when viewed from above (fig. 9.3). Such pruning increases the portion of the tree canopy that is exposed to light, providing for maximum productivity.

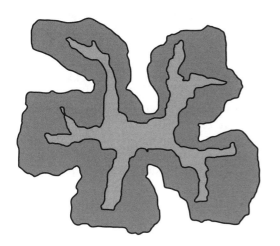

Figure 9.3. Top view diagram of a lobular-shaped tree showing the increased bearing surface.

Pruning for Harvest

Hand Harvest. Hand pickers use ladders to harvest olives. For safe hand picking, tree height should not exceed 15 to 18 feet (4.6 to 5.5 m). Tall, upright limbs that extend beyond this must be removed. If trees are taller than the safe limit at harvest, growers often cut the tall limbs at picking time and harvest them on the ground rather than from an unsafe position on the ladder.

Shaker Harvest. This method of harvesting olives requires that energy from a trunk or limb shaker be transmitted from the shaker to the fruit with enough force to break the fruit stem. Unlike many fruit species, olive trees are not well suited for this process. At the time of harvest, the fruit is immature, small, weighing 3 to 7 grams, and has little inertia. The long, willowy shoots of an olive tree do not transmit energy well, and the brushy clumps of shoots, natural to the tree's growth habit, absorb the shaker's energy before it reaches the fruit. Also, energy is poorly transmitted to fruit on limbs growing at angles greater than 45° from vertical. The result is poor fruit removal.

If a shaker is to be used, proper pruning is essential to maximize fruit removal. First, the tree's normal shape must be modified for machine harvest. The Manzanillo tree's low, rounded shape must be changed to one that is more upright, with a few stubby limbs and branches of thinned clumps of shoots that transmit energy well. Ascolano, Sevillano, and Mission trees grow more upright than Manzanillo and usually require less modification. Also, the shaker must be able to operate quickly and efficiently in the orchard to economically harvest olives. Most older olive trees must be limb shaken. A maximum of five, well-spaced upright scaffold branches should be left on each tree; more limbs congest the operating area and slow harvest (color plate 9.1).

Restructuring for mechanical shaker harvest should be done gradually, several years in advance. This avoids both immediate production loss from severe pruning and the resulting profuse, unfruitful vegetative growth. A good rule of thumb is to use saw cuts, removing no more than one-fourth of the leaf surface in any one year.

Once the tree has been restructured, annual maintenance pruning is needed for best fruit removal. Fruit wood must also be renewed and should be attached as directly as possible to the scaffold branch to receive the most energy. All suckers on the trunk and limbs must be continually removed.

Vertical Rotating Comb Harvest. Rotating combs mounted on vertical drums have been developed for olive harvesting (fig. 9.4). Such machines, called comb or hedge harvesters, operate in one direction and harvest olives in a flat plane on the tree's side. Trees must be maintained by hand pruning or hedging to develop the flat side required for this type of harvest (fig. 9.5).

Figure 9.4. "Comb" or "hedge" harvester.

Figure 9.5. This hedged tree row shows the flat side required for comb harvesting.

Mechanical Pruning. Mechanized hedging and topping are attractive substitutes for expensive hand pruning. The mechanized method of pruning is indiscriminate in that all the shoots on the top and the sides are cut to the plane of the saws; discriminate pruning, as is practiced to manage cropping, is impossible with this method. Hedging and topping can be useful in lowering tree height and managing the harvest plane in hedgerow plantings to be harvested with a comb or hedge harvester.

Mechanized pruning strategies are being researched. Although no thorough data exist yet, hedging one side every other year or every third year seems to be least disruptive to cropping. Hedging every year would probably reduce cropping considerably as new shoots that will bear the subsequent crop are removed. Flat topping and relatively severe hedge pruning, as would be done to prepare an established grove for mechanized comb harvest, have been shown to substantially reduce crop and per acre income for at least 2 years following one operation. Further, profuse growth develops, which is expensive to hand prune later. Although undocumented, a compromise for flat topping is developing a roof-shaped tree that may minimize crop loss. Trees pruned as a roof should be done so to accommodate the vertical rotating comb harvester. Regardless of tree shape following hedging, heavy branches greater than 2 inches (5 cm) in diameter should be cut 12 inches (30 cm) further back into the canopy than the rest of the tree. This reduces production for 1 to 2 years, but large branches extending out to the periphery interfere with the rotating comb, damaging the equipment.

Limiting Tree Space

Crowded olive trees decline in production as fruiting shoots become shaded. First, the tree's lower parts die out, followed by higher fruitwood. If not effectively managed through pruning, production eventually becomes confined to the top of the tree and the side canopies are lost.

The olive tree must be confined to its allotted space to give it enough light for productive shoots to develop. Pruners should remove or shorten longer branches that interfere with or congest adjoining trees. Undercutting nonproductive branches and pruning older, dead wood from brushy clumps accomplishes this objective (fig. 9.6).

The lower canopy of crowded, shaded trees cannot be restored to productivity by top pruning. In addition to removing highly productive parts of the tree that quickly fill in again and block light access to the lower canopy, top pruning causes substantial loss of production. When tree height is to be lowered, judicious, selective pruning to outside lateral limbs should be practiced.

Rejuvenating Old Trees

As olive trees age, their capacity to generate productive shoots declines, and they must be rejuvenated to regain productivity. Usually, these trees are well spaced but have become so large that they shade out lower shoots and cause production to become confined to the top, which is difficult to harvest. To rejuvenate trees, it is necessary to cut scaffold branches back to a height of 6 to 8 feet (1.8 to 2.4 m), preferably to a lateral branch, and to thin any scaffolds congesting the tree, leaving three to five branches for the main framework (color plate 9.2). Once such heavy pruning is completed, exposed limbs must be protected from sunburn with a whitening agent.

Profuse growth develops along limbs and at cuts after rejuvenation pruning. These shoots need judicious thinning to properly space and rebuild the tree's secondary framework. Once shoots are thinned, further pruning should be minimized to allow trees to return to productivity as soon as possible; continued, severe thinning of shoots delays bearing. Also, nitrogen fertilizers should be withheld from healthy rejuvenated trees to discourage excessive growth. Once trees regain bearing, normal fertilization should be reestablished.

Figure 9.6. Undercutting branches helps to confine tree growth without reducing production.

Managing Alternate Bearing

Olive trees characteristically bear heavy crops one year and light crops the next. This alternate bearing results when the heavy crop suppresses shoot growth and exhausts food reserves (color plate 14.1). Flowering and fruit set the following year are then reduced.

Fruit thinning is the only effective method of reducing olive crops to prevent overcropping and subsequent alternate bearing. Fruit thinning improves the leaf-to-fruit ratio by reducing crop but not leaves, which remain to manufacture food for vegetative growth. Pruning, on the other hand, removes both leaves and fruit indiscriminately and is only partially effective because the leaf-to-fruit ratio is not altered. Pruning does stimulate new shoot growth that can be partially fruitful the season after a heavy crop.

The best use of pruning to alleviate alternate bearing is in crop management. Prune heavily in a heavy-bearing year and remove clumps of fruit with relatively few leaves. In a light crop year, wait to prune until the bloom is present, and prune to leave as much bloom as possible for maximum crop. Such a strategy does not eliminate alternate bearing but minimizes it by physically controlling crop size each year.

Removing Frost Damage

The olive is a subtropical tree. Freezing temperatures of 15° to 22°F (–9° to–6°C), depending on cultivar sensitivity, cause the bark to split, leaves to fall, and, occasionally, limbs to die. On damaged trees, profuse growth occurs from uninjured buds, as if the trees had been severely pruned. Injured trees should be left unpruned until new growth reveals the extent of damage. Then prune to remove dead shoots and branches and lightly thin out new shoots early in the growing season. Avoid heavy pruning until normal bearing is restored.

10

Olive Irrigation Management

ROBERT H. BEEDE AND DAVID A. GOLDHAMER

Water management in orchards is critical for tree uniformity and sustained high yields of superior quality. Unfortunately, the often laborious task of irrigation is sometimes delegated to people without the technical skills to assess water use, soil moisture content, and application uniformity. Evaluating existing practices and implementing improved methods can be challenging. Considering such issues as increasing water and energy costs, changing water allocations to agriculture, groundwater overdraft, and pollution of drinking water, many growers realize that scientific water management pays off ecologically, politically, and financially. Applying the principles presented here can significantly improve olive orchard quality and productivity. Knowledge of crop evapotranspiration (ET) throughout the season, along with often simple modifications of irrigation procedures, can bring the olive grower substantially greater returns.

Olives are considered drought tolerant. Their small leaves are thick and leathery with a waxy cuticle on the upper surface and hairs on the lower surface to limit water loss (transpiration). The stomata are located primarily on the lower surface in depressions that also reduce water loss. Although these adaptations allow olive trees to survive dry conditions, they do not produce well without proper irrigation.

WATER AND OLIVE PERFORMANCE

Unlike deciduous trees, which are dormant in winter, olives retain their canopy and use water year-round. However, like other tree crops, olives have certain developmental periods that are especially sensitive to low soil moisture (table 10.1). The bloom period is very sensitive to dry soil conditions, particularly in warm, dry weather. These conditions also cause excessive fruit thinning when naphthaleneacetic acid (NAA) is used.

Table 10.1. Critical periods for adequate soil moisture in California olive orchards

Period growth events		Effect of low soil moisture
February to June	1. flower bud development	1. reduced flower formation
	2. bloom	2. incomplete flower
	3. fruit set	3. poor fruit set
	4. shoot growth	4. increased alternate bearing
		5. decreased shoot growth
June to July	1. stage 1 of fruit growth due to cell division	1. small fruit size due to decreased cell division
	2. shoot growth	2. fruit shrivel
		3. decreased shoot growth
Late September to harvest	1. stage 3 of fruit growth due to cell enlargement	1. small fruit size due to reduced cell expansion
	2. shoot growth	2. fruit shrivel
		3. decreased shoot growth

Too Little Water

July and August are typically the months when olives need the most water. Insufficient soil moisture during these months reduces shoot growth and carbohydrate production and, if severe enough, causes fruit shrivel. Shriveled fruit recover with irrigation but may shrivel again during processing. Final fruit size may also be affected by the reduced carbohydrate production. Irrigation research on olives suggests that mild, short-term water stress from June to mid-August can conserve water without affecting fruit production or quality (Hartmann 1949). The details of this practice, referred to as regulated deficit irrigation (RDI), are explained in chapter 11: Effects of Water Stress on Olive Tree Performance.

Mature orchards require substantial shoot growth to replace old fruitwood and maintain high yields. Shoot growth is of major importance to young, developing orchards as early production depends on tree size. Olive shoot growth, most noticeable in June and July, is reduced by low soil moisture. Therefore, shoot growth can be used as a visual indicator in determining whether water is sufficient in both bearing and non-bearing orchards.

Another, less obvious, effect of poor water management is a reduction in nutrient absorption. Nitrogen and potassium deficiency could occur in marginal soils due simply to inadequate irrigation. Trees obtain needed nutrients from the soil by way of the water absorbed by the roots. Excessively dry soil limits the amount of nutrients that dissolve into the water from the soil particles. Deficiencies in elements required in large quantities (macronutrients), therefore, occur when plant demand exceeds the rate of absorption. Extended periods of dry soil can also markedly reduce the root mass available for water and nutrient absorption.

Too Much Water

Too much irrigation is just as detrimental to olives as is too little. Poorly drained or layered soils can become waterlogged, resulting in poor aeration and root deterioration. This is more common in winter and early spring, causing poor shoot growth, yellow foliage, and tree loss. Soil that becomes saturated after fruit set contributes to fruit shrivel. Olives suffering from root damage do not tolerate winter cold as well, presumably because they have lower amounts of stored carbohydrates. *Phytophthora* is also a greater problem in excessively wet orchards.

A second, equally significant soil pathogen in olives is *Verticillium dahliae*, a soilborne fungus (see chapter 17: Diseases of Olive). The relationship between soil temperature, water content, infection potential, and symptom expression is complex and not well understood. However, field observations suggest a greater incidence of *Verticillium* during cool, wet springs and in areas of the orchard where excess water persists (such as the field end to which water drains). Consequently, growers in high-inoculum soil attempt to reduce spring symptoms by filling the root zone to near field capacity in January and then avoiding excessive irrigation from February through April.

WATER REQUIREMENTS FOR OLIVE TREES

The research on the specific water requirement for olive is relatively recent, possibly because much of the world's acreage is not irrigated. Where irrigation is practiced abroad, the water supply is so limited in most producing areas that only a small fraction of the potential orchard water need is met. In California—where irrigation water is relatively plentiful and inexpensive, excellent distribution systems serve the state, and high-intensity agriculture is practiced—irrigation designed to meet the water needs of trees is practiced on virtually all olive acreage. As competition for California's water increases from the municipal and industrial sectors, however, maximizing the beneficial use of applied water is an increasing priority for olive growers.

The Concept of Evapotranspiration

Water use in an olive orchard depends on two processes: evaporation (E) of water from the soil around the tree and transpiration (T) of water from the tree's foliage. Crop water use is the sum of these two and is called evapotranspiration (ET).

Weather conditions largely determine ET rates. Because both processes that make up ET involve water vaporization, the energy status of the atmosphere determines water loss. Components of this energy status include solar radiation, temperature, humidity, and wind speed. Bare ground upwind of an orchard can also markedly increase ET rates since warmer air (and more energy) can move horizontally from it into the orchard.

Rainfall can supply a significant part of the olive tree's water requirement. Not all rainfall is stored in the soil; depending on its intensity and duration, up to 50 percent of the rainfall can evaporate or run off the end of the field. A practical method of evaluating effective rainfall is augering into the soil at the beginning of the season to determine wetted depth.

Evaporation from the soil is important only when the soil surface is wet. After irrigation, wet soil can evaporate water at the same rate that trees transpire. As the soil dries out, surface evaporation decreases quickly. Thus, the amount of water evaporated depends on the wetted orchard floor area and irrigation frequency. Localized irrigation, including drip systems, can lower evaporation significantly and save water in young orchards, but less so in mature orchards (Schwankl, Hanson, and Prichard 1998). This is due to the fact that percent of shaded area becomes more dominant in mature orchards.

Covercropping. Although cover crops can have many benefits, they use considerable amounts of water. Cover crops or resident vegetation can increase ET by up to 30 percent in mature orchards and by much more in young trees. Therefore, the cost and availability of water should be taken into account when considering cover crops.

ET and Canopy Size. The most significant plant factor affecting ET is the total leaf area intercepting solar radiation. Thus, tree canopy size, planting density, and leaf-development stage all influence crop water use. The degree of orchard floor plant cover (shade) is known to correlate well with the area exposed to sunlight. The relationship between shaded area and ET is key to estimating the water requirement of developing orchards. The relationship between percent ground cover and ET, shown for almond in figure 10.1, is not one to one. Almond ET is greatest when about 55 to 60 percent of the ground is shaded by tree canopies at midday. Full cover is not required to reach maximum ET, presumably because the orchard floor area receiving direct sun heats up and transfers energy to the tree canopies, which increases transpiration. While the relationship for olive trees has not been established, the results with almond can be taken as a first approximation.

Estimating Evapotranspiration

Two main techniques are used to estimate baseline ET and to create reference indexes of evaporative demand. Evaporative demand is the potential of the atmosphere to vaporize water. One index is based on measuring water lost from a round metal pan 4 feet (1.2 m) across and 10 inches (25 cm) deep placed in irrigated, close-cut grass. Water loss is measured daily in the pan using a depth gauge. This index of ET, referred to as Epan, is commonly reported by weather stations and local newspapers.

The other, more recent, ET index uses weather data and meteorological mathematical models. The data come from a statewide network of about 70 automated weather stations—developed by the University of California and operated by the California Department of Water Resources—called the CIMIS (California Irrigation Management Information System). Each station measures solar radiation temperature, relative humidity, wind speed, and wind direction. These parameters are used in a formula (modified Penman equation) to estimate water use for a close-cut grass, referred to as ETo. This index correlates better with short-term crop water use than Epan because it is based on parameters that are directly related to the physiology of transpiration rather than simple evaporation from a free water surface. Also, automated weather stations allow rapid estimates of ETo as their data are readily accessible electronically. The remaining discussion considers only ETo and how to use it. To convert Epan data to ETo, divide Epan by 1.24.

Current weather information and ETo estimates are available to growers in local newspapers and by computer via the Internet. The California Department of Water Resources supplies current (real time) and historic water use information at the CIMIS Web site: http://www.cimis.water.ca.gov. Access to the automated weather stations can also be obtained

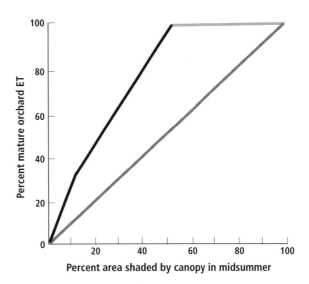

Figure 10.1. The relationship between tree canopy size and water usage (Fereres 1982). Solid line is experimental data.

through the University of California Statewide Integrated Pest Management Program's (IPM) Web site: www.ipm.ucdavis.edu. Though a less precise guide to irrigation scheduling than real-time data, long-term historical average monthly ETo data have also been compiled for all locations in California in Snyder, Pruitt, and Shaw (1995). Table 10.2 provides average ETo information for California's major olive-growing counties.

The Crop Factor (Kc)

As described above, ETo provides an estimate of crop water use for close-cut grass. For many crops, field research has been conducted to determine their actual water requirement (ETc). Information derived from such studies is site and time specific and is not accurate under different weather conditions; however, the relationship between ETo and ETc has been found to be relatively constant. Thus, researchers have used this ratio to develop crop factors, or coefficients (Kc), that allow growers to relate crop ET to ETo. In California's interior valleys, crop factors are relatively independent of location and vary primarily with the tree species and its stage of growth. From the ETo for an olive-growing region, the Kc for the specified period of the season can be applied to obtain an estimate of olive ET. Crop factor values assume that soil water content and disease are not limiting plant water use. If either condition exists, the Kc will overestimate the water requirement for the orchard.

Recent research in California with the Manzanillo cultivar indicates that irrigating mature trees with a Kc of less than .65 results in tree water stress based on predawn

Table 10.2. Average reference evapotranspiration (ETo) for major olive-growing counties in California (inches per month)

	Jan	Feb	Mar	Apr	May	June	July	Aug	Sept	Oct	Nov	Dec
Sacramento Valley												
Butte (Oroville)	1.22	1.65	2.81	4.72	6.10	7.56	8.54	7.32	5.31	3.66	1.65	0.98
Glenn (Orland)	1.22	1.65	3.05	4.84	6.71	7.44	8.79	7.32	5.79	3.78	1.65	1.10
Shasta (Redding)	1.22	1.43	2.62	4.13	5.61	7.09	8.54	7.32	5.31	3.23	1.42	0.85
Tehama (Corning)	1.22	1.76	2.93	4.49	6.10	7.26	8.06	7.20	5.31	3.66	1.65	1.10
Regional average	1.22	1.62	2.85	4.55	6.13	7.34	8.48	7.29	5.43	3.58	1.59	1.00
Regional total: 51.1												
San Joaquin Valley												
Fresno (Reedley)	1.10	1.54	3.17	4.72	6.35	7.68	8.54	7.32	5.31	3.42	1.42	0.73
Kern (Shafter)	0.98	1.65	3.42	4.96	6.59	7.68	8.30	7.32	5.43	3.42	1.54	0.85
Kings (Kettleman City)	0.98	1.76	3.42	5.31	7.20	7.91	8.42	7.44	5.91	3.66	1.65	0.98
Madera (Madera)	0.92	1.43	3.17	4.84	6.59	7.80	8.54	7.32	5.31	3.42	1.42	0.73
Tulare (Porterville)	1.22	1.76	3.42	4.72	6.59	7.68	8.54	7.32	5.31	3.42	1.42	0.73
Regional average	1.04	1.63	3.32	4.91	6.66	7.75	8.47	7.34	5.45	3.47	1.49	0.80
Regional total: 52.3												
Southern California												
Riverside (Riverside)	2.07	2.87	4.03	4.13	6.10	7.09	7.93	7.57	6.14	4.15	2.60	1.95
Regional total: 56.3												

Source: Snyder, Pruitt, and Shaw 1995.

leaf water potential (Goldhamer, Dunai, and Ferguson 1994). No stress was observed when a Kc of .65 to .85 was used. Canning olives must maximize the production of large sized fruit in order to optimize revenue. When shoot growth, fruit load, and size are all considered, crop revenue was greatest when a Kc of .75 was used for season-long irrigation scheduling. In contrast, oil production in the same cultivar was not maximized by optimizing fruit size. Oil production was significantly greater when a Kc of .65 was used. Based on these production responses, we suggest that olives grown for canning use a Kc of .75 for conservation irrigation scheduling in California. See chapter 11: Effects of Water Stress on Olive Tree Performance, for further information.

Table 10.3 lists monthly Sacramento Valley and southern San Joaquin Valley Kc values and ETc estimates for canning olives grown under clean-cultivated conditions during a normal year. Table values apply to mature orchards (60 percent shaded area or more). Note that there is very little difference in seasonal crop water requirements between the Sacramento Valley (38.2 in [97.3 cm]) and the southern San Joaquin Valley (39.3 in [99.6 cm]). Cover crops increase crop ET rates significantly, especially during spring, and require higher Kc values.

Long-term average ETo data can be successfully used for irrigation scheduling even though a "normal" year seldom occurs. Common sense should be used to modify irrigations if temperatures or wind conditions are quite different from normal.

SCHEDULING IRRIGATIONS: THE WATERBUDGET METHOD

The most common method of water management is to schedule irrigations based on past experience. However, rising water costs, decreasing availability, high energy prices, and the potential to improve orchard productivity now call for more scientific irrigation scheduling based on sound agronomic principles.

There are several different approaches to improving irrigation scheduling. One is to monitor soil moisture levels by touch ("feel method") or by using various instruments, and to replenish soil water in a timely fashion. This strategy, if applied on a regular basis, can be effective. Another is to estimate crop water use, as previously discussed, and then irrigate to match that water requirement. This is known as the water budget method.

Experimental methods (still primarily in the research phase for trees) measure the water status of a plant with specialized equipment such as the pressure bomb and infrared gun. These devices measure the tension of water in leaf tissue and canopy temperature, respectively; predetermined thresholds are used to decide when to irrigate. This technique is used for scheduling the irrigation of cotton in California. Research is continuing on tree and vine crops to develop reliable thresholds.

The water budget method is the most comprehensive management technique now available; it uses

Table 10.3. Average estimated water requirements for clean-cultivated olives in the Sacramento and southern San Joaquin valleys

Month	ETo (in)	Kc*	Crop Etc (in) Etc	Etc (in/day)	Etc (gal/tree/day)
Sacramento Valley					
Jan	1.2	0.75 (1.05)	0.9	0.03	17
Feb	1.6	0.75 (1.05)	1.2	0.04	24
Mar	2.9	0.75 (1.05)	2.1	0.07	39
Apr	4.6	0.75 (1.05)	3.4	0.11	64
May	6.1	0.75 (1.05)	4.6	0.15	83
June	7.3	0.75 (1.00)	5.5	0.18	103
July	8.5	0.75 (1.00)	6.4	0.21	115
Aug	7.3	0.75 (1.00)	5.5	0.18	99
Sept	5.4	0.75 (1.00)	4.1	0.14	76
Oct	3.6	0.75 (1.00)	2.7	0.09	48
Nov	1.6	0.75 (0.95)	1.0	0.04	22
Dec	1.0	0.75 (0.95)	0.8	0.02	14
TOTAL	51.1		38.2		
San Joaquin Valley					
Jan	1.0	0.75 (1.05)	0.8	0.03	14
Feb	1.6	0.75 (1.05)	1.2	0.04	24
Mar	3.3	0.75 (1.05)	2.5	0.08	45
Apr	4.9	0.75 (1.05)	3.7	0.12	69
May	6.7	0.75 (1.05)	5.0	0.16	90
June	7.8	0.75 (1.00)	5.8	0.19	108
July	8.5	0.75 (1.00)	6.4	0.20	115
Aug	7.3	0.75 (1.00)	5.5	0.18	99
Sept	5.5	0.75 (1.00)	4.1	0.14	76
Oct	3.5	0.75 (1.00)	2.6	0.08	47
Nov	1.5	0.75 (0.95)	1.1	0.04	21
Dec	0.8	0.75 (0.95)	0.6	0.02	11
TOTAL	52.4		39.3		

Source: Goldhamer, Dunai, and Ferguson 1994.

*The Kc in parentheses are for orchards with cover crops.

information on crop ET, rainfall, irrigation system efficiency, and, in some cases, soil water-holding capacity to guide an irrigation program. It also answers the two most important questions for effective irrigation: when to irrigate and how much water to apply. The following discussion focuses on the water budget method.

Determining Available Water Content (AWC)

Furrow, basin, and sprinkler irrigation techniques rely on the soil to serve as a reservoir between irrigations. The size of the soil water reservoir and the rate that water is used (ETc) determine when to irrigate and how much water to apply to refill the reservoir.

The capacity of soil to store water depends primarily on its texture and structure. Fine-textured soils hold more water than coarse-textured soils. A soil's capacity to hold water for plant use is defined by three terms. The first, field capacity (FC), is the water remaining in the soil 2 or 3 days after being saturated. This is the amount of water a soil can hold after drainage has reached a very slow rate. The second term is permanent wilting point (PWP), the point at which the water remaining in the soil pores is held so tightly that plants cannot extract it and remain wilted when watered. The third term, the difference between the first two, is available water content (AWC). This is the soil water (commonly expressed in inches per foot of soil or total inches in a defined root zone) that is available for plant use. Table 10.4 gives estimates of AWC for various soil textures.

Sandy soils hold less water than loams and clay loams. This is related to both the number of soil pores and the size of individual pores. Coarse-textured sands have larger pores but less total pore space than silty clay loams; the result is less water holding capacity. Hence, most of the water in coarse-textured soil is easily removed by plant roots. Clay soils possess a large number of small pores and hold the most water. However, a large percentage of these small pores do not easily release the water; this must be taken into account in making irrigation decisions.

The wide range in AWC within a soil textural class indicates that the pore size distribution can widely affect water-holding capacity. However, precise AWC determinations are generally not necessary to improve irrigation scheduling. Using the averages provided in table 10.4, growers can obtain a rough estimate of the total water available to their olives by multiplying the AWC for their soil(s) by the depth of the root zone.

Determining the Root Zone

An accurate estimation of root depth is essential for determining the potential available water content (AWC). The olive root zone is commonly 3 to 4 feet (0.9 to 1.2 m). An excellent method for evaluating root depth is to backhoe along the drip line at three or four sites in the orchard. These excavations also provide valuable information on soil texture and the existence of compacted layers or hardpans limiting water intake. Based on the average AWC estimation of 1.5 inches per foot (3.8/30.5 cm) for a medium-textured soil (see "sandy loams" in table 10.4) and an estimated olive root depth of 4 feet (1.2 m), 6 inches (15.2 cm) of water (1.5

Table 10.4. Estimates of available water content (AWC) for different soil textures

Soil texture	Range (in/ft)	Average (in/ft)
Coarse-textured sand	0.50–1.25	0.90
Sandy loams	1.25–1.75	1.50
Silty clay loam	1.50–2.30	1.90
Clay	1.60–2.50	2.30

in/1 ft × 4 ft [3.8 cm/30.5 cm × 121.9 cm]) should be applied to fill the soil reservoir to capacity if it was initially at the permanent wilting point. However, due to postharvest irrigation and winter rainfall, it is very unlikely that the soil is at PWP. Hence, estimates of soil water content must be made using techniques described later in the chapter to determine how much water would be needed to refill the root zone to field capacity.

Establishing Allowable Depletion

As soil water content decreases from field capacity (FC), roots must expend more energy to extract water even though it is well above the permanent wilting point (PWP). This is because water is extracted first from the larger pores where it is held less tightly than in smaller pores. Small pores also hold less water, and conduction to the roots is slower. Together, these factors limit water uptake as soils dry out. This decline in water extraction decreases crop growth before the entire root zone reaches the PWP. Therefore, olive growers should irrigate before the soil water is depleted to a point that restricts growth. An exception may be spring irrigations when root rot or V0erticillium wilt could be aggravated by soil water contents near FC.

No single soil water level can be recommended for all situations. Management allowable depletion (MAD), or yield threshold depletion (YTD), is the target percentage or amount of the total available water in the root zone that indicates irrigation is needed. It depends on several factors including root depth, soil texture, weather, the season, and any regulated stress level the grower may wish to induce. Providing that infiltration does not limit the amount of water effectively applied per irrigation, olive growers typically irrigate when the AWC reaches about 50 percent depletion. In the previous example, assume a 50 percent MAD. Since the total AWC was estimated at 6 inches (15.2 cm) (1.5 in/1 ft × 4-ft [3.8 cm/30.5 cm × 121.9-cm] root depth), the next irrigation should be applied when ETc indicates that 3 inches (7.6 cm) has been used (6 in [15.2 cm] × 0.5 [1.3 cm] MAD) since the last irrigation. In stress-sensitive periods such as during flower and fruit development, trees should be irrigated at relatively small depletion levels (30 to 40 percent MAD).

The MAD and AWC concepts are important only for surface and sprinkler irrigation systems. Localized systems (such as drip and micro-sprinkler systems) are designed to replenish ETc on a daily to weekly basis as the crop consumes water. Hence the soil is not being used for water storage to the same degree as with surface or conventional sprinkler systems. Orchards with conventional irrigation systems and slow infiltration also require increased irrigation frequency for the same reason.

APPLICATION EFFICIENCY

The information in the paragraphs above can be used to estimate how often to irrigate and the amount of water required to refill the soil water reservoir. However, when water is applied to an orchard, some losses occur that are not due to crop use, and these must be considered in calculating the actual amount of water to be applied. The type of irrigation system used, soil, weather conditions, and water management practices largely determine application efficiency.

Water applied to a field can be lost by runoff, percolation below the root zone, and (with sprinklers) spray evaporation and drift. The goal of water management is to minimize these losses. For instance, runoff can be minimized by designing an irrigation system that matches application rate to soil infiltration rate or that collects and reuses tailwater. Application efficiency (Ea) is a term commonly used to describe how efficiently growers irrigate. It is defined as the percentage of applied irrigation water that is stored in the root zone (and thus available for crop use).

Application efficiency is directly related to how uniformly water can be applied to an orchard. Therefore, the irrigation method is of prime importance. Most olive orchards use surface (basin, furrow, and border strip) irrigation methods although sprinkler and drip or low-volume systems are becoming more popular. Each method differs in its application uniformity. With surface irrigation, the variability in water intake properties of the soil and the rate that water advances over the surface determine uniformity; uniformity is greatest when irrigation water is applied rapidly from the head to the tail of the field. With sprinklers, uniformity depends largely on system design—nozzle spacing, type, size, riser height, operating pressure, and wind conditions. The efficiency of drip or low-volume systems depends on their design, operation, and maintenance. In general, sprinkler and drip or low-volume systems can be operated with higher efficiencies than surface methods. Because application efficiencies vary, Ea must be estimated for each orchard. The University of California Cooperative Extension, USDA Farm Services, and private irrigation consultants offer assistance in evaluating irrigation systems. Some general application efficiency estimates for different systems are shown in table 10.5. An Ea estimate is necessary to determine how much water must be delivered to the orchard (the gross irrigation requirement). For example, assuming a 75 percent efficiency (0.75), the amount of water that must be delivered to achieve an effective 3-inch (7.6-cm) irrigation would be 3 inches/0.75 = 4 inches (7.6 cm/0.75 = 10 cm). Irrigating 12 acres (4.9 ha) at this rate would require 4 inches × 12 acres = 48 acre-inches (10 cm × 4.9 ha = 49 cm/ha) (4 acre-feet) (4,932 m³).

Table 10.5. Irrigation efficiency (Ea) of olive orchard systems

System	Ea (%)
Basin	70–80
Border	strip 70–80
Furrow	65–75
Sprinkler	75–85
Drip	85–95

A major component of the water budget irrigation method is the amount of water actually being delivered to the orchard. This is more difficult to estimate with ditch water than with wells, but not impossible. Many ditch tenders are quite good at estimating water delivery, usually expressed in "second-feet" (technically known as cubic feet per second or cfs); one second-foot is equal to 1 acre-inch per hour (103 m^3/hr) (27,154 gallons [102,778 L]). USDA Farm Services, UC Cooperative Extension, or commercial irrigation designers can assist growers in selecting inexpensive flow measurement devices that can be installed to help determine delivery rates.

Pumping stations can be tested easily for discharge by contacting a local pump company to provide data on pump efficiency, static water table and drawdown, and the cost per acre-foot of water delivery. After determining actual pump capacity, the time required to apply the desired amount of water can be calculated. Assuming a pump capacity of 1,000 gallons per minute (3,785 L/min), the running time necessary to apply 48 acre-inches (4,944 m^3) to the 12-acre (4.9-ha) example would be:

$$(27,154 \text{ gal/ac-in} \times 48 \text{ ac-in})/1,000 \text{ gal/min}$$
$$= 1,303 \text{ min} = 21.7 \text{ hr}$$

$$(102,778 \text{ L}/103 \text{ m}^3 \times 4,944 \text{ m}^3)/3,785 \text{ L/min}$$
$$= 1,303 \text{ min} = 21.7 \text{ hr}$$

IRRIGATION PROGRAM EVALUATION

The above discussion describes the many components to developing an irrigation management program that provides optimal soil moisture for tree health and productivity. The final and essential component is timely evaluation of soil moisture status. Monitoring soil moisture determines the accuracy of water budget–based irrigation scheduling.

The most valuable information from soil moisture monitoring is obtained just before an irrigation and 3 to 4 days after irrigating. Assessing the soil moisture prior to irrigation verifies that the soil has dried out as expected based on the water budget method and the estimated allowable depletion (AD). For example, too low a soil moisture (depletion greater than that desired) requires more frequent irrigation or, in the case of well-drained soil, the application of more water at the existing frequency. Evaluation of the soil moisture 3 to 4 days after irrigation determines the depth and uniformity of the irrigation. Together, these two evaluations provide information essential to confirming that the root zone was refilled after irrigation and that the estimation for water use (ETc) between irrigations is accurate.

The "Feel Method"

The simplest but most subjective method of evaluating soil moisture is to sample the soil directly with an auger and assess its water content by feel. Guidelines for relating the feel of various soil textures to water content are available through USDA Farm Services or UC Cooperative Extension. Although time-consuming, assessing soil moisture by the feel method is very effective in determining soil water content and irrigation requirements.

Tensiometers

Another method of monitoring soil moisture is with a tensiometer, which consists of a vacuum gauge connected to a piece of PVC tubing with a porous ceramic cup at its tip. Tensiometers are filled with distilled water and then purged of air using a simple suction device. As soil water is depleted, soil moisture tension increases. This creates a vacuum at the ceramic cup-soil interface which exerts tension on the column of water in the tubing. The tension is then registered in units of atmospheric pressure (centibars) on the gauge. Charts provided with the instruments relate the gauge reading to percent soil moisture depletion based on soil texture. Tensiometers are better suited to sandy soil than clay because they are not mechanically capable of measuring the high tensions at which water is still available in fine-textured soils. Tensiometers break suction above 80 centibars and become inoperable before finer-textured soil (loams to clay loams) has reached sufficient depletion for irrigation. Tensiometers are also most valuable when two or three are placed at different depths in a single location. This provides information on the rate and depth of depletion. Used in combination with the water budget method, tensiometers can be helpful in evaluating soil water status. It is essential that their porous cup maintains contact with the soil and that they are checked regularly for breaks in vacuum caused by leaks or excessively dry soil.

Electrical Resistance Block

A third instrument used for soil water measurement is the electrical resistance block. It consists of a small block of gypsum or ceramic-sand material containing two separate wires; the blocks are installed at different depths in the root zone using a device similar to a soil push-tube. The wires leading up to the surface are attached to a stake or to the tree trunk to avoid damage. A hand-held meter is used to measure the electrical resistance (in centibars of soil moisture tension) between the wires in the block. Electrical resistance and meter readings increase as the soil becomes drier. Rewetting the soil causes water to move back into the block, which reduces the resistance to electrical current flow and lowers the reading. Resistance blocks made from gypsum are more suited for use in surface irrigation systems because they are less accurate in the wet soil moisture range than those constructed from ceramic-sand. Blocks constructed from ceramic-sand can be used in microirrigation systems where frequent irrigation keeps soil relatively wet. Table 10.6 shows the relationship between percent of available water content (AWC) depletion and tension for several soil textures.

Soil salinity should be considered when using electrical resistance blocks. Salt-affected soils give lower resistance readings, which suggest higher soil moisture levels than are present. Electrical resistance blocks buffer the effects of salinity on reading accuracy up to ECe (electrical conductivity of the soil saturation extract) values of 1.5 dS/m.

Neutron Probe

Another soil water measurement device increasingly used is the neutron probe. It consists of a radiation source and a recording unit. The radiation source is lowered into a 2-inch (5-cm) diameter PVC or metal tube carefully installed in the soil to a depth of about 5 feet (1.5 m). The very low-level radiation source emits high-energy neutrons that collide with hydrogen atoms in the water and soil. The collision results in energy loss and the creation of slow neutrons. Some slow neutrons are reflected back to the source and counted by a neutron detector. The readings are interpreted from a calibration curve that relates the instrument readings to soil water levels. Measurements are usually taken at 1-foot (30-cm) increments.

The neutron probe is primarily used by large farms and by irrigation consultants providing service for a fee. Because the probe is radioactive, it is strictly regulated by state agencies and requires a license for operation. Like all devices installed in the soil, it is site-specific; the access tubes must be placed in soils representing an average texture and infiltration for a given orchard. The tubes can be damaged by equipment since they must be located in the irrigated area. The soil surrounding the tube at ground level must not crack sufficiently to allow water to run down the outside of the tube, which would create a wetted area not representative of the root zone.

Other Methods of Evaluation

Recently, new instruments that measure the dielectric constant of the soil have become available. This constant is a measure of the ability of a material to establish an electric field. Since water is about 20 times more capable of this than dry soil, changes in soil water content can be monitored using this concept. The most common dielectric methods are frequency-domain-reflectometry (FDR) or capacitance and time-domain-reflectometry (TDR) sensors.

Calibration equations have been developed to relate dielectric constant and soil moisture content. The effects of soil texture and salinity on these calibrations are not well known although the salinity effect is thought to be small. Since these sensors are most sensitive to the moisture content of soil immediately adjacent to it, air gaps from soil cracking or poor installation greatly affect reading accuracy. Dielectric sensors measure soil moisture about 4 inches (10 cm) away from the electrodes. Instruments using dielectric constant technology have the advantage of taking continuous measurements. This allows the observation of trends in soil moisture, which are more difficult to detect with instruments that are read only periodically. However, the difficulty in developing a calibration equation and the small area measured by the electrodes can limit the accuracy of individual soil moisture readings.

Table 10.6. Percent of available water depleted at various soil moisture tensions

Tension (bars*)	Loamy sand	Fine, sandy loam	Sandy loam	Loam	Clay
0.3[†]	55	50	35	15	7
0.5[†]	70	62	55	30	13
0.8[†]	77	70	63	45	20
1.0[‡]	82	75	68	55	27
2.0[‡]	90	82	78	72	45
5.0[‡]	95	93	88	80	75
15.0[‡]	100	100	100	100	100

*1 bar = 100 centibars
[†]Tensiometers operate within this range.
[‡]Gypsum blocks operate within this range.

REFERENCES

Fereres, E. 1982. Drip irrigation saves money in young almond orchards. Calif. Ag. Sept.–Oct.:12–13.

Goldhamer, P. A., J. Dunai, and L. Ferguson. 1994. Irrigation requirements of olive trees and responses to sustained deficit irrigation. Acta Horticulturae 356:172–176.

Hartmann, H. T. 1949. Growth of the olive fruit. Proc. Amer. Soc. Hort. Sci. 54:86–94.

Schwankl, L., B. Hanson, and T. Prichard. 1998. Micro-irrigation of trees and vines. Oakland: University of California Agriculture and Natural Resources, Publication 3378.

Snyder, R. L., W. O. Pruitt, and D. A. Shaw. 1995. Determining daily reference evapotranspiration (ETo). Oakland: University of California Agriculture and Natural Resources, Publication 21426.

11

Effects of Water Stress on Olive Tree Performance

DAVID A. GOLDHAMER AND ROBERT H. BEEDE

Due to a lack of water resources or infrastructure development, most of the world's olives are grown under dry land conditions. When irrigation is practiced, applied water is often far less than potential water use (ETc) of the trees. It is clear that the olive tree is drought tolerant, able to survive severe water stress, and still produce a crop. However, numerous studies have shown that top yields of high-quality fruit require supplemental irrigation.

Most California olive growers are able to fully irrigate their orchards due to relatively abundant water resources and a highly developed distribution system throughout the state. However, increased competition for California's water supply from a growing population and the environmental sector suggests that growers will be increasingly accountable for their water use. Future water costs will likely be higher. Thus, knowledge of olive tree response to water stress can be important in developing irrigation management strategies. Two recent field studies established relationships between applied water, yield, and revenue. This chapter summarizes these studies and answers the questions of whether and under what conditions deficit irrigation should be used. (Goldhamer 1999; Goldhamer, Dunai, and Ferguson 1994)

Water stress studies (ibid.) examining effects of sustained and regulated deficit irrigation on olive tree performance were conducted for two consecutive seasons in a mature commercial Manzanillo orchard in California's San Joaquin Valley where effective rainfall averages about 4 inches (10 cm) per year. Irrigation was provided via microsprinklers or drip emitters.

WATER STRESS

The lack of adequate soil water results in plant water deficits, what is referred to as water stress. As leaf stomata, the small openings on the underside of olive leaves, open early in the morning in response to sunlight, water vapor moves from the interior of the leaf through the stomata and into the atmosphere. This process is known as transpiration. It causes the leaves to become slightly deficient in water and creates an energy gradient between the leaves and other parts of the plant—shoots, trunk, and roots. At the root-soil interface, this gradient results in soil water extraction. The transpiration rate depends primarily on weather conditions. As soil water becomes limited, the transpiration rate exceeds the soil water extraction rate. Without some type of regulation, leaves would dehydrate, resulting in damage or death. Stomata provide this regulation: they begin to close in response to water stress, thus maintaining a favorable internal water balance in the plant. However, this comes at a price.

Leaf stomata are not only the conduits for transpiration but also for carbon assimilation. Carbon dioxide diffuses from the atmosphere through the stomata and into the leaf where photosynthesis converts it into sugars, the building blocks necessary for plant and fruit growth and the fuel that powers important plant processes. In essence, the plant trades water for carbon since both water and carbon dioxide use the same plumbing system at the leaf surface. Maximum transpiration and thus maximum photosynthesis occur when plants are fully irrigated. Reducing carbon uptake and thus photosynthesis will negatively affect one or more plant organs—roots, shoots, branches, leaves, fruit, and so on.

SUSTAINED DEFICIT IRRIGATION (SDI): SEASON-LONG WATER STRESS

Eight irrigation regimes were imposed for the entire season based on using crop coefficients (Kc's) of 0.16, 0.26, 0.36, 0.46, 0.55, 0.65, 0.75, and 0.85 and reference crop water use (ETo). (See chapter 10, Olive Irrigation Management, for an explanation of crop coefficients). With these regimes, seasonal applied water ranged from 8 to 40 acre-inches/acre (2,035 to 10,175 m³/ha) (hereafter referred to as inches).

Fruit load (number of fruit per tree) was only minimally affected with applied water amounts equal to or

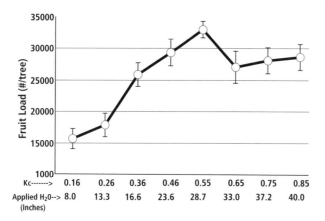

Figure 11.1. Mean values of fruit load for the final 2 years of the sustained deficit irrigation study. (Vertical bars indicate ± one standard error.)

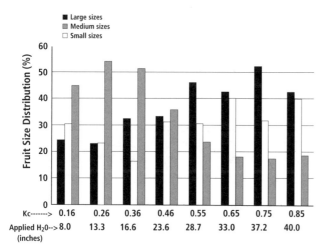

Figure 11.2. Mean values of fruit size distribution for the final 2 years of the sustained deficit irrigation study.

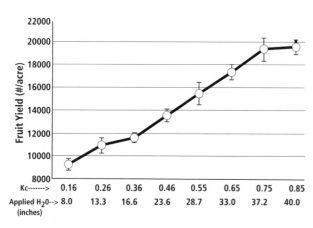

Figure 11.3. Mean values of fruit yield for the final 2 years of the sustained deficit irrigation study. (Vertical bars indicate ± one standard error.)

greater than about 17 inches (fig. 11.1). Below about 13 inches of applied water, fruit load was significantly lower, presumably due to reduced shoot growth and thus fewer fruiting positions.

There was a direct relationship between fruit size and applied water (fig. 11.2). Undesirable, small fruit (undersize and culls) accounted for the majority of the harvested fruit with 17 inches or less of applied water. The greatest percentages of larger fruit were produced with the higher levels of applied water.

Total fruit yield per tree depends on both fruit load and fruit size. Fruit yield was strongly related to applied water between approximately 8 and 37 inches (fig. 11.3). While yield was reduced by 55 percent with 8 inches of water, there was also a significant yield loss of 35 percent when about 24 inches of seasonal applied water was used.

Crop value is based primarily on fruit size. Crop value from treatments ranging from 8 to 24 inches of applied water was about \$300/ton (\$300/.907 metric t) (fig. 11.4). Between 24 and 37 inches, crop value increased linearly to about \$550/ton (\$550/.907 metric t).

Gross revenue, based on yield and crop value data, was highly correlated with irrigation amounts (fig. 11.5). Revenue increased exponentially between 8 and 37 inches of applied water. Revenue produced per unit of applied water ranged from about \$200/acre-ft (\$200/1,233 m^3) for 1 acre-ft (1,233 m^3) of applied water to about \$1,300/acre-ft (\$1,300/1,233m^3) for 3 acre-ft (3,699 m^3) of applied water.

Although olives are used primarily for canning in California, most olives worldwide are cultivated for oil. During the last experimental year, harvest was delayed for some trees until January to simulate a harvest date for oil olives. The measured oil content increased under very limited irrigation (fig. 11.6). With only 8

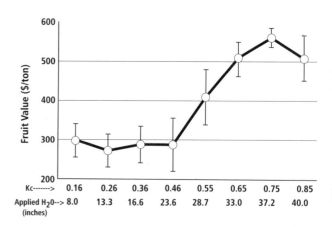

Figure 11.4. Mean values of crop value for the final 2 years of the sustained deficit irrigation study. (Vertical bars indicate ± one standard error.)

inches of applied water, the measured oil content approached 16 percent on a fresh weight basis compared with about 12.5 percent for trees that received 40 inches of water. Thus, the most stressed trees had an apparent oil content increase of about 40 percent. However, any benefit from increased oil was offset by the more than 55 percent decrease in gross yield in these deficit treatments. Free fatty acid content also tended to increase with increased, sustained deficit irrigation although not to the same magnitude as oil. (The analytical technique used to extract oil for testing may be more complete for stressed fruit and thus, partly responsible for the apparent higher oil content of the severely stressed treatments.)

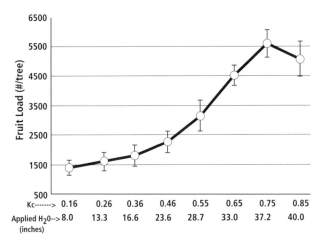

Figure 11.5. Mean values of gross revenue for the final 2 years of the sustained deficit irrigation study. (Vertical bars indicate ± one standard error.)

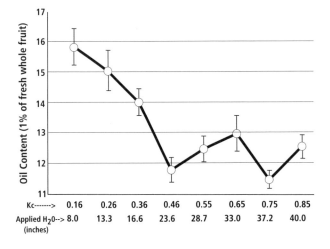

Figure 11.6. Olive oil content on a fresh, whole fruit basis. Values are means from a normal canning date harvest and a season when some trees were not harvested until January. (Vertical bars indicate ± one standard error.)

REGULATED DEFICIT IRRIGATION (RDI)

Negative effects of sustained or season-long deficit irrigation on olive production are well recognized. However, growers may still be faced with the reality of reduced and more costly irrigation supplies in the future. With RDI, stress is limited to the most stress-tolerant growth periods of the season. The goal is to reduce water use while minimizing negative effects on the crop.

The most stress-tolerant period for canning olives in California is in June and July. Three RDI regimes were imposed for four consecutive seasons (table 11.1): reductions of approximately 16, 25, and 44 percent from the 30 inches [76 cm] for the most heavily irrigated trees.

During severe deficit irrigation, fruit diameter growth slowed (fig. 11.7). However, after reintroduction of full irrigation, growth accelerated. This phenomenon resulted in full or near full recovery of fruit size of formerly stressed fruit. Fruit size recovery was due to both rehydration and increased dry matter accumulation immediately following increased irrigation and indicates that potential fruit size is not limited by water deficits that develop in late June because cell division is unaffected. Temporary slowing of cell growth and eventual full recovery in size suggest that cell walls are not damaged by stress and maintain flexibility needed to expand.

Regulated deficit irrigation did not significantly affect fruit load, dry fruit weight, and fruit value for the 4 experimental years (table 11.2). However, fresh fruit weight was somewhat smaller in the most severe RDI regime. Mean gross revenue, calculated from yield and crop value for each year, was virtually identical for all but the most severe RDI regime (table 11.2).

Table 11.1 Regulated deficit irrigation (RDI) regimes evaluated

Irrigation regime	Deficit irrigation period	Duration (days)	Irrigation rate (%)*	Mean applied water (in/yr)
T1: Control	—	—	—	30.2
T2	mid-June–July	42	50	25.4
T3	June–mid-Aug	70	50	22.8
T5a	mid-May–mid-June	28	50	27.0
T5b	mid-June–mid-Aug	56	25	27.0
T5c	mid-Aug–mid-Sept	28	50	27.0

Source: Goldhamer, Dunai, and Ferguson 1994.
*Percent of normal irrigation
T = Treatment

Table 11.2. Regulated deficit irrigation (RDI) operational and production mean values for the 4-year study

Regulated deficit irrigation regime	Yearly applied water (in)	Gross fruit yield (ton/acre)	Fruit load (number/ tree)	Fresh fruit weight (gm/ fruit)	Dry fruit weight (gm/fruit)	Crop value ($/ton)	Gross revenue ($/acre)	Oil content[‡] (% of whole fresh fruit)	Oil production[§] (gal/acre)
**T1: Control[**]	30.2	5.89 ab[*]	17290	4.13 a	1.34	558	2,690 b	11.1 a	171
T2	25.4	6.07 b	18080	4.24 ab	1.37	577	2,700 b	12.9 b	205
T3	22.8	6.11 b	18010	4.36 b	1.40	586	2,680 b	13.8 bc	221
T5	17.0	5.30 a	17480	4.10 a	1.37	545	2,020 a	14.4 c	200
			NSD[†]		NSD	NSD			

Source: Goldhamer, Dunai, and Ferguson 1994.

[*] Numbers not followed by the same letter are statistically different using Duncan's Multiple Range Test at the 5% confidence level.

[**] T = Treatment

[†] NSD indicates no statistically significant differences.

[‡] Data only from last experimental year.

[§] Based on single year's oil data and 4-year mean yield values.

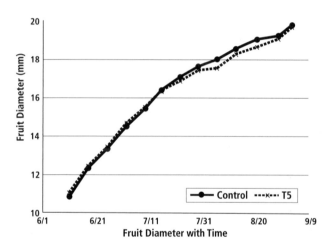

Figure 11.7. Fruit growth for the control and the most severe RDI regime (T5) for an "off" bearing year.

Oil content was significantly higher for all RDI regimes relative to the control (table 11.2). For the most severely stressed regime, the increase was about 30 percent. This outweighed the 10 percent reduction in yield (tons/acre) suggesting that higher oil production (gals/acre) can be achieved with applied water significantly lower than fully irrigated trees.

REFERENCES

Goldhamer, D. A. 1999. Regulated deficit irrigation for California canning olives. Acta Horticulturae 474(1):369–372.

Goldhamer, D. A., J. Dunai, and L. Ferguson. 1994. Irrigation requirements of olive trees and responses to sustained deficit irrigation. Acta Horticulturae 356:172–175.

1 2
Mineral Nutrient Availability

MARK FREEMAN AND ROBERT M. CARLSON

Soil is a complex mixture of soil particles, soil solution, organic matter, and biological organisms. Plants obtain most of their mineral nutrients from the soil solution, but each of the other components affects how easily nutrients are absorbed by roots. An olive tree found deficient in a mineral nutrient does not always simply need fertilizer. The cause of that mineral deficiency should be investigated before a solution is attempted.

Olives are more tolerant of high soil boron levels and less fertile soils than are most other commercial tree crops. In fact, highly fertile soils and high nitrogen levels are undesirable because they lead to excessive shoot growth and the production of many small fruit. Olives do not tolerate poorly drained soils, however.

Only three mineral nutrient deficiencies have been observed in commercial California olive orchards: nitrogen, potassium, and boron. Annual applications of nitrogen and in some situations potassium result in the greatest nutrient uptake efficiency. However, not all olive orchards require annual fertilizer additions, and nutrient deficiencies other than nitrogen, potassium, and boron can occur. This chapter is intended to help growers understand how mineral deficiencies occur.

ESSENTIAL NUTRIENTS

Normal growth and optimal production requires that most plants obtain 14 nutrients from the soil. Carbon, hydrogen, and oxygen, the other three essential plant nutrients, are taken up by plants as carbon dioxide and water from the atmosphere or soil. Nutrients obtained from the soil are separated into two groups based on the relative amounts needed by the plant. The macronutrient group includes nitrogen, phosphorus, potassium, calcium, magnesium, and sulfur. The micronutrient group includes zinc, iron, manganese, boron, copper, chlorine, molybdenum, and nickel. The most important management objective for the 14 elements should be that none of them is in such short supply that plant growth and yield are reduced. Growth and production are limited by the single element that is most deficient (or, in some cases, too abundant or toxic). Until that element's concentration is increased (or decreased when a toxicity occurs), growth will be subnormal.

The concentration of nutrients needed for normal development in a particular part of the plant changes throughout the year. For example, older olive leaves accumulate and store nitrogen, only to have it translocated to developing fruit and new leaves. However, olive trees do not require most essential nutrients to be added through a regular fertilizer program. Most essential elements are supplied in adequate amounts from most soils, except for nitrogen and perhaps potassium and boron. Only small amounts of some essential nutrients are removed through harvesting, pruning, and other orchard practices from olive trees. Finally, the leaves of fruit trees translocate much of the total supply of these essential nutrients back into the tree before they fall off.

Nutrients in the soil can be contained in the soil solution or attached to colloids (very small particles) of soils or organic matter, but plant roots absorb most of the nutrients from the soil solution. Nutrients exist in solution as ions with a positive electrical charge (called cations), ions with a negative electrical charge (anions), and ions with no electrical charge (neutral molecules). Some nutrients, such as nitrogen, can occur in both negatively and positively charged forms. Table 12.1 summarizes the forms of the elements in the soil solution that are utilized by plants. Cations added to the soil form salts that precipitate or become fixed onto the surfaces of clay particles and thus become unavailable to roots until returned to the soil solution. Microbes such as bacteria and fungi in the soil are often involved in bringing these nutrients into the soil solution. Mycorrhizal fungi are specifically involved in the uptake of both nutrients and water by the tree.

Table 12.1. Forms of nutrient elements found in soil solutions utilized by plants

Class of nutrient	Element	Cationic forms	Symbol	Anionic forms	Symbol
Primary nutrients	nitrogen	ammonium	NH_4^+	nitrate	NO_3^-
	phosphorus	—	—	dihydrogen phosphate	$H_2PO_4^-$
				hydrogen phosphate	HPO_4^{2-}
	potassium	potassium ion	K^+	—	—
Secondary nutrients	calcium	calcium ion	Ca^{2+}	—	—
	magnesium	magnesium ion	Mg^{2+}	—	—
	sulfur	—	—	sulfate	SO_4^{2-}
Micronutrients	iron	ferrous ion	Fe^{2+}	—	—
		ferric ion	Fe^{3+}		—
	manganese	manganous ion	Mn^{2+}	—	—
	zinc	zinc ion	Zn^{2+}	—	—
	copper	cupric ion	Cu^{2+}	—	—
	boron	—	—	borate	$H_2BO_3^-$
				neutral boric acid	H_3BO_3
	molybdenum	—	—	molybdate	MoO_4^{2-}
	chlorine	—	—	chloride	Cl^-

SOIL REACTION (PH)

Soil pH refers to the relative concentrations of hydrogen (H^+) and hydroxyl (OH^-) ions in the soil solution. Soil pH is measured on a scale from 0 to 14. This measurement is important because it indicates whether a soil is acidic (pH less than 7), neutral (pH of 7), or basic (pH greater than 7). The lower the pH, the more acid a soil is, having a higher concentration of hydrogen ions in solution. The higher the pH, the more basic (alkaline) a soil is, having a higher concentration of hydroxyl ions. Soil pH influences which nutrients are soluble and at what concentrations they are present in the soil solution. Thus, pH has a definite effect on nutrient availability to tree roots (fig. 12.1). For most plants, a soil pH range between 6.5 and 7.0 is best for overall nutrient availability.

Four processes are largely responsible for lowering the pH in orchard soil: growing leguminous crops, such as vetch or clover, that fix nitrogen from the atmosphere; adding fertilizers that contain or form ammonium; leaching cations (such as Na^+, Ca^{2+}, Mg^{2+}, and K^+) to lower depths in the soil; and removal of those cations by the crop. Fine-textured soils (with a high clay content) or those containing free lime (calcium carbonate), as many California soils do, have a considerable buffering capacity that reduces the acidification effect. However, sandy soils with smaller amounts of clay or those soils having little or no free lime may be acidified rapidly. These soils are especially vulnerable if irrigation water has low concentrations of calcium or magnesium, legumes that fix nitrogen are present, or

ammonium-based fertilizers are used regularly. Soil pH should be monitored regularly.

The optimal range of soil pH for olive is not established although olives are generally grown on soils having a pH of 5.5 to 8.3. Many California soils where olives are grown have a pH greater than 7.0, and they grow well in these calcareous soils.

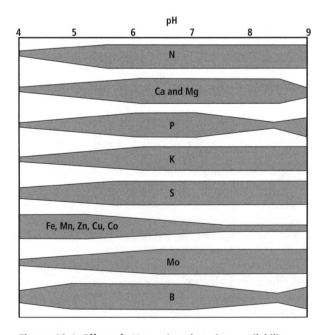

Figure 12.1. Effect of pH on mineral nutrient availability.

SOIL BUFFER SYSTEMS

Soil contains many chemical mechanisms, called buffer systems, that limit or buffer against drastic changes in pH or nutrient concentrations. These systems help ensure that a steady supply of nutrients is available, but if a major imbalance occurs over time, these same buffer systems make it difficult to effect rapid changes. Soil minerals (like clay) and organic matter tend to buffer changes in the composition of the soil solution. For example, growing legumes or applying ammonium-based fertilizers over many years lowers soil pH. A clay soil requires much more lime than a sandy soil to raise its soil pH by the same amount. Three important processes in the buffer action of soils are cation exchange, specific adsorption, and the precipitation of compounds having limited solubility.

Cation Exchange Capacity

Cation exchange capacity (CEC) expresses a soil's ability to hold onto cations against leaching and is defined as the sum total of exchangeable cations that a soil can adsorb. Many cations are mineral nutrients that olive roots can absorb from the soil solution. Mineral soils with a higher CEC are typically more fertile as they have a greater storage capacity for mineral nutrients. Cation exchange, the exchange of one cation for another, occurs primarily on the surface of clay mineral particles and on active sites of organic matter (fig. 12.2).

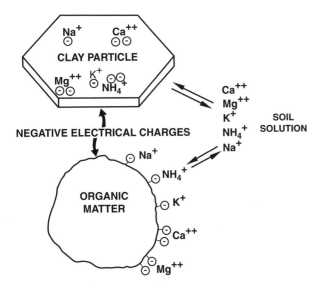

Figure 12.2. Cation exchange (Ramos, D. E., ed. Walnut orchard management. 1985. Oakland: University of California Agriculture and Natural Resources, Publication 21410).

The exchange occurs when a plant takes up a cation like calcium in exchange for two hydrogen ions. Clay particles and organic matter have negative electrical charges that must maintain a balance of positively charged cations.

Concentrations of calcium, magnesium, potassium, and sodium in soil solution are controlled primarily by cation exchange. The extent to which these nutrients are held depends on the kinds and amounts of clay and organic matter in the soil. Very sandy soils with lower clay and organic matter contents have a smaller capacity to hold these nutrients. Thus, loss of nutrients by leaching below the root zone can be a problem. However, nutrients added to sandy soils can be readily leached to the plant roots. In clay soils, penetration of certain fertilizer nutrients (such as potassium) into the root zone of deep-rooted crops is slow because the negatively charged soil particles remove them from the soil solution and retain them in the top surface soil. Cation exchange also plays a role in buffering soils against pH changes. Soil colloids hold some cations more tightly than others; however, any cation in solution can replace any cation held on a soil colloid's surface (exchangeable cation) to some extent if the concentration is high enough.

CEC is important because cations are retained by soil colloids with different intensities based on the type and concentration. Generally, calcium and magnesium predominate, and calcium is often added to displace sodium. This is significant when correcting soils high in sodium.

Specific Adsorption

Specific adsorption is a highly selective phenomenon with respect to each nutrient. Nutrients are held on the soil colloid's surface (adsorbed) by forces much stronger than the electrical attraction forces that bind exchangeable cations (fig. 12.3). Adding water is not enough to overcome these forces and put these nutrients back in solution.

Specific adsorption helps control the phosphorus concentration in the soil solution. In neutral-to-acid soils, phosphorus is specifically adsorbed onto the surface of iron and aluminum oxide particles. It is not appreciably displaced from them by other components of the soil solution. This effect becomes more pronounced as the soil becomes more acid; hence, one problem with acid soils is the reduced availability of phosphorus. Specific adsorption also appears to help control the availability of copper and zinc; thus, they are less available in basic soils. Fortunately, deficiencies of these three nutrients have not been observed in California olive orchards.

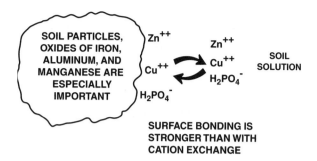

Figure 12.3. Specific adsorption (ibid.).

Precipitation and Dissolution of Compounds

Some nutrient compounds dissolve only to a small extent in the soil solution. When such a compound comes to exceed its solubility, usually due to a change in pH, the excess portion forms solid particles (precipitates). Thus, nutrient ions are taken out of solution and become unavailable to plant roots. Calcium phosphate compounds precipitate in neutral to basic soils as their solubility decreases and as soil pH increases. For acid, iron and aluminum phosphates may precipitate (in addition to the specific adsorption of phosphate on iron and aluminum oxide surfaces). These phosphates become less soluble as soil pH decreases. Iron and manganese concentrations are controlled partly by the solubility of their oxides, which decreases rapidly as soil pH increases.

SOIL TEXTURE

Soil texture, defined in terms of the proportions of sand, silt, and clay that comprise a particular soil, also affects nutrient availability to roots. Clay mineral particles are the smallest in size, and they have the capacity to store and exchange cations. Silt- and sand-sized particles do not participate in the exchange process. With their higher CEC, clay soils lose fewer nutrients to leaching than sandy soils. Clay particles can also store more available water in the same volume of soil than silt and sand. Many California soils planted to olive are layered, and nutrient availability varies depending on the soil's parent material and the different soil layers present.

Many olive orchards are planted on two or more soil types. This spatial variation mainly affects water infiltration rates but may also influence water holding capacity. These soil differences along with nonuniform irrigation practices can lead to water-logging. In that situation, the plant experiences a decrease in root health and nutrient availability. Water stress can occur in areas of lower infiltration or lower water storage capacity.

Much of California's olive acreage is planted on foothill soils (in Butte County) or terrace soils (in Tulare and Fresno counties), which are less fertile than deeper valley soils. Trees on shallow soils exhibit more growth and yield in response to nitrogen fertilizer applications than those on valley soils. Too much nitrogen can lead to increased fruit set, small fruit size, and alternate bearing. Some of these shallow soils are low in boron. Land leveling, especially within the cut areas, can result in a need for more nitrogen or potassium where the surface soil is removed. Shallow soils, however, can yield more fruit than deeper, more fertile soils because they do not promote excessive vegetative growth.

ORGANIC MATTER

To a lesser extent, soil organic matter plays a major role in controlling the availability of nitrogen, phosphorus, sulfur, zinc, and the other nutrients. These nutrients are released to the soil solution when organic matter is decomposed or mineralized by microorganisms (fig. 12.4). Conversely, these nutrients may become unavailable to plants when microbes, decomposing materials such as straw and compost, incorporate them from the soil into their own bodies.

Organic matter benefits the soil by aggregating soil particles as well as increasing its cation exchange capacity and water-holding capacity (especially in sandy soils). It can also act as a chelate, making certain micronutrients more available to roots. In addition, under some conditions it can increase air and water movement into soil and help moderate soil temperature. Unfortunately, most California soils have less than 1.5 percent organic matter, and many are less than 0.5 percent. Warmer soil temperatures over longer periods of time provide for more oxidation and microbial decomposition of the organic matter that is added each year.

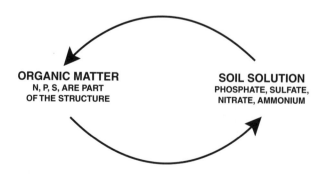

Figure 12.4. Organic matter cycling.

BIOLOGICAL ORGANISMS

Plants act as a pumping system, continually cycling nutrients to the soil surface. The nutrients added to the soil surface tend to be bound by soil particles, from which they replace nutrients removed from the soil solution. Plant roots extract nutrients from throughout the root zone and transport them to the plant tops. As plant leaves and other parts die and decompose, their nutrients are released to the soil surface again (fig. 12.5). Thus, in undisturbed soil most nutrients are concentrated near the surface. When surface soil is removed by land leveling or erosion, a major part of the organic matter and nutrient pool is removed, as well.

Roots also excrete many substances, including carbon dioxide (which forms carbonic acid in the soil solution) and organic materials, that tend to lower the pH of the soil adjacent to them. Except in acid soils, this tends to increase the availability of nutrients to the plant. Some of the excreted organic materials can form complexes with micronutrients such as zinc and iron (natural chelates); this, too, can increase the availability of nutrients from soil.

Microorganisms contribute to nutrient availability by decomposing inorganic and organic materials and oxidizing certain nutrients, which then become available for root uptake. Oxidation is important with nitrogen and sulfur. When materials added to the soil are high in carbon but low in nitrogen, like straw or compost, microbes can tie up nitrogen, making it less available. In addition, certain fungi called mycorrhizae aid root uptake of nutrients like phosphorus and zinc, particularly for most tree species. Soil microorganisms are a significant aid to soil nutrient availability.

SOIL MOISTURE LEVELS AND NUTRIENT AVAILABILITY

Nutrients (in the soil solution) are obtained by roots in three ways: root interception, mass flow, and diffusion. Nutrient uptake can occur through root interception as roots continually grow into new, undepleted soil. Nutrients can also move in the soil water that the plant needs for transpiration. This process is called mass flow (fig. 12.6). In some soils and for some nutrients, mass flow can supply much of the plant's needs. Plants can continue to take up nutrients even when water is not being drawn into the roots. *Diffusion* (fig. 12.7) describes the process where the root depletes the nutrient supply at its surface, and a gradient in concentration develops in the soil solution near the root. The nutrient diffuses down this gradient toward the root surface.

The amount of a nutrient delivered to the plant root by root interception, mass flow, and diffusion increases

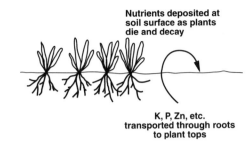

Figure 12.5. Movement of nutrients to soil surface by plant cycling.

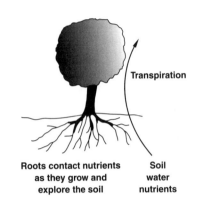

Figure 12.6. Root exploration and mass flow.

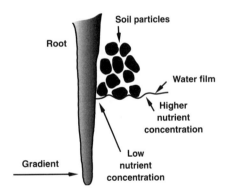

Figure 12.7. Nutrient diffusion to roots.

with the nutrient's concentration in the soil solution and the rate of root growth. However, these delivery mechanisms are also sensitive to the soil's moisture content and temperature. Delivery by all processes slows as soil moisture and temperature decrease. Little can be done to alter soil temperature, but maintaining adequate soil moisture can enhance the supply of nutrients to a plant. Conditions that promote new root growth, such as less compacted soil, also increase nutrient availability because more nutrients become available as roots explore new areas of soil.

TOXIC SOIL CONDITIONS

Plant growth is limited when soils contain excessive (or inadequate) soluble salts, are too acidic or too basic (alkaline), or lack adequate oxygen. High levels of soluble salts reduce the amount of soil water that roots can absorb. Excessive sodium, boron, and chloride are toxic to plants. Accumulated sodium also displaces exchangeable calcium and magnesium from soil particles, imparting undesirable physical properties to the soil, such as low water infiltration rates.

Water with high or low levels of soluble salts can adversely affect plant growth. When irrigation water adds soluble salts to soil, and tree roots then extract the water or it evaporates from the soil surface, most of the soluble salts are left behind. These salts concentrate in the soil profile unless irrigations and rainfall in excess of evapotranspiration leach the salts below the root zone. Water with low levels of soluble salts can create different problems. Canal water originating from the Sierra Nevada has a very low salt concentration; it also moves calcium to slightly deeper depths in the soil (perhaps less than ½ inch [1.3 cm]), and adds a small amount of sodium. These three factors combine to reduce water infiltration into the surface of soils.

Acid soils may occur naturally or may develop over time with the addition of ammonium based nitrogen fertilizers or nitrogen fixed by legumes. Very acid soils (pH <5.0) may cause a number of conditions that are unfavorable to plant growth. Among these are reduced nutrient availability, phosphorus in particular, as well as increased solubility of aluminum and manganese (which may become toxic). Liming materials, such as calcium carbonate lime, sugar beet lime, and wood ash, can be incorporated into the soil to neutralize soil acidity. Since liming materials are not easily moved in soils by rainfall or irrigation water, they must be incorporated directly to the desired soil depth to alter the pH.

Alkaline soils, with a pH greater than 7.5, have reduced nutrient availability, particularly zinc, iron, and manganese. Soils with higher pH (>8.3) usually have higher sodium concentrations that decrease water infiltration, increase ponding of water on the soil surface, and reduce oxygen concentration in the soil. Reduced oxygen concentrations can also be caused by soil compaction resulting from tillage or equipment travel on the soil when it is wet.

When the supply of oxygen is restricted, soil microorganisms may make chemical transformations that produce toxic levels of certain substances, including hydrogen sulfide, methane gas, and other toxic organic materials. Production of these toxins depends on temperature—it occurs much more rapidly in warm soil. In addition, root growth is significantly less when oxygen levels are lower under saturated conditions and nutrient uptake is reduced. Olive trees are sensitive to poor drainage and waterlogging.

....

NUTRIENT BEHAVIOR IN SOIL

In soil, the behavior of each nutrient or group of similar nutrients is summarized below. Individual nutrient elements may occur in more than one form in the soil solution and may also be taken up by the plant in several chemical forms such as ammonium and nitrate nitrogen. Nutrients added as fertilizer behave exactly the same way as nutrients from organic sources when they enter the soil solution; plant roots cannot distinguish whether a nutrient is derived from organic or inorganic sources.

Nitrogen

Most nitrogen in soil is stored as organic forms that are unavailable to tree roots. As soil organisms and organic matter break down, nitrogen is slowly released to the soil solution where roots can absorb it. The amount released, however, is usually insufficient to replace nitrogen removed by the tree to harvests and prunings. Nitrogen occurs in the soil solution primarily as nitrate (NO_3^-) and ammonium (NH_4^+) ions. Nitrate, being an anion, is very soluble and is not attracted to the negatively charged soil colloids. So it can readily move to the plant roots in soil solution. It can also be leached as water moves past the root zone. Ammonium has a positive charge and is held as an exchangeable cation on the surface of the negatively charged clay minerals and organic matter. Thus, its mobility is restricted. Ammonium forms of fertilizer left on the soil surface may be converted to ammonia gas, which can volatilize into the atmosphere. Ammonium applied to the soil surface as fertilizer does not move far into the soil except in very sandy soils. Incorporation of ammonium fertilizer into the soil by tillage to several inches of depth minimizes ammonia gas loss.

Nitrogen is constantly recycled through different forms in the soil, air, and plants. Some soil microorganisms break down complex organic forms of nitrogen to water-soluble forms that roots can absorb. This process is called mineralization. Bacteria are primarily involved in the conversion of ammonium to nitrate through a process called nitrification. Adequate moisture and warm temperatures favor these reactions. When the oxygen supply in a soil is low (as in a compacted or waterlogged soil), other microorganisms can convert nitrate to nitrogen gas. This process, called denitrification, occurs most rapidly at higher temperatures and lower oxygen concentrations.

Phosphorus

The total amount of phosphorus in most soils is low, and the solubility of most phosphorus compounds is also low. The soluble sources of phosphorus added as fertilizers and manure are fixed or tightly held by soil colloids. Fortunately, phosphorus deficiency in California tree crops, including olive, is practically non-existent. Mycorrihizal fungi, growing in a symbiotic relationship with roots of tree crops, take up phosphate ions from the soil solution and make them available to the trees. These crops do not respond to phosphate fertilizers even when grown in soils that need additional phosphorus for annual crops. Generally, there is no reason to apply phosphate to olive orchards other than to supply the needs of a cover crop. Phosphorus deficiency has been reported in olive in Europe.

Potassium

Soils having parent materials consisting of micas and feldspar minerals usually have large amounts of potassium. This is particularly true on the east side of the San Joaquin Valley. Over time, sandy soils having lower amounts of these potassium-bearing minerals can become deficient. A number of the soils in the Sacramento Valley, particularly on the east side, are potassium deficient. This becomes evident when crops that require large amounts of potassium, such as almonds, prunes, and alfalfa, are planted in those soils.

The concentration of potassium in the soil solution is influenced mostly by the exchangeable potassium on soil colloids. The amount of exchangeable potassium is in turn controlled largely by the release of fixed potassium in clay minerals, and the breakdown of micas, feldspars, and the primary minerals. Tree roots absorb potassium from the soil solution or exchange sites on soil colloids. In some cases, potassium fertilizers applied in bands at the drip line have been effective in increasing leaf concentrations. Potassium fertilizers injected through micro-sprinklers that applied water to approximately two-thirds of the soil surface have given excellent yield response in almonds.

Calcium and Magnesium

Calcium and magnesium are closely related elements, and their soil chemistry is somewhat similar. Of the 14 essential plant nutrients coming from the soil, calcium and magnesium occur in the soil solution in the greatest abundance. Their availability is largely controlled by the cation exchange process and dissolution of carbonate minerals. They typically occupy 80 to 90 percent of the exchange sites on soil colloids of productive soils. It is desirable that the concentration of calcium on the exchange sites be equivalent or up to six times higher than the magnesium ions. In very acid soils, calcium and magnesium are removed by crop uptake or leached to lower depths in the soil profile. Sites previously occupied by calcium are replaced with other cations like hydrogen, manganese, and aluminum. Calcium held on exchange sites promotes good soil structure by holding soil colloids together with its double positive charge. Applying lime (calcium carbonate) or dolomitic lime (calcium magnesium carbonate) neutralizes the acidity and replenishes calcium and magnesium. Occasionally, magnesium deficiency is seen in orchards growing in sandy, acid soils, or where calcium carbonate lime or high rates of potassium have been applied. Fertilization with epsom salts (magnesium sulfate) or magnesium potassium sulfate fertilizer can correct this deficiency.

Sulfur

Sulfur is similar to nitrogen in that it exists in soil principally in organic forms and the sulfate ion (SO_4^{2-}) in soil solution. Bacteria are responsible for the oxidation of organic forms to the sulfate ion. There is a tendency for small amounts of sulfate to be adsorbed by soil particles in certain acid soils, but generally it is somewhat mobile. In waterlogged soils with lower oxygen concentrations, sulfate sulfur may be chemically reduced to hydrogen sulfide and other forms that are unavailable to plants. Sulfur deficiency is not very likely to occur in California orchards. Many commonly used fertilizers contain sulfur (for example, ammonium sulfate and some mixed fertilizers). Small amounts of sulfur are also delivered to the soil in rainfall.

Iron and Manganese

Iron and manganese availability are largely controlled by the solubilities of their oxides. These elements also undergo transformations called oxidation-reduction reactions. For iron, the transformation from the ferrous (Fe^{2+}) to the ferric (Fe^{3+}) form is the oxidation reaction; the reverse is reduction. In well-aerated soils, the oxidized ferric form, which is of low solubility, is dominant. In soils that are waterlogged, flooded, or acidic and poorly drained, the solubility of iron and manganese can greatly increase and supply toxic quantities to plants.

Solubilities of both iron and manganese dioxide are pH dependent: the solubilities are greatest at a pH of 4.0 to 5.0 and decrease rapidly as soil pH increases. Soils contain large amounts of both iron and manganese, far more than what is necessary for plant growth. Deficiencies occur because these elements are unavailable to plants at a higher soil pH; thus, their availability can be increased by lowering soil pH. The easiest way to do this is to apply acidifying materials to the soil such as sulfuric acid or elemental sulfur, which is converted to sulfuric acid by microorganisms.

Zinc and Copper

Specific adsorption and the formation of precipitates at soil pH greater than 7.0 dominate the availability of zinc and copper. Their amounts in soils are much less than those of iron and manganese, but like those elements they become much less available to plants at a soil pH greater than 7.0. A soil pH of 6.5 or less is the most desirable for zinc availability to plants. Zinc deficiency has been observed in a number of tree and annual crops, but not in olives. Copper deficiency in plants is seldom observed in California.

Boron

Boron occurs in the soil solution as neutral boric acid (H_3BO_3) and, to some extent, as the borate anion ($H_2BO_3^-$) in neutral to alkaline soils when its activity increases at higher pH. Boron is most available to plants in acid soils with pH less than 7.0 and is rather easily leached from acidic, sandy soils. It is least available to plants between pH of 7.0 and 9.0. Boron deficiency is observed in California on the sandy, often acid soils on the east side of the San Joaquin Valley. With olive, boron deficiency has only been observed in the east side of the Sacramento Valley (Butte County). Boron is more soluble and thus leachable in these soils. Boron toxicity has not been observed in California olive orchards.

Molybdenum and Chlorine

The amount of molybdenum required by plants is very small. It occurs in soil as the molybdate ion (MoO_4^{2-}), and soil pH is most important in influencing plant availability. The plant availability is lowest below pH 5.0 and increases as the soil pH increases. Molybdenum deficiency is unknown in California orchards.

Plant need for chlorine is very small. It occurs in the soil as the highly mobile chloride ion (Cl^-). Chlorine is added to the soil in large quantities by the use of fertilizers such as potassium chloride and to the atmosphere in the salt spray from ocean waves. Enough chlorine to meet plant needs reaches the soil in annual rainfall. Chlorine toxicity is a more serious problem than deficiency, but as the chloride ion is quite mobile, it is easily leached out of the root profile with adequate water.

13

Diagnosing and Correcting Nutrient Problems

MARK FREEMAN, KIYOTO URIU, AND HUDSON T. HARTMANN

Diagnosing a nutrient problem involves two basic techniques: careful observations and asking the right questions. Three general diagnostic categories of observations can be used: (1) visual symptoms (on the tree and in the environment), (2) tissue analysis, and (3) soil and water analyses. All three categories have their strengths and weaknesses; the category to be used depends on the problem to be solved.

VISUAL SYMPTOMS

One approach in diagnosing nutritional problems is to look for abnormal symptoms in foliage or growth. Visual diagnosis is the quickest way to identify deficiencies or toxicities. However, a tree may already have suffered in growth or yield by the time visible symptoms appear. Also, it takes experience to recognize the symptoms of all the deficiencies and toxicities. Borderline deficiencies or deficiencies of more than one element may be hard to diagnose; moreover, problems other than nutrition may cause similar symptoms. Thus, diagnosis from visual analysis alone may be difficult. However, visual symptoms can be an invaluable aid when interpreting soil or leaf analyses. And there is no substitute for observing the orchard regularly.

Successful diagnosis depends on observing symptoms continually. One deficiency may cause symptoms early in the season whereas another may show up later. It is important to consider the effects of environmental factors on trees. For example, abnormal fruit and foliage can reflect poor irrigation practices or a soil problem. Too much water can induce an iron deficiency; too little can adversely affect growth, leaf color, and yield. Olive trees survive for centuries on poor, rocky hillside soils in the Mediterranean region, but to achieve economic crops under California conditions, management of soil and water must be optimal for good nutrient availability. Fertilizer may not correct a problem if the real limiting factor is not found and addressed.

In California, field observations have recorded deficiencies for only three nutrients: nitrogen, potassium, and boron (see indications—in percentages or parts per million—in table 13.1). Potassium and boron deficiencies are illustrated in color plates 13.1 and 13.2, respectively. Other nutrient deficiencies have been noted in the field outside California, however, and could occur here in the future. Table 13.2 describes the visual symptoms of olive trees grown experimentally without six different nutrients.

PLANT AND TISSUE ANALYSES

Tissue analysis involves testing plant parts for actual concentrations of nutrients. Olive leaves are sampled and chemically analyzed for mineral deficiencies and toxicities. A leaf's mineral composition depends on its maturity, current climatic conditions, the availability of mineral elements in the soil, cultural practices, and other factors. The mineral nutrient level in the leaf integrates all these factors and thus reflects the nutrient status of the tree.

Optimal concentrations of different elements, the critical levels below which deficiency occurs, and the levels above which toxicity can develop, have all been established for olive (table 13.1). Results of leaf analyses can be compared with these standard values to determine current nutrient status and future fertilization needs. Leaf analysis can help confirm a visual symptom or identify a potential problem that is not yet showing visual symptoms. Results from leaf analysis are best used in a long-term fertilizer program or to prevent a developing problem.

Seasonal Use and Level of Mineral Elements

In interpreting leaf analyses, knowledge of the seasonal use pattern of mineral nutrients is helpful. At bud break in the spring, when root activity is minimal, many elements that have been stored in the budwood and roots

Table 13.1. Critical nutrient levels (dry-weight basis) in July olive leaf samples

Element	Nutrient concentration	Occurrence of deficiency in CA	Visual deficiency symptoms in field
Nitrogen (N)			
deficient below	1.4%	uncommon (due to small,	yellowish leaves; shoot growth of less than 8 in
adequate at	1.5–2.0%	routine fertilizer applications)	
Phosphorus (P)			
adequate at	0.1–0.3%	unknown	
Potassium (K)			
deficient below	0.4%	occasional	light green leaves, tip burn; dead areas in tree
adequate over	0.8%	(Butte County)	
Calcium (Ca)			
adequate over	1.0%	unknown	
Magnesium (Mg)			
adequate over	0.1%	unknown	
Sodium (Na)		unknown	
excessive over	0.2%		
Chlorine (Cl)		unknown	
excessive over	0.5%		
Boron (B)			
deficient below	14 ppm	occasional	misshapen fruit (monkey face); short, branched growth;
adequate at	19–150 ppm	(Butte County)	limb dieback; rough bark; small leaves with tip dieback
excessive over	185 ppm		
Copper (Cu)			
adequate over	5 ppm	unknown	
Manganese (Mn)			
adequate over	20 ppm	unknown	
Zinc (Zn)			
deficient below	unknown	unknown	visual deficiency not observed in field, even at very low levels

become available to the rapidly developing buds. Much of the nitrogen, phosphorus, zinc, and perhaps potassium, initially required, comes from the stored (for instance, in older leaves) supply and is redistributed to the growing points. Stored nitrogen then becomes important. The more nitrogen stored, presumably, the more available for fruit set. As root activity increases in spring, nitrogen, as well as other mineral elements, is increasingly taken up from the soil. Most of the phosphorus and zinc that accumulates in the leaves has done so by the time the leaves reach full size. This means that these elements, like nitrogen, must initially come from storage tissues. Calcium, essential in cell wall formation, is not redistributed but comes directly from the soil by root absorption during the growing season. Thus, it accumulates in the leaves as the season progresses and reaches its highest level at summer's end. Magnesium, boron, chloride, and sodium also tend to increase, but to a much lesser extent than calcium. If boron and chloride exist in toxic amounts in the soil, they increase rapidly during the season and reach their highest levels in the leaves at the end of the summer, as does calcium.

A single leaf analysis does not show the use pattern of mineral nutrients. Concentrations are determined for those elements and expressed as percentages (or parts per million) on a given weight of dried leaves. The concentration of mineral nutrients in leaves changes as the leaves first emerge and then expand to full size. For many elements the smallest change in concentration occurs from late June through early August. Olive leaf samples should be taken then, because critical levels have been established for that time period. The optimal concentration level (or range of values) is known, along with critical levels below which fertilizer should be added.

There are exceptions. For example, sampling to compare the nutrient status of a healthy tree with an unhealthy one can be done at any time, as long as how the concentration of each element changes during the season (fig. 13.1) is considered along with the analysis results. Concentrations of nitrogen, phosphorus, zinc, and potassium start off high early in the season, decline rapidly, reach a fairly steady state after mid-June, and then (except for potassium) drop in the fall. Concentrations of magnesium, manganese, boron, and

Table 13.2. Visual symptoms of mineral nutrient deficiencies in Manzanillo olives under experimental conditions[*]

Nutrient withheld	Trees	Shoots	Leaves	Fruit
Zinc	normal	normal	young leaves slightly lighter green than older leaves	fruit appearance and number are about the same, but fruit matures earlier
Nitrogen	small tree size; sparse foliage; heavy defoliation; light crop	individual shoots less than 8 in; very little shoot growth; dieback of shoots	small, yellow leaves; heavy defoliation	few fruit but normal in appearance
Calcium	small tree size, similar to trees without nitrogen	terminal dieback, with subsequent lateral growth (early growth); many lateral shoots; then whole shoot dies	terminal leaves curl, turn yellow; then tips become necrotic and leaves drop; basal leaves on shoot normal in size and color; terminal leaves small; some basal leaves turn yellow	fruit production sparse but fruit normal in size, with no chlorosis evident
Magnesium	same size as normal; good crop	long shoot growth; no terminal bud necrosis	basal leaves on shoot become chlorotic, turn yellow, and drop; terminal leaves normal in size and color; just before leaves drop, banding appears: tips yellow, midsection somewhat green, basal area yellow	fruit has yellowish, chlorotic appearance, but not to the extent found in iron-deficient trees
Potassium	tree has weeping willow appearance (not upright); branches may lack strength; total tree size normal	short internode (space between leaves on shoot) very characteristic; short shoot growth; total node number may be normal	pale, yellow-green leaves similar to start of nitrogen deficiency; slightly smaller-than-normal leaf size; no excess defoliation; basal leaves show more yellowing than terminal leaves	color normal
Iron	tree size normal; moderate crop associated with trees having slight leaf symptoms	shoot growth normal	small leaf size; whitish, bleached-out appearance in all leaves, especially terminal ones; then terminal leaves drop, with shoot dieback; symptoms more severe each year; no leaf necrosis; midrib and veins more green than interveinal areas; network of small green veins appears	fruit develops pronounced chlorotic, yellow appearance

Source: Uriu 1981; Hartmann and Brown 1953.
[*]Nutrient deficiencies were induced over 5 years by withholding a specific mineral element from a nutrient solution added to trees potted in sand. This does not mean that an element is not essential if the tree exhibited normal growth.

chloride do not start high, but remain fairly constant or increase slightly during the season. Boron and chloride levels increase steadily if excessive amounts are in the soil. Calcium levels start low and increase noticeably.

Sampling Procedure

Remove mature leaves from the middle of nonbearing, current-season shoots from late June through early August. A sample of 80 to 100 leaves is sufficient. Ideally, a sample should be taken from a uniform block of trees. This means that trees of different varieties or different ages, trees on different soil types, and trees under different irrigation systems should be sampled separately.

Samples should consist of a few leaves from as many trees as possible, selected at random from throughout the orchard. Avoid any leaves that are abnormal in appearance or leaves from abnormal trees unless that is the problem to be solved. In that instance, the abnormal leaves or trees should become a separate sample.

Interpretive Guides

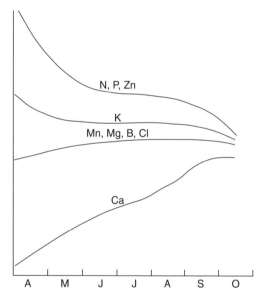

Figure 13.1. Generalized shapes of concentration curves of mineral nutrients in the leaf during the growing season. Curves show trends, not actual values.

Correlations between leaf analysis levels and the expression of deficiency symptoms are shown in table 13.1. Leaf analysis is very useful for all the nutrient elements when their levels can be interpreted together with visual symptoms.

SOIL AND WATER ANALYSIS

Tree crops, including olives, have extensive root systems that occupy a larger volume of soil than do those of most annual crops. Soil can vary widely within such a large area; thus, it may be difficult to take a soil sample that accurately represents the root area and nutrient levels that the roots extract. Furthermore, reliable soil standards for mineral nutrient levels are lacking for fruit trees. It is difficult to diagnose most nutrient imbalances from soil analysis alone. Soil analysis, however, does help in diagnosing toxicities from excessive concentrations of such elements as sodium, chlorine, and boron salts. Soil analysis is also useful in locating where these elements occur in excess, which helps in planning corrective treatments.

Sampling Procedure

In general, soil samples can be taken for analysis at any time because soil nutrient levels are relatively stable. Nevertheless, some precautions should be taken in collecting samples to test for a few of the nutrients. Under prolonged wet soil conditions, for example, nitrogen is subject to loss from de-nitrification. Thus, nitrogen levels in the soil after a lengthy rainy season can be lower than before. In many soils, nitrate, chloride, and, to some extent, boron can be leached by winter rains and irrigation. A new source of water could change the soluble salt content of the top foot of soil fairly quickly. Interpretations of soil analyses for mineral elements need to account for these changes.

The sampling procedure depends on the problem and area involved. Is one tree affected, or are many? Is there a pattern in the orchard—down the row, by soil type, in the low areas? Because olive tree roots occupy a large volume of soil and soil variability can be high, 3 to 10 spots in a site should be sampled. Because soils differ in composition at different depths, it is desirable to keep samples from different depths separate, starting with a sample of the top 6 to 12 inches (15 to 30 cm) and moving downward, with samples taken at 12-inch (30-cm) increments. Samples taken from different distances from the trunk may be combined. Samples should represent the effective rooting zone (where most of the roots are located). Situations differ; some soils may need to be sampled down to 4 or 5 feet (1.2 or 1.5 m) if roots are that deep.

A soil auger can be used to obtain samples. Two pounds of soil per sample is enough material for a laboratory.

Interpretive Guides for Soil and Water Testing

The following three tables and discussion present general guidelines for fruit trees, indicating where specific information applies to olive. Table 13.3 lists laboratory analyses commonly used for water and soil quality determinations. Some laboratories may use different units, which are also listed. The following text discusses specific laboratory tests and how to interpret and use their results to solve problems. For further explanation of terms and concepts used in this section, refer to chapter 12: Mineral Nutrient Availability.

Saturation Percentage

Saturation percentage (SP) is a measure of soil texture used to estimate water-holding capacity and cation exchange capacity (table 13.4). It is expressed as the grams of water required to saturate 100 grams of soil.

One-half of the SP is approximately the amount of water that soil holds at field capacity (the moisture content of soil in the field 2 or 3 days after a thorough wetting). One-fourth of the SP approximates the permanent wilting point (PWP) of the soil (the soil moisture percentage at which plants wilt and fail to recover turgidity). The available water is the difference between field capacity and PWP; it represents the amount of water the soil can store that is available to the plant. The SP can indicate changes in soil texture at different depths; for instance, a large variation of SP with depth indicates a stratified layer or layers within the soil profile. Layering can be visually confirmed with an auger or backhoe. Soil layers may be places where nutrient availability varies or where poor drainage may cause a toxicity.

Soil Reaction (pH)

The soil pH is indicated on a scale reading from 0 (acid) to 14 (basic, or alkaline). Within the pH range of 6.5 to 7.5, nutrient availability should not be limiting (table 13.6). Soil pH has not been observed to limit California olive production. Most California soils where pH exceeds 8.5 have either Verticillium wilt or very poor soil structure due to high sodium levels. If pH problems are suspected, soil samples should be taken at 6-inch (15-cm) increments, or where soil layers change, to locate problem areas.

Lime is commonly used to correct acidic soils (below pH 6.0). The lime required to raise the pH varies with soil texture; it can be estimated by laboratory analysis. The approximate amount of finely ground limestone needed to raise the pH of a 7-inch (18-cm) layer of soil by one pH unit from an initial pH of 4.5 or 5.5 ranges from about ½ ton per acre (1.1 metric t/ha) for sandy soil to about 2 tons per acre (4.5 metric t/ha) for a clay loam. Usually, only the top 12 inches (30 cm) of soil become acidic enough to require liming. Research on tree crops under drip irrigation has documented very low soil pH levels, but the effects of low pH on tree growth and yield are not known.

Cation Exchange Capacity

The cation exchange capacity (CEC) measured in the laboratory indicates the ability of the soil to hold cations against leaching. Many soil cations are mineral nutrients that olive roots absorb from the soil solution. Soils with a higher CEC are typically more fertile as they have a greater storage capacity for mineral nutrients. Usually expressed in milliequivalents per 100 grams of soil, the CEC of a soil depends directly on its clay and humus content. Fertilizer should be applied more frequently and in smaller amounts to soils with lower CEC.

Table 13.3. Laboratory analyses used to evaluate soil and water quality for olive production

Laboratory analyses	Reporting symbol	Reporting units	Soil	Water	Equivalent* weight (mg/meq)
Saturation percentage	SP	%	X	—	—
pH	pH	—	X	X	—
Electrical conductivity	EC_e	dS/m†	X	—	—
	EC_w	dS/m†	—	X	—
Calcium	Ca^{+2}	meq/L	X	X	20.0
Magnesium	Mg^{+2}	meq/L	X	X	12.2
Sodium	Na^+	meq/L	X	X	23.0
Carbonate	CO_3^{-2}	meq/L	—	X	30.0
Bicarbonate	HCO_3^-	meq/L	—	X	61.0
Chloride	Cl^-	meq/L	X	X	35.4
Sulfate	SO_4^{-2}	meq/L	—	X	48.0
Boron	B	ppm‡	X	X	—
Adjusted sodium adsorption ratio	adj.SAR_e	meq/L	X	—	—
	adj.SAR_w	meq/L	—	X	—
Exchangeable sodium	ESP	%	X	—	—
Lime requirement	LR	ton/acre	X	—	—
Gypsum requirement	GR	ton/acre	X	—	—
Lime	$CaCO_3$	%	X	—	—

*ppm = meq/L x equivalent weight (mg/meq)
— = not applicable
†dS/m = mmho/cm
‡ppm = mg/L

Table 13.4. Relationship of saturation percentage (SP) to soil texture, cation exchange capacity (CEC), and available water for a loam soil

SP	Soil texture	CEC k(meq/100 g)	Available water (in/ft)
<20	sandy or loamy sand	2–7	<0.6
20–35	sandy loam	7–15	0.6–1.0
35–50	loam or silt loam	15–30	1.0–1.5
50–65	clay loam	30–40	1.5–2.0
>65	clay or peat	>40	>2.0

Table 13.5. Soil salinity guidelines for olives

Soil problem	Degree of problem		
	Starting	Increasing	Severe
Salinity (affects crop water availability)			
EC_e (dS/m)	4	5	8
Olive yield decrease (%)	10	25	50
Sodium (ESP)			
Soil permeability and plant toxicity problems stunt growth (%)	20–40		
Boron (ppm)	2		
pH			
Range for most crops: 5.5–8.4			
Optimal range for most crops: 6.5–7.5			
Known harmful in olive: >8.5			

Salinity

Salinity is a measure of all the soluble salts present in a soil solution. Salinity damage to trees may be due to specific ions or to the total salt content. Specific ions that constitute salinity, such as sodium, chloride, and boron, can cause damage by themselves if levels are high enough. Damage to olives from high soil levels of these three elements has not been observed in California. High total soil salinity reduces the amount of soil water available to roots. The problem of high total soil salinity has been known to affect olive orchards in California. Soil salinity is measured in a laboratory from a saturated extract of soil. The soil water is analyzed for water-soluble compounds formed by three cations—sodium, calcium, and magnesium—with the anions chloride, carbonate and bicarbonate, sulfate, borate, and nitrate nitrogen. Total salinity is measured in terms of electrical conductivity because salts in solution conduct electricity. As salt concentration increases, so does the conductivity. A saline soil is defined as having an electrical conductivity of the soil-saturated extract (EC_e) of more than 4 decisiemens per

meter (dS/m) at 25°C. In water, 1 dS/m of electrical conductance corresponds to about 1,700 pounds per acre-foot (640 mg/L) of salt. Olive trees can experience a 10 percent yield loss if total soil salinity reaches 4 dS/m (table 13.5). Yields and tree growth are substantially reduced as EC_e increases to 8 dS/m. Most of the saline soils used for agriculture in California grow annual crops that carry Verticillium wilt. Olive growers have avoided these areas for that reason. Orchards are usually located on well-drained soils and are irrigated with good-quality water; thus, winter rainfall is adequate to leach out annual salt accumulations. However, when soil analysis indicates excessive salt accumulation in the root zone, additional irrigation in spring or fall or heavier irrigations are necessary. For proper leaching, irrigation distribution and uniformity may need to be improved by changing the field level or the system design, or soil structure may need to be modified by ripping an impervious hardpan or mixing a stratified soil. Drainage lines may be required when a high water table is present. Soil amendments, such as gypsum, are generally not necessary to correct saline conditions unless excess sodium is present. The amount of extra water needed (above evapotranspiration) to leach soluble salts from the soil profile depends primarily on the initial soil salinity, the technique used for applying water, and the soil type. The extra water needed, called the leaching fraction, can be calculated for specific orchards; a general rule of thumb is that 1 acre-foot (1,233 m³) of extra water reduces the salinity of the upper 1 foot (30 cm) of soil by 70 to 80 percent. Salinity can be a problem in irrigation water. Saline water values are listed in table 13.6. The best remedy to saline water is to find another water source; otherwise, the soil salinity will increase.

Table 13.6. Irrigation water quality guidelines for olives

Irrigation problem	Degree of problem		
	None	Increasing	Severe
Salinity (affects crop water availability)			
EC_w (dS/m)	<2.0	2.5–4.0	>5.5
Permeability (affects soil infiltration rate)			
EC_w (dS/m)			
if SAR = 0–3	>0.7	0.7–0.2	<0.2
if SAR = 3–6	>1.2	1.2–0.3	<0.3
Specific ion toxicity			
Boron (ppm or mg/L)	0–1.0	>1.0	

Sodic (Alkali) Soils

Soils that contain excessive amounts of exchangeable sodium in proportion to calcium and magnesium are termed sodic, or alkali, soils. Sodic soils are characterized by a dispersion of soil particles that reduces a soil's permeability to water and air. By definition, a sodic soil has an exchangeable sodium percentage (ESP) of greater than 15. That means that 15 percent of the soil's cation exchange capacity is associated with sodium and the remainder with calcium, magnesium, and other cations. Olive trees are affected when ESP levels reach 20 to 40 (table 13.5). Most California soils with this problem are planted to annual crops. When a sodic condition is identified, a laboratory analysis can be performed to determine the gypsum requirement. This indicates the amount of calcium required to displace sodium. After an amendment is applied, the displaced sodium must be leached below the root zone. Organic materials, such as manure, cover crops, or crop residues, may help improve the soil structure for leaching. In established orchards, heavy irrigation to leach sodium during the dormant period minimizes damage to tree roots caused by lack of aeration. Some soils are both sodic and saline. The problem is best dealt with by leaching out the soluble salts, such as chloride and borate, with irrigation water. It is necessary to apply a source of calcium to displace sodium from the exchange sites on the soil particles and then leach the sodium displaced into the soil solution.

Sodium Hazard in Water

There is a close association between the composition and concentration of salts in the soil and salts in irrigation water. When used for irrigation, water with a high level of sodium relative to calcium and magnesium is likely to result in a sodic soil. The sodium hazard of water is indicated by the sodium adsorption ratio (SAR). The adjusted SAR (adj.SAR) is commonly used and includes the hazard that carbonate and bicarbonate add to that of sodium by precipitating some of the exchangeable calcium and magnesium. Water with a low adj.SAR dissolves lime from the soil, increasing exchangeable calcium. Water with a high adj.SAR precipitates calcium, decreasing exchangeable calcium, and can lead to sodic conditions. Irrigation water should have adj.SAR values below 6; when values exceed 9, problems can occur. Gypsum should be used to replace precipitated calcium when using water with a high adj.SAR. It is normally applied to the bottom of furrows or to that part of the soil surface that is wetted by irrigation water. Two to four tons per acre (4.5 to 9.0 metric t/ha) of gypsum every year or so is a common rate. Soil incorporation is not necessary.

Boron and Chloride Toxicity

Leaf analysis is the most useful tool for diagnosing salt injury in trees. Soil and water analyses may also be needed to determine the source of salts or whether a problem exists before planting. Problems with chloride toxicity often occur in orchards planted on saline soils not fully reclaimed or when high-chloride irrigation water is used. Because it is much more difficult to correct a salinity problem after the orchard is planted, the soil should be completely reclaimed before planting. Chloride toxicity sometimes occurs after fertilizers containing chloride (in the form of potassium chloride, KCl) are applied to poorly drained soils. The problem can easily be corrected by leaching excess chloride from the root zone, but severe damage can occur. Boron (borate) toxicity problems typically occur on the west side of the Central Valley, where native soils are derived from marine sedimentary material. Both soil and groundwater can be high in boron. The boron levels that affect olives are listed in tables 13.5 and 13.6. Boron-affected soils are reclaimed only slowly, with great difficulty and much water.

Slow Infiltration—Low Salt Water

Irrigating with water that is very pure may slow infiltration into sandy loam or fine-textured soils. This can occur when water contains less than 250 parts per million (ppm) of soluble salts (EC_w < .4 mmho/cm). It is a common problem on the east side of the San Joaquin Valley, where the canal water originates as snowmelt from the Sierra Nevada and contains only 50 to 100 ppm total salts. With certain soils water infiltration can drop to less than .1 inch (2.5 mm) per hour, making it difficult to satisfy the orchard's water requirements.

Gypsum applications can help correct this water penetration problem. The infiltration rate can be increased as much as fivefold by applying 1 to 2 tons per acre (2.3 to 4.5 metric t/ha) of gypsum in late spring or early summer, just before peak evapotranspiration. Gypsum is generally beneficial for three to five irrigations. Infiltration can also be improved by mixing gypsum directly into the irrigation water with specially designed equipment. Also, manure applied to the wetted areas can add soluble salts to the irrigation water.

REVIEW OF SPECIFIC MINERAL NUTRIENTS

Nitrogen

Nitrogen deficiency symptoms are not common in California olive orchards now because nitrogen fertilizer is applied routinely. The visual symptoms and critical leaf nutrient levels are listed in table 13.1. Soil levels of nitrogen do not correlate well with leaf levels or deficiency symptoms. One study found that leaf nitrogen content in olives is fairly constant through the fall and winter but drops when vegetative growth starts in the spring (Hartmann and Brown 1953). The leaf levels reach a low point in August and then increase. Nitrate nitrogen (NO_3–N) in groundwater can contribute significant amounts of nitrogen toward a fruit tree's nutritional requirement and should be considered when planning a fertilizer program. Nitrogen levels in irrigation water often range from 5 to 50 pounds (2 to 23 kg) of nitrogen per acre-foot (1,233 m^3). Laboratories report nitrate concentrations in parts per million (ppm, or mg/L). This is converted to pounds of nitrogen per acre-foot by multiplying by 2.7.

Nitrogen levels directly affect fruit set, yield, and shoot growth. Many field trials in California (and around the world) have shown yield and growth increases in olive from nitrogen fertilization. In experiments in the 1950s (Hartmann 1958), orchards on a foothill soil (with naturally low fertility) and a fertile valley clay soil received nitrogen fertilizer. The foothill orchard showed increased fruit set, yields, and leaf size, and also delayed fruit maturity. (Some trees on low-fertility soils given heavy nitrogen applications have large crops of small fruit and tend to bear alternately.) The valley orchard showed no immediate response in fruit set or yields. Nitrogen was withheld for 3 years, and leaf nitrogen levels were still adequate. Both nitrogen deficiencies and excesses, then, can hurt yields. Nitrogen

levels in leaves differed in on- and off-crop years but stayed above critical levels.

Liquid fertilizers, due to their lower cost, are the most common form of nitrogen used to correct deficiency. Many nitrogen fertilizers are available (table 13.7) and can be easily applied if nitrogen levels are approaching a deficiency. However, fertilizing should not be viewed as a specific step used to change nitrogen levels. Even with no added nitrogen, the level in the trees tends to remain adequate, and in deeper soils with less leaching and rainwater, soil nitrogen levels remain fairly stable.

Nitrogen can also be applied to olives with foliar sprays. Experimental work on Manzanillo, Mission, and Sevillano olives in the early 1990s (Ferguson, Connell, and Krueger 1994) demonstrated 2 percent low biuret urea plus 0.25 percent spreader sticker solution, sprayed to leaf runoff, increased nitrogen content in leaves within 72 hours. The average nitrogen application was approximately 0.4 pound (0.2 kg) per tree, or 38 pounds per acre (42.6 kg/ha) at 96 trees to the acre (237 trees/ha). If applied during the early stages of fruit enlargement through July, leaf levels returned to prespray levels within 1 month. If applied after July, leaf nitrogen levels remained elevated. These results were similar to earlier nitrogen research results (Klein and Weinbaum 1984) that demonstrated the rapidly growing fruit is a strong sink for nitrogen applied early in the growing season. This suggests that supplemental foliar nitrogen applied during the early stages of fruit growth (when cell division and rapid cell enlargement are occurring) could better support these processes and produce a better crop. It also suggests that supplemental foliar nitrogen applied during early, rapid fruit growth could supply the requirements of both: (1) the current season's fruit growth and (2) shoot growth bearing the subsequent season's crop. This could alleviate alternate bearing. However, application of foliar nitrogen to trees with sufficient nitrogen did not increase the value of the current crop or any yield component of the subsequent crop.

In summary, olive leaves absorb foliar nitrogen readily throughout the season. However, unless trees are nitrogen deficient and require rapid correction, there is no economic advantage to foliar nitrogen applications.

First, leaf analysis should be used routinely to monitor annual changes in the nitrogen levels and help plan the future fertilizer program. Nitrogen must be absorbed into the tree before March 1 to influence the crop set in the spring. Some growers apply

Table 13.7. Nitrogen-containing fertilizers

Fertilizer	Formulation	Nitrogen (%)	Water-soluble potash K$_2$O (%)	Equivalent acidity or basicity (in lb CaCO$_3$) Acid	Equivalent acidity or basicity (in lb CaCO$_3$) Base
Urea ammonium nitrate solution*	$NH_4NO_3 \cdot CO(NH_2)_2$	32.0		57	
Calcium ammonium nitrate solution*	$Ca(NO_2)_2 \cdot NH_4NO_3$	17.0		9	
Ammonium nitrate	NH_4NO_3	33.5–34.0		62	
Ammonium sulfate†	$(NH_4)2SO_4$	21.0		110	
Anhydrous ammonia	NH_3	82.0		148	
Aqua ammonia	NH_4OH	20.0		36	
Calcium nitrate	$Ca(NO_3)_2$	15.5			20
Manure (dry)‡		10–30 lb/ton			
Urea	$CO(NH_2)_2$	45–46		71	
Potassium chloride	KCl		60–62	neutral	
Potassium sulfate	K_2SO_4		50–53	neutral	

Source: California Fertilizer Association Editorial Committee 1985.

*Often injected through low-volume irrigation systems.

†Will acidify the soil when used exclusively over a period of time.

‡Also improves soil structure but can contain high levels of salt.

nitrogen during winter; however, research with some tree crops indicates that root uptake of nitrogen is slowest in winter. If urea is applied at the soil surface at that time, the ammonia it yields can be lost to the atmosphere. To avoid this loss, either incorporate urea or to irrigate it into the soil shortly after application.

The goal of using nitrogen fertilizer is to maintain leaf nitrogen levels of 1.5 to 1.8 percent. This results in adequate (but not excessive) shoot growth of 8 to 20 inches (20 to 51 cm) per year with optimal bloom and fruit set. It is common practice to apply 1 to 2 pounds (.45 to .9 kg) of actual nitrogen per tree per year. In the southern San Joaquin Valley, some soils carry over adequate nitrogen, so fertilizer is only applied in alternate years. Manures can supply nitrogen (table 13.7) though it is not as quickly available as synthetic sources. Midseason foliar urea applications have not been shown to increase fruit size.

Potassium

Low levels of potassium in olive leaves and deficiency symptoms have been observed only in foothill orchards of Butte County. Soil levels of potassium do not correlate well with leaf nutrient levels or deficiency symptoms (table 13.1). However, potassium levels below the critical leaf level can occur long before leaf symptoms appear. Therefore, it may be important to monitor this nutrient in orchards planted in sandy soils or where much land leveling has been done, because some fruit trees exhibit potassium deficiency symptoms under those conditions. Researchers worldwide find a correlation between high yields and high levels of leaf potassium. Potassium levels in leaves differ during "on" versus "off" crop years, but are always above the critical level.

Potassium deficiency can be corrected more easily in sandy than in clay or silty soils. Applications of potassium sulfate (K_2SO_4) made during early winter in doses of 10 to 20 pounds (4.5 to 9.0 kg) per tree, should be effective for several years. On heavier soils, the K_2SO_4 should be shanked in below the surface within the drip line. On lighter soils, it can be shanked in or surface applied. Potassium chloride (KCl) is less expensive, but because of the chloride it should not be used on sandy or sandy loam soils. Possibly, foliar sprays of potassium nitrate could be used, or potassium compounds applied along with irrigation. Guidelines for amounts are not available.

Boron

Like potassium, boron deficiency in olive has only been observed in Butte County. There, the boron content in leaves correlates very well with deficiency symptoms (table 13.1). Trees showing severe deficiency symptoms have 7 to 13 ppm boron in the leaves. Leaves having 19 or greater ppm of boron do not show symptoms. Olive is much less sensitive to high boron levels than most other commercial tree crops grown in California. Olive in high-boron soil apparently does not accumulate much boron in the leaves.

Boron deficiency can be corrected with soil applications of borax at rates of 1 pound (.45 kg) per tree. Do not apply higher rates as toxic levels may result. This treatment should be sufficient for many years. Foliar sprays such as Solubor aid the current season's growth, but the effect does not last as long as a soil application.

Phosphorus

Neither phosphorus deficiency nor a growth response to the addition of phosphorus fertilizer has been observed in California olive orchards. A survey of California olive trees found low phosphorus leaf levels to be associated with poor soil drainage. Actual phosphorus deficiency has been reported in Europe.

Magnesium and Calcium

Deficiencies of magnesium and calcium have not been observed in California olive orchards. The deficiency symptoms noted in table 13.2 were induced under sand culture. Under sand culture, calcium and magnesium leaf levels increase or decrease together. In olive leaves, low potassium levels are associated with high calcium levels, and vice versa.

Zinc, Copper, Iron, Manganese, and Molybdenum

Little information is available about the requirement of olives for these five minor nutrients. Zinc deficiency has not been observed in California olives, and it has not been induced when zinc has been withheld from olive trees grown in sand culture (table 13.2). Nonetheless, zinc deficiency is common in many other California tree crops.

Sodium and Chloride (excess or toxicity)

Compared with most tree crops, olives are very tolerant of saline and sodic soils, which usually contain high levels of sodium and chloride (table 13.6). In many tree crops, these two mineral toxicities cause leaf tip burn that progresses up the leaf. Leaf analysis is used to identify which nutrient is involved. Sodium or chloride toxicity has not been observed in California olive orchards except where potassium chloride was misused.

REFERENCES

California Fertilizer Association Editorial Committee. 1985. Western fertilizer handbook, 7th ed. Danville, IL: The Interstate.

Ferguson, L., J. H. Connell, and W. H. Krueger. 1994. Unpublished data. Department of Pomology, University of California, Davis.

Hartmann, H. T. 1958. Some responses of the olive to nitrogen fertilizers. Proc. of the Amer. Soc. Hort. Sci. 72:257–266.

Hartmann, H. T., and J. G. Brown. 1953. The effect of certain mineral deficiencies on the growth, leaf appearance, and mineral content of young olive trees. Hilgardia 22(3):199–30.

Klein, I., and S. A. Weinbaum. 1984. Foliar application of urea to olive: Translocation of urea nitrogen as influenced by sink demand and nitrogen deficiency. J. of the Amer. Soc. of Hort. Sci. 109 (3):356–360.

Uriu, K. 1981. Unpublished data. Department of Pomology, University of California, Davis.

Plate 5.1. Olive grove with sufficient sunlight for optimal production.

Plate 9.1. Mature olive pruned to five upright scaffolding branches, ideal for use with a tree shaker.

Plate 9.2. Old olive pruned back for rejuvenation.

Plate 13.1. Symptoms of potassium deficiency in leaves.

Plate 13.2. Boron deficiency can cause misshapen, "monkey-faced" fruit.

Plate 14.1. Overabundant fruit set is evident in heavy crop year of the alternate bearing cycle.

Plate 14.2. Results of a post-bloom application of naphthalene acetic acid to thin fruit; unsprayed sample on left.

Plate 14.3. Manzanillo olive at full bloom.

Plate 15.1. Adult olive fly, *Bactrocera* (Dacus) oleae.

Plate 15.2a & b. Olive fly larvae in fruit.

Plate 15.3. Olive fly pupa in fruit during summer.

Plate 15.4. Internal fruit damage from olive fly larvae.

Plate 15.5. Damage to pulp by olive fly larvae renders it useless for canning.

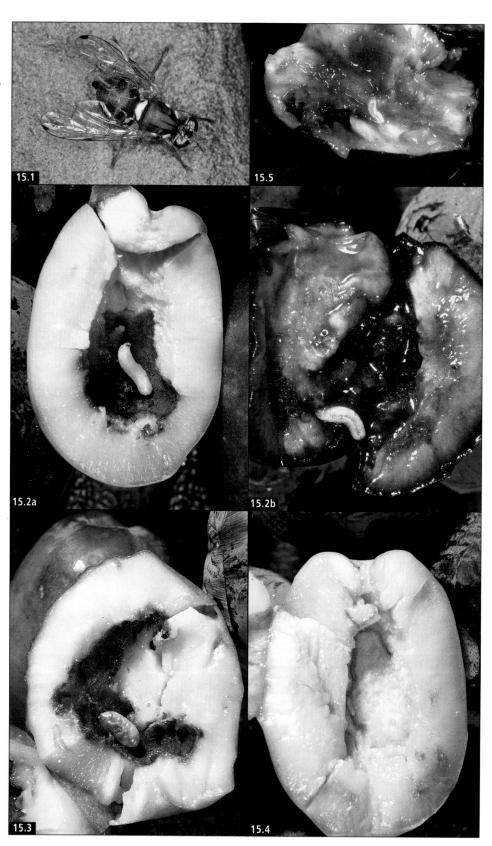

15.7

15.6

15.8

15.10

15.9

15.11

15.12

Plate 15.6. Adult female black scale, Saissetia oleae, showing "H" pattern.

Plate 15.7. Black scale eggs, cast egg shells, and first instar nymphs, or crawlers, underneath the adult scale.

Plate 15.8. Pre-ovipositional adult black scale in the "rubber" stage, showing very distinctive "H" pattern.

Plate 15.9. Sooty mold growing on black scale honeydew secretion.

Plate 15.10. Dense, closed canopies favor survival of scale.

Plate 15.11. Open, well-pruned canopies promote higher temperatures and unfavorable conditions for black scale.

Plate 15.12. Young female olive scale.

Plate 15.13. Purple spotting on fruit caused by second-generation olive scale.

Plate 15.14. Development stages of the parasitoid *Aphytis maculicornis,* from egg to pupae, on olive scale.

Plate 15.15. Cluster of oleander scale on olive leaves and twigs.

Plate 15.16. Adult latania scale, showing characteristic ridges (the exuvium) forming a point on one side.

Plate 15.17. Latania scale damage on fruit.

Plate 15.18. Cluster of greedy scale (on acacia).

Plate 15.19. Surface of olive fruit infested with California red scale.

Plate 15.20. Olive mites and "silvering" damage on leaf undersurface.

Plate 15.21. Fruit scarred and dimpled by western flower thrips.

Plate 15.22. Adult branch and twig borer.

Plate 15.23. Adult black vine weevil (on euonymus).

Plate 17.1. Olive knots on twig.

Plate 17.2. Lesions caused by olive leaf spot (peacock spot, bird's eye spot) on leaves.

Plate 17.3. Evidence of Phytophthora root rot in heavy, saturated soil.

Plate 17.4. Plaques of fungal mycelium between bark and wood due to Armillaria root rot.

Plate 17.5. Typical elliptical diplodia canker on twig.

Plate 17.6. Verticillium wilt in 80-year-old orchard.

Plate 18.1. Example of herbicide strip treatment in tree rows.

Plate 20.1. Characteristic white juice of mature olive fruit.

Plate 20.2. Quality (by color) of Manzanillo fruit at harvest

Plate 20.3. Quality (by color) of Mission fruit at harvest.

Plate 20.4. Quality (by color) of Ascolano fruit at harvest.

Plate 20.5. Quality (by color) of Sevillano fruit at harvest.

Plate 20.6. Relative olive color change, from green to black, throughout the harvest season.

Plate 22.1. Intercultivar differences in chilling sensitivity after storage at 36°F (2°C) for one month.

MANZANILLO

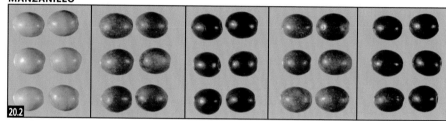

| Early season Pale green to straw Optimal | Early season Pale green to straw Optimal | Early season Black Unacceptable | Late season Light red blush Borderline | Late season Dark red Unacceptable |

MISSION

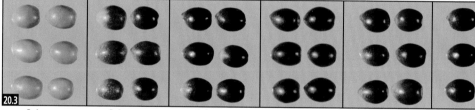

| Early season Pale green to straw Optimal | Early season Light pink to dark red Acceptable | Early season Dark purplish Borderline | Early season Black Unacceptable | Late season Light pink to dark red Borderline | Late season Dark purplish Unacceptable |

ASCOLANO

| Early season Pale green to straw Optimal | Early season Slight blush Unacceptable | Late season Pale green to straw Optimal | Late season Slight blush Unacceptable |

SEVILLANO

| Early season Slight blush stem end Acceptable | Early season Half or more dark red Unacceptable | Late season Straw Optimal | Late season Slight blush stem end Unacceptable |

SEVILLANO   **ASCOLANO**   **MANZANILLO**   **MISSION**

Plate 23.1. Olive fruits at three stages of maturity: (left) maturity index 7; (center) maturity index 3; (right) maturity index 2.

Plate 23.2. Rotten olives (left) and desiccated fruit (two at right) will yield defective oil.

Plate 23.3. Clean rinse water sprayed onto olives just as they are leaving the washer.

Plate 23.4. Traditional Italian-type stone mill.

Plate 23.5. Opened hammer-mill and exposed screen.

Plate 23.6. Jacketed two-compartment malaxator. Paste in the right chamber is downloaded into the separator while the left chamber is filled with new paste.

Plate 23.7. Spreading paste onto a filter mat.

Plate 23.8. Stacking filter mats onto the press cylinder.

Plate 23.9. New oil exiting a vertical centrifuge.

Plate 23.10. Solid waste (pomace) from a press.

Plate 23.11. Fruit water or water of vegetation ejected from the port of a vertical centrifuge.

14

Olive Fruit Thinning

WILLIAM H. KRUEGER, JOSEPH MARANTO, AND G. STEVEN SIBBETT

Olives normally produce crops in alternate-year cycles. Flowers and fruit are produced exclusively on the previous year's shoot growth. Light crops result in abundant summer shoot growth that flowers and sets excessively the following "on," or heavy, year (color plate 14.1). Because fruit is a strong carbohydrate sink, the large fruit population receives resources at the expense of shoot growth, which diminishes the crop potential for the following year, the "off," or light, year. The price per pound received by growers is often lower and harvest costs higher during heavy years, with large tonnages of small, low-value fruit. Although prices may be higher in light years when fruit is in shorter supply, it does not make up for the reduced production. Alternate-year bearing is, therefore, disruptive to orderly marketing and grower profitability. Additionally, fruit maturity is retarded with excessive crops, which increases the risk of damage from early fall freezes.

To mitigate alternate bearing, excessive crops must be reduced. Crop control can be achieved by chemical thinning, pruning, or hand thinning. Fruit thinning is more effective than pruning because the leaf to fruit ratio is increased, while pruning removes both leaves and fruit.

The ideal crop load varies with cultivar and with tree age and vigor. In the Manzanillo cultivar, fruit density of approximately six to eight fruit per 1 foot (30 cm) of fruiting shoot growth appears optimal to size the fruit while ensuring moderate shoot growth for the following year's crop.

Chemical Thinning

Chemical thinning is the most useful tool available to olive growers for crop control. Postbloom application of naphthalene acetic acid (NAA) can regulate crop size to improve fruit quality and result in shoot growth for return bloom the following year (color plate 14.2). NAA is a synthetic form of auxin, a plant growth regulator that enhances the naturally occurring June drop of olives. NAA is absorbed by the leaves and fruit and is translocated to the fruit stems. Within 2 weeks of application, an abscission zone is formed, causing some fruit to drop. NAA effectively thins Manzanillo, Ascolano, and Mission cultivars. Although it was generally accepted that the Sevillano cultivar was nonresponsive, recent research indicates that postbloom application of NAA also removes Sevillano fruit (Krueger and Heath 2001). Rates and timing are yet to be determined.

NAA in the sodium salt formulation is currently the only material registered and recommended for thinning olives. NAA in the potassium salt formulation is equally as effective, but not currently available.

Chemical thinning with NAA has been available for more than 25 years. Widespread adoption has been slow because thinning must be done before the crop load can be accurately judged, therefore presenting the risk of over- or underthinning. Additionally, chemical costs have increased dramatically in recent years.

The greatest obstacle connected to chemically thinning olives is the variable thinning response related to temperatures following material application. Thinning response can vary from none with unseasonably cool temperatures to almost complete removal with excessive temperatures. This is the main reason why many growers are reluctant to use this procedure. However, the potential benefits are so great, both for the year of the thinning and the subsequent year, that they cannot be ignored. In a 1999 study on the Manzanillo cultivar, all chemical thinning treatments increased income per acre, after harvest costs were deducted, by an average of nearly $1,000 per acre ($2,470/ha), and more than doubled the return bloom rating. (Krueger, Heath, and Mulqueeny 2002.)

> NOTE: Always leave some unsprayed control areas to gauge the effectiveness of spray thinning.

Treatment Timing

Timing of NAA sprays is critical for optimal results. Olives are successfully thinned with NAA between 12 and 18 days after full bloom. Earlier or later treatment may result in excessive or insufficient fruit removal. In the Central Valley, olive bloom begins in the southern San Joaquin Valley and moves northward to the Sacramento Valley, usually taking place from the last week in April to the third week of May, depending on the location and the weather. Thinning is done between the second week in May and the first week in June. Two methods can be used to accurately time NAA applications: (1) fruit size, and (2) days after full bloom (DAFB).

Fruit Size. This is the most commonly used method. NAA is applied when average fruit size is between 1/8 to 3/16 inch (3 to 5 mm) in diameter. Fruit size varies within the orchard and within a tree, so measurements should be made at different locations in the orchard and on the north and south sides of trees to obtain an average. The indicated size is usually reached 12 to 18 days after full bloom, but may be delayed or advanced by cool or warm temperatures, respectively.

Days after Full Bloom (DAFB). To use this method, the date of full bloom must be established for each orchard. The full-bloom date is determined as follows: As flowers begin to open, a contrast in color between the green leaves and white flowers can be observed in the orchard from a distance. At full bloom, the tree appears to be white, with shoots containing 80 to 90 percent open, fresh flowers, with bright yellow anthers exposed (color plate 14.3). The remaining 10 to 20 percent of the flowers include those not yet open and those whose petals have dropped. Pollen release is abundant at full bloom, and it should be possible to collect pollen by shaking bloom into one's hand. Tapping a limb in full bloom should release a puff of yellow pollen and falling petals. These reference points indicate the date to designate as the full-bloom point. Three to four days after full bloom, as the flowers age, the tree develops a yellow-bronze cast. Determining and recording the full bloom date by block is useful for predicting treatment timing. NAA should be applied 12 to 18 days after full bloom.

NAA Concentration and Active Ingredient. NAA concentration depends on how spray timing is determined (see Fruit Size and Days after Full Bloom, below) and whether a spray oil is used. Traditionally, thinning treatments have been applied as dilute sprays (300 to 500 gallons per acre [gpa] [2,800 to 4,700 L/ha]), using 150 ppm NAA. Research has shown that concentrate sprays (100 gpa or less) can be as effective as dilute sprays provided adequate active ingredient is applied (Krueger et al. 1987). However, as of the publication date of this manual, concentrated application is not registered for use in California. Although thinning response can vary

dramatically from year to year and is largely determined by temperatures during the few days following application, research has demonstrated that an active ingredient of greater than 4.1 ounces per acre (287 g/ha) (72 oz per acre [5.04 kg/ha] of the concentrate 200 product) is necessary for satisfactory thinning (Krueger, Heath, and Mulqueeny 2002).

Fruit Size. If fruit size is used to time NAA sprays and a dilute spray without a spray oil, apply a concentration of 150 ppm NAA with a wetting agent or spreader-sticker, according to the chemical manufacturer's recommendation. The commercially available NAA formulation, Liqui-Stik Concentrate, does not contain a wetting agent. If you use a spray oil, mix 100 ppm NAA with a light or light-medium summer oil at a rate of 1½ gallons (5.7 L) of oil per 100 gallons (378.5 L) of spray mix (1.5 percent vv) and apply as a dilute spray. Do not use a wetting agent if you use oil.

Days after Full Bloom (DAFB). If a spray is timed according to DAFB, apply NAA as a dilute spray (300 to 500 gallons per acre [2,800 to 4,700 L]) 12 to 18 days after full bloom using 10 ppm for each day after full bloom (for example, if you spray 15 days after full bloom, use 150 ppm NAA) (table 14.1). Abnormally cool weather delays fruit growth. In this case, the fruit size method for spray timing should be used.

Application

To be effective, the NAA spray must cover the undersides of leaves on fruiting branches, but a heavy drenching application such as that used for scale control is usually unnecessary and wasteful.

Air Blast Sprayers. When most trees bear a heavy crop, an air blast sprayer does the best job of covering the whole tree. For good spray distribution, drive a properly adjusted air blast sprayer at 1½ to 2 miles per hour (2.4 to 3.2 km/hr).

Table 14.1. Amount of naphthalene acetic acid (NAA) from Liqui-Stik concentrate* required for various application rates

Water per acre (gal)	Concentration (ppm)	Product (oz)/100 gal water	Product (oz)/acre
300	100	24	72
300	150	36	108
400	100	24	96
400	150	36	144

*NAA ammonium salt, 200 grams active ingredient per gallon of product

High-Pressure, Hand-Gun Sprayers. For spot treatment, use high-pressure, hand-gun sprayers with number 8 discs at 200 to 300 pounds per square inch (psi) (14 to 21 kg/cm²) pressure.

Chemical Thinning Precautions

Chemical thinning is a sensitive operation, and under- or overthinning can occur. As discussed above, the response to NAA is influenced by environmental conditions (primarily temperature within a few days of application) and tree stress during and after the thinning application. Tree stress tends to accelerate the thinning response, so growers should avoid stressing trees during and after thinning.

Only well-watered, healthy trees should be chemically thinned. Young shoot tips may be injured by NAA, but there is no lasting effect. Treatments should be avoided when warmer or cooler than normal temperatures are predicted for the 3 or 4 days following treatment.

NAA should not be used with oil when daytime temperatures are 90°F (32°C) or higher, or when soil moisture is low. Failure to observe these precautions may result in leaf and shoot burn, defoliation, fruit injury, and excessive thinning.

Chemical Thinning Each Year

Ideally, fruit thinning is done every year. Annual thinning should remove enough fruit so that shoot growth and return bloom are balanced.

Often the fruit thinning response is not uniform from season to season. Enough fruit may be removed to increase the fruit size and value, but not enough to eliminate poor tree bloom and alternate bearing. In addition, if the bloom is light, chemical thinning can further reduce a light crop and should not be done.

Complete Fruit Removal

Occasionally, it is desirable to remove an entire crop, such as when olives are used as ornamentals, and the ripe olives that drop create a nuisance. For complete crop removal, use a solution of 150 ppm NAA applied in two sprays, the first 2 to 3 days before full bloom, and the second 1 week later. If the bloom period is short, a second spray may not be necessary. A single spray may be applied at full bloom, but often crop removal is incomplete. Warm weather following this application will increase fruit removal. For large trees, a power sprayer is required; 5 to 10 gallons (19 to 38 L) of solution per tree may be required for good coverage. Although NAA is not normally used to thin the Sevillano variety, treatments for complete or near complete fruit removal are effective. Note that spraying with NAA when the temperature exceeds 100°F (38°C) can injure new growth and may also cause some leaf drop. Tender ornamentals nearby should be covered, and drift should be avoided by spraying only under calm conditions and by using moderate pressure to apply a coarse spray.

PRUNING

Pruning, the traditional method used to moderate alternate bearing, is especially useful if chemical fruit thinning is not practiced, such as on the Sevillano variety. Pruning to thin fruitwood reduces the crop, thereby promoting shoot growth to bear fruit the following year. Pruning is an expensive cultural practice and is not as effective in moderating alternate bearing as thinning because it removes both fruit and leaves and does not increase the leaf-to-fruit ratio. Pruning removes entire shoots, and fruit set may still be excessive on remaining shoots.

To control the crop and affect alternate bearing, pruning must be done in the spring or early summer of the heavy year when bloom or crop load can be seen. Pruning should be detailed, removing branches with heavy bloom or crop and leaving lighter-cropped branches. Pruning for crop control should be done more heavily in heavy years, and lightly or not at all in light years.

HAND THINNING

Fruit thinning by hand is effective, but due to high labor costs it is not practical. However, for a few trees in the home garden, it may be an acceptable alternative. For maximum benefit, thinning should be completed within 4 weeks of full bloom. Later than that, thinning contributes less to larger fruit size and does not reduce alternate bearing as much. The following points should be observed when hand thinning:

- To protect hands and fingers, wear heavy rubber gloves or tape the fingers. With both hands, strip the fruit from twigs that have heavy fruit set. Take care not to damage or remove leaves.

- Thin only those twigs from which at least 5 or 6 olives can be removed at one pull. Try to leave an average of 6 olives per 1 foot (30 cm) of twig. Unless enough fruit is removed from the entire tree, thinning is not useful.

REFERENCES

Krueger, W. H., and R. Heath. 2001. Response of the Sevillano olive cultivar to postbloom thinning with napthalene acetic acid. Abst. Amer. Soc. Hort. Sci.

Krueger, W. H., Z. R. Heath, and B. Mulqueeny. 2002. Effect of spray solution concentration, active ingredient, certain additives, and sequential treatments of naphthalene acetic acid for chemical thinning of Manzanillo table olives. Acta Horticulturae 586:267–271.

Krueger, W. H., G. C. Martin, C. Nishijima, and J. E. Dibble. 1987. Using concentrate postbloom NAA sprays to thin olives. California Agriculture. March–April.

15

Arthropod Pests of Olive

K. M. DAANE, R. E. RICE, F. G. ZALOM, W. W. BARNETT, AND M. W. JOHNSON

Insect and mite pests in California olive groves could, until recently, be kept below economically damaging levels through a combination of biological and cultural controls. If insecticide treatments were needed, selective programs that target specific pests could achieve control without disturbing the natural regulation of other insect and mite pests. With the recent introduction of the olive fly into California, pesticide treatment is becoming essential in many commercial orchards. An important component of the integrated pest management (IPM) approach for olives is monitoring pest and beneficial species to determine if and when pesticides are necessary, and choosing controls that prevent the occurrence of secondary pest outbreaks. Therefore, controls for olive fly must be integrated with other pest management decisions.

OLIVE FLY

The olive fly, *Bactrocera oleae* (Gmelin), poses a new and serious threat to the California olive industry. A native of the Mediterranean region, this insect is considered to be the most damaging pest of olives in southern Europe, North Africa, and the Middle East. In 1998, the olive fly was first observed in North America infesting olives on landscape trees in Los Angeles County. Detection surveys in 1999 and 2000 showed olive fly infesting coastal areas from Napa and Sonoma counties, south to San Diego, and in Baja California and the Caborca (Sonora) areas of Mexico. More critical to the olive industry, the olive fly is now found in most of the Central Valley, as well as in some Sierra Nevada foothill regions. Presently, the olive fly occurs in at least 41 California counties.

Given such a widespread infestation, state and federal regulatory officials have concluded that it is not possible to eradicate olive fly from California. Consequently, commercial table and olive oil producers must learn to manage this pest economically and in a manner that does not cause outbreaks of secondary pests. Olives grown by homeowners for home curing or oil are also at risk.

Olive flies now commonly infest ornamental olive plantings in urban and landscape situations in which they are not actively managed. These noncommercial olive trees may serve as an important source of invasion for commercial groves.

Description

The adult olive fly is approximately 3/16 inch (4.8 mm) long with clear wings containing dark veins and a small dark spot at each wing tip (color plate 15.1). The head, thorax, and abdomen are brown with darker markings and several white or yellow patches on the top and sides of the thorax. Adult flies can live from 2 to 6 months depending on food availability (honeydew, rotting fruit, bird feces, and so on) and temperature. Male flies are polygamous; females are normally monogamous.

Olive fly females have been reported to lay from 10 to 40 eggs per day, and from 200 to 500 eggs during their lives, thus the reproductive potential for olive flies is extremely high if host fruit is available for oviposition. Olive fly eggs are small and difficult to see, embedded under the fruit surface.

The larvae are maggot-like and have a pointed head; their color varies from pale white to light yellow, with the color intensity depending on the color of the olive pulp that they infest (color plate 15.2). Unlike most other tephritid species, mature olive fly larvae pupate in fruit during the summer (color plate 15.3), but leave fruit in the fall and winter to pupate in the soil under the tree.

Field Biology

The seasonal phenology of olive fly varies considerably, depending on temperatures and host availability. In general, there are from three to as many as six generations of olive fly in California each year, depending on microclimate and host availability. The life cycle is currently being studied in many olive growing regions of the state. Olive flies overwinter in the adult or pupal stages. In warmer climates, adults can lay eggs throughout the winter; however, this overwintered adult population declines to generally low levels by February or March. New adults from overwintering pupae begin to emerge in early spring. The next generation of adults represents offspring from overwintered adults and pupae and appears between June and August, depending on regional temperatures. In Mediterranean areas of Europe, olive fruit susceptibility begins at the time of pit hardening, usually in July, and corresponds with the first olive fly adult flight during summer. However, in California, pit hardening was observed in olives in Tulare County (along with many trapped flies) in June 2001. Mature, mated female flies with eggs were collected throughout June 2001 in the San Joaquin Valley. Therefore, olives may be infested earlier in the season in some areas of California as compared with the Mediterranean area.

Additional generations of olive flies are produced from late August through December, depending on temperatures and fruit maturity and availability. Olives that are left on trees can produce high numbers of flies from late fall to early spring if these fruit are unharvested or allowed to mature and drop naturally from the trees onto the ground. There are undoubtedly significant differences in the seasonal phenology and biology of olive fly in California due to the numerous microclimates found within our coastal and interior regions. For example, in coastal regions with mild winter temperatures, such as in San Diego or Santa Barbara counties, olive fly development is continuous throughout the year if old olive fruit remains on trees (through the winter into early summer).

The adult olive fly activity threshold is approximately 60°F (16°C). In summer olive flies can complete a generation in as little as 30 to 35 days with optimal temperatures. The eggs hatch in 2 to 3 days and larvae develop in about 20 days during the summer and fall. Pupal development requires 8 to 10 days during the summer but may last for six months in winter. Unlike other tephritid species, olive flies pupate within the host fruit during warmer months, but leave the fruit to pupate in the ground or in any protected niche during winter.

In the Mediterranean region, olive flies survive best in the more humid coastal climates but are also known to heavily infest olives that are grown in interior dry regions of Greece, Italy, and Spain. High temperatures of 100° to 105°F (38° to 41°C) and dry conditions are detrimental to adult flies and to immature stages in fruit. However, adult flies are very mobile and can seek out protection from the heat in more humid areas within olive groves or urban landscapes, particularly those that are heavily irrigated. The adult fly has been reported to move from 650 feet (200 m) in the presence of olive hosts to as much as 2.5 miles (4 km) to find hosts.

Damage

The larva of the olive fly feeds exclusively on olive fruit and is the only life stage that causes significant damage (color plate 15.4). In areas of the world where olive fly is established, it has been responsible for losses of up to 80 percent of oil value and 100 percent of some table cultivars. Economic olive fly damage at harvest results from as little as an adult fly oviposition "sting" on the fruit surface of table olives, to fruit drop caused by feeding larvae, to direct pulp destruction that renders fruit useless for canning (color plate 15.5). Olive fly larval damage also increases acidity of the oil, lowering its quality and value.

Monitoring and Control

Early detection of olive fly is essential to prevent crop losses in commercial production areas. The California Department of Food and Agriculture initially developed a statewide management plan to detect and combat olive fly in the commercial and urban olive growing districts, including olive-fly trapping and then control procedures when flies were caught. However, once an area becomes widely infested with flies, as in most of California's olive growing regions, eradication is not feasible, and monitoring and control become the responsibility of individual growers or pest control districts formed by growers.

Adult olive fly populations are monitored with yellow sticky traps containing a sex pheromone (spiroketal) and/or ammonium carbonate, ammonium bicarbonate, or diammonium phosphate bait. The sex pheromone attracts male olive flies. The ammonium carbonate and related compounds produce ammonia which is also associated with protein decomposition. Females need protein for egg production, and they are attracted to the volatile ammonia. Both sexes are attracted to the yellow color of the trap and become stuck on the sticky trap surface. Olive flies can also be monitored effectively with glass or plastic McPhail traps that contain yeast hydrolosate plus the same ammonia producing chemicals as the yellow sticky trap. MacPhail traps capture more flies than do yellow sticky traps, but they can be more difficult to use. Plastic McPhail traps are easier to use than are glass ones. Researchers are currently working on improving detection tools. Crop sanitation, insecticide applications, and various trapping techniques are required to prevent extensive damage to fruit and oil quality.

Cultural Control. Sanitation is important to help prevent the spread of olive fly. After harvest, olive fruit left on trees or ground can result in continuing development of the olive fly. Homeowners and commercial growers should collect fallen olives and remove as much fruit as possible from their trees.

Sanitation of landscape and unmaintained trees, which may serve as a habitat for flies, can help reduce the overall densities present in an area. Unused or fallen fruit should be disposed of in landfills or buried.

Growth regulators can be used to prevent fruit formation in ornamental plantings, but proper application timing is critical for effective fruit suppression. Growth regulators must be applied thoroughly to flowers during bloom and before fruit set. They should only be sprayed during bloom to prevent commercial fruiting in ornamental olives, but they may also be used prior to bloom to thin olives in production situations. Read and follow the manufacturer's label directions for use.

Fruitless olive varieties should be used in new landscape plantings not intended for olive production. These varieties have the additional advantage of producing less pollen that may aggravate peoples' allergies.

Biological Control. The olive fly is attacked by a number of parasitoid species in the Mediterranean and also in sub-Saharan Africa, where the fly is thought to have originated.

Currently, there are no effective biological control agents of the olive fly in California. University of California and state scientists have recently imported and are testing several small parasitic wasps from Africa, Europe, and Hawaii. Economic control of olive fly in commercial olive groves using only biological controls may prove difficult, due to the commercial requirements of very low infestation levels. Nevertheless, suppressing olive fly populations on untreated landscape trees, which serve as a source of adult flies that disperse into commercial groves, will help to reduce overall fly densities and potentially reduce the number of sprays necessary to achieve control in commercial orchards.

Chemical Control. Most insecticidal controls are applied as a bait and insecticide mixture, but cover sprays are also used in some European commercial production areas. The baits attract adult flies that must feed to prolong life and produce eggs. Ground application is recommended for bait sprays rather than aerial application, which results in droplet sizes that are too small to be effective. Large droplets about $3/16$ inch (4–5 mm) in diameter are preferred so that they do not dry out too quickly, and the droplets should be applied at a rate of 3 to 6 per square foot of foliage to a minimum of a 2-foot diameter area within the upper part of the canopy on the north or east side of each tree. Begin treatments when the number of olive fly males responding to a pheromone-only trap increases sharply, which occurs at

or just prior to pit hardening. See the *University of California Pest Management Guidelines: Olives* for currently recommended pesticides and preferred treatment timing.

"Attract and kill" devices or panels, baited with olive fly attractants and coated with a long-residual insecticide, may also be used for control. The devices are hung in trees as high as possible on the side that receives the most sun. Flies attracted to the panels die after they contact the pesticide-treated surface. At the end of the season, the panels should be disposed of in a sanitary landfill, in accordance with local regulation. In Spain, some growers utilize an OLIPE trap to suppress olive fruit fly populations in organic orchards and in sensitive areas near homes and natural parks. The OLIPE trap consists simply of a 1- to 2-liter plastic bottle with 5-mm holes melted into the shoulder. This is filled about two-thirds with a 3–5% solution of one of the ammonia-producing attractants and water and hung in the trees. The flies are attracted to the trap, crawl inside, and die.

BLACK SCALE

From 1970 to 2000, black scale, *Saissetia oleae* (Olivier), was the major insect pest of California olives. Prior to that period, black scale was generally controlled by insecticide treatments targeting the olive scale *Parlatoria oleae* (Colvee), which was the more serious pest at that time (see **Olive Scale**, page 109). When the biological control of olive scale became fully effective during the late 1960s, annual treatments for it were discontinued, and black scale emerged as the predominant insect pest. Today, with the improved biological and cultural controls for black scale, the olive fly has now displaced black scale as the primary insect concern.

It is important that controls for olive fly are used within an IPM framework to prevent disruption of scale insects in commercial olive groves and the renewed need to target pesticides for scale control.

Black scale is native to southern Africa. This soft scale is currently found in most Mediterranean and semitropical regions of the world. Hosts include almond, apple, apricot, citrus coyote brush, fig, fuchsia, grape, grapefruit, oleander, peppertree, plum, prune, and rose. With such a wide host range it is found throughout California and readily infests olive and citrus orchards where it causes serious economic losses.

Description

Adult females are brown when young and change to black with a pronounced hemispherical shape as they mature. Mature females deposit their eggs under the scale covering (color plate 15.6). The eggs are very small, 0.2 to 0.3 millimeter long, and light colored when first laid, becoming pinkish 2 or 3 days later and a red-orange color just a few days before hatching.

First-instar nymphs, called crawlers, are about 0.5 millimeter long and pale yellow to light brown, with dark eyes (color plate 15.7). After emerging from the eggs, crawlers search for a suitable feeding site for up to 7 days before they insert their mouthparts and begin to feed. The nymphs double in size before their first molt, which occurs 3 to 8 weeks after hatching (depending on temperature and host plant condition). Second-instar nymphs are about 1 millimeter long when the distinctive "H"-pattern on the top of the scale begins to form.

The next stage, the sexually immature adult (third instar), is quite different in appearance. It is dark, ash-gray to brown and about 2 to 3 millimeters long, with the legs hidden beneath the body. The "H" is quite distinct. This stage is often referred to as the rubber stage (color plate 15.8) but could be more correctly called the pre-ovipositional adult stage because the reproductive organs have formed and egg production is about to begin. In the adult or ovipositional stage, the outer shell covering (integument) turns black and becomes quite hard, belying its common name of soft scale. Adult scale size varies greatly, from 3 to 5 millimeters long, and can be up to 3 millimeters high. The number of eggs per female varies with adult size and host condition and can range from 300 to 3,000, with the upper range indicating the explosive nature of scale outbreaks.

Male black scale are rarely found in California. Young males are identical to the females until the second instar stage, when the male becomes more elongate. After 4 to 6 weeks, in warm weather, the male scale molts to a prepupal and then again to a pupal stage, which has a red head with black eyes; antennae, legs, and wing pads become minute. The adult is light yellow and winged.

Field Biology

In California's interior valleys, black scale typically overwinters as a second- or third-instar nymph. As temperatures increase in spring, there is a period of rapid growth and development, accompanied by a large amount of honeydew excretion. By April most scale have progressed to the pre-ovipositional and adult stages. Egg hatch and crawler emergence begins shortly thereafter, peaks in May or June, and is often not completed until July. Crawlers settle and begin to feed on leaves and twigs. In late summer and fall, most of the scale that are still feeding on leaves migrate to more favorable feeding and overwintering sites on twigs, where they develop to the second or third instar.

Black scale typically has one generation per year; however, because black scale development is driven by temperature and host quality, there can be two generations when conditions permit. For example, in California's interior valleys, scale development is slower during winter and summer because temperatures approach the scale's intolerable levels, resulting in one generation per year. In fact, prolonged periods of high temperatures cause significant mortality at the early developmental stages. Therefore, cultural practices that lower canopy temperatures in summer (for example, closed pruning and flood irrigation) reduce scale mortality and can alter scale development to result in a second or partial second generation. On the coast, where temperatures are milder, there are often two generations per year.

Damage

Black scale feeds by inserting its needle-like mouthparts into a leaf or twig to extract plant juices. As the scale feeds, it excretes unused material, called honeydew, because it is rich in carbohydrates. The honeydew can accumulate on leaves, forming a sticky, sugary fluid, and providing a substrate for sooty mold, which can form a dense black covering that shades leaves and reduces photosynthesis and respiration. The combination of insect feeding and buildup of honeydew can reduce fruitbud formation, cause leaf drop and twig dieback, and reduce the following year's crop (color plate 15.9).

Monitoring and Control

The presence of honeydew droplets on olive leaves in March and April, corresponding to a rapid increase in scale size, is often the earliest signal of increased scale density in the orchard. To monitor, check about 40 trees per block in April for honeydew droplets on the leaves. With new infestations, the scale is often found on just a few trees, so it is important to check trees throughout the block. Be sure to check in the inner canopy where the scale population typically starts to build.

If honeydew is found, sample for adult scale in May, focusing on 2 to 3 areas in each block, particularly those that have had scale problems in the past. At least 10 trees should be searched in each 10 acre section. On each tree, count the number of mature scale (third instar to adult scale) on the terminal 20 inches (51 cm) of 10 branches; again, be sure to include the inner sections of the tree. Sum the numbers of black scale in each 10-branch sample and divide by 10 to get the average infestation level. We have categorized infestations into four levels: light (less than 1 per branch), moderate (1 to 3 per branch), heavy (4 to 10 per branch), and severe (more than 10 per branch).

Light Infestation. If no scale are found, no treatment is needed. Light infestations typically do not require treatment in open-canopy orchards (see Cultural Control, below). Closed-canopy orchards should be pruned to increase air circulation and raise temperatures. If trees cannot be pruned or if spring and summer temperatures are lower than average, an application of a dormant oil can be considered as a safeguard.

Moderate Infestation. A small infestation can build to a moderate infestation following a cool spring and summer or within a closed-orchard canopy. A moderate scale infestation typically does not cause damage; however, the offspring from adult scale found in spring can cause substantial damage to the crop. In trees with open canopies, the scale population should decrease or remain stable, depending on summer temperatures; however, application of a dormant oil should be considered to reduce scale densities. Orchards with closed canopies should be pruned. If trees cannot be pruned, an insecticide application should be considered.

Heavy Infestation. Heavy infestations will cause economic damage if left untreated. If the orchard has not been pruned for years and the trees have closed, an in-season insecticide treatment should be used to prevent further damage at harvest. After harvest, trees should be pruned to open the canopy and make the environment less hospitable for scale survival.

Severe infestations typically occur in closed-canopy orchards in which treatment of moderate or heavy scale infestation was delayed. Economic loss can be extensive because the adult scale population in spring represents a potentially great increase during the summer. An in-season insecticide treatment is needed to protect the crop and trees. After harvest, the trees should be pruned to open the canopy. Severely infested or damaged branches should be removed.

Cultural Control. Crawler and first and second instar black scale cannot survive prolonged periods of hot, dry weather because the small scale cannot feed fast enough to replace the fluids they lose. The scale desiccate. The natural reduction of black scale, even when natural enemies are present, depends on a 70 to 90 percent kill—or desiccation—of the early developmental stages during the spring and summer. Therefore, canopy structures that affect the microclimate influence black scale mortality and development. When left unpruned for many years, the canopy becomes dense, or closed, and the spring and summer heat is moderated (color plate 15.10); in this protected environment scale can better survive hot summers and develop to outbreak levels in mild summers. Regular pruning opens the canopy (color plate 15.11) and exposes scale to higher temper-atures and drier conditions. This is the best cultural control available.

Natural Control. Many natural enemies have been imported and released in California to control black scale. About 15 parasitoid species have become established. The most common parasitic wasps are *Metaphycus helvolus* Compere, *Metaphycus anneckei* Guerrieri and Noyes, *Metaphycus hageni* Daane and Caltagirone, *Coccophagus ochraceus* Howard, *Coccophagus lycimnia* (Walker), *Coccophagus scutellaris* (Dalman), and *Scutellista caerulea* (Fonscolombe). Insect predators are also present, such as green lacewings (*Chrysoperla* spp.) and lady beetles (for example, *Hippodamia convergens* and *Hyperaspis* sp.). These predators feed primarily on young black scale.

Unfortunately, parasitoids and predators have had only partial success in controlling black scale below economic injury levels. One problem is that the parasitoids cannot reproduce without suitable black scale host stages. Because the scale often has only one generation per year, there can be periods when the proper host stage, or size, is not available and the parasitoid numbers drop to very low levels.

Chemical Control. Dormant oil treatments are effective against light to moderate infestations, especially when used in conjunction with pruning to open the orchard canopy. However, for heavy or severe infestations, more toxic pesticides should be considered. Pesticides are most effective against crawlers, the first- and second-instar nymphs found in summer. Before application, check the adult scale to make sure egg hatch is complete (the adult shell may protect crawlers from pesticide exposure). Postharvest treatments are also possible, until the rubber stage is reached the following spring.

OLIVE SCALE

Olive scale, *Parlatoria oleae* (Colvee), is a pest of many crops and has been collected from over 200 plant species. Olive scale is widely distributed throughout the world's olive-growing regions, including Argentina, India, the Mediterranean, Middle East, Russia, and Turkey. In the United States, it was first noted on privet in Maryland in 1924, although it may have been in Phoenix, Arizona, as early as the 1890s. In California, it was found near Fresno in 1934 and spread rapidly through olive-growing areas in the Central Valley, reaching areas south of the Tehachapi Mountains by 1961. It became a major pest of olives and required annual pesticide treatments to protect fruit from economic damage. Today it ranges from San Diego to the northern Sacramento Valley. However, due to successful biological control (see **Monitoring and Control**, below), this pest is rarely a problem.

Description

The adult female cover—or shell—is almost circular, about 1 mm across, slightly convex, and light to dark gray with a brownish nipple or exuvium. Under the scale cover, the young female's body ranges from a reddish to deep purple (color plate 15.12). The male's covering is elongate, white, and flat; the exuvium is to one end rather than central, and is brownish or blackish.

Field Biology

There are two generations of olive scale each year. The scale overwinters as an immature, mated, third-instar female. Overwintered females mature and begin laying eggs in late April and early May. Crawlers begin emerging in May and wander for a short time, then settle on twigs, leaves, and, in some cases, newly set fruit. Emergence of first-generation crawlers is usually completed by June or early July. Both male and female scales are produced. Females from this generation mature and begin egg production in August and early September. The eggs of this fall generation hatch, and crawlers settle on leaves and twigs, but to a much greater extent on fruit. Males complete their development in fall and fertilize immature female scales before winter.

Damage

High olive scale densities can cause defoliation and twig death, and frequently reduce tree productivity. The major damage results from scale settling on fruit. Fruit infested by the first generation become badly misshapen. Infestation by the second generation causes pronounced purple spotting of the green fruit, rendering it worthless for pickling (color plate 15.13).

Monitoring and Control

The best time to detect an increasing olive scale population is at harvest because of the characteristic discoloration of the infested fruit. Chemical control is normally not required. Two species of introduced parasites provide excellent control of olive scale. *Aphytis maculicornis* (DeBach and Rosen) (color plate 15.14) was introduced in 1952 and provided good control in some groves, but it was less successful in others because it is inhibited by the hot, dry summers of California's interior valleys. *Coccophagoides utilis* (Doutt) was introduced in 1957; in combination, the two parasites currently provide widespread biological control of olive scale in California.

Chemical treatment to control olive scale is rarely needed unless biological control is disturbed by treatments for other pests. If olive scale was detected in the previous season or if chemicals are used in the orchard or on nearby crops, watch closely to detect crawlers moving onto the fruit in summer. If treatment is needed, apply chemicals against the first generation in May or June. A postharvest treatment is also effective.

OLEANDER SCALE

Oleander scale, *Aspidiotus nerii* (Bouche), also known as ivy scale, occurs throughout the warmer parts of the United States and is one of the most common scale insects in California. It attacks a wide range of plants, including acacia, aloe, avocado, azalea, Boston ivy, boxwood, cactus, camellia, cherry, grape, grapefruit, lemon, magnolia, mistletoe, Monterey pine, oleander, rose, sago palm, and yucca. It rarely requires treatment on other hosts, but on olive, infestations occasionally become sufficient to damage fruit.

Description

Oleander scale resembles greedy scale (see **Greedy Scale**, below) except that its scale covering is less convex, and the exuvium is almost central. Oleander scale is 1 to 2 mm across, flat, and gray with yellow or light brown exuvium (color plate 15.15). The male covering is smaller than the female and more elongate, with the exuvium at one end. The mature scale, found under the covering, and the crawlers are yellow.

Field Biology

Little is known about the life cycle of oleander scale. The majority of overwintering individuals are adult females. Egg production and crawler emergence begins in April, and females continue producing progeny for almost 2 months. A second generation is produced in July and August, but because progeny production is spread over such a long period, there is often an overlap of the first and second generations.

Damage

Oleander scale is generally found on leaves and, to a lesser extent, on twigs in the lower, inner canopy. Leaves and twigs can tolerate heavy populations before any reduction in crop occurs. When population density is high, oleander scale infests olive fruit. Infested fruit is characterized by green spots on purple fruit, as scales delay maturity of the tissue around the scale. Early infestations seriously deform fruit, and later fruit spotting renders olives worthless for pickling.

Monitoring and Control

The best way to decide whether a treatment may be needed is to examine the previous season's grade sheet and determine the amount of culled fruit caused by this pest. This is a relatively good measure for all the diaspid, or armored, scales. Oleander scale can also be monitored with double-sided sticky cellophane tape, placed around branches with adult scales present, to detect crawler emergence. However, it is difficult to determine which of the armored scales are present from the small crawlers caught on sticky tape. Like the other armored scales, there is no economic injury level. Parasitoids and predators most often keep oleander scale in check. When monitoring scale, look for holes caused by parasite emergence to estimate the level of biological control. If pesticides are required, treat first-generation crawlers in late May or June when they are first seen moving onto fruit.

LATANIA SCALE

Latania scale, *Hemiberlesia lataniae* (Signoret), has been found on a wide range of hosts in tropical and subtropical areas. It is very common in California, being recorded on such diverse hosts as acacia, avocado, bramble, cedar, euonymus, fuchsia, gladiolus, Kentia, kiwifruit, philodendron, rose, willow, and yucca.

Description

The adult scale covering is gray or white, with a darker exuvium. The covering is quite convex, with the exuvium toward one side (color plate 15.16). The body of the female under the scale cover is yellow to orange, in contrast to the purple color of the olive scale. Apparently, male scales do not occur in California although they have been observed in other parts of the United States. The crawler through second-instar bodies are orange.

Field Biology

Latania scale overwinters as a second-instar nymph. In early spring the scale mature; the female scale initially lays eggs in batches of 15 to 20, and then 3 to 5 a day until she dies. Eggs are laid beneath the scale covering, where they hatch.

Young crawlers migrate a short distance from the mature female, settle down, insert their mouthparts, and begin feeding. The legs of the crawlers become functionless after they settle. The first generation may complete its development in as little as 2 months. Crawlers are reported to be active in May, July, and then in September, indicating that 2 to 3 generations per year occur in California. The short distance that the crawlers move is one reason they are often clumped together.

Damage

Latania scale feed on leaves, bark, and fruit. If the population density is high, twig dieback may occur. Most damage occurs when scales develop on the olive fruit (color plate 15.17), rendering it worthless for pickling.

Monitoring and Control

Pesticides are rarely needed because parasitoids are commonly present and can significantly reduce latania scale. However, as with most of the armored scales, if the grade sheet from the previous season indicated an economic infestation, closer monitoring is needed and pesticides should be considered. Time the pesticide application to the emergence of crawlers in May or June. Double-sided sticky cellophane tape is useful to determine when crawlers are active.

GREEDY SCALE

Greedy scale, *Hemiberlesia rapax* (Comstock), is the most common and widely distributed species of armored scale in California. It infests innumerable hosts throughout the United States and may attack almost any woody plant. However, it is not as damaging to its hosts as many of the other scale species mentioned.

Description

The scale covering is usually light gray, circular, and very thin and convex in side view (color plate 15.18). It measures about 1 to 1.5 millimeters across when fully grown. The exuvium is yellow to dark brown and slightly off center. The body of the mature female under the scale cover is yellow and circular or pear shaped. This scale is easily confused with latania scale and can be distinguished only by microscopic examination. Adults also resemble ivy or oleander scale but are less convex, and the exuvium is more centrally positioned.

Field Biology

Little is known about the biology of this insect. Most overwinter as adult females although other development stages have been found overwintering. As this scale may be found in various stages of development, it presumably has several overlapping generations per year.

Damage

Greedy scale may become abundant on the bark of branches, especially on older suckers. However, like other armored scales, little damage occurs unless it develops on the fruit, where it can cause deformation and off-colored marks.

Monitoring and Control

Parasites and predators play a prominent role in regulating greedy scale populations. If grades indicate that greedy scale is causing fruit loss, monitor crawlers in the following generation with double-sided sticky tape and apply treatments when crawlers are present.

CALIFORNIA RED SCALE

Although California red scale, *Aonidiella aurantii* (Maskell), is a significant pest of citrus, infestations on olive rarely require treatment. It is widely distributed throughout Central and Southern California on citrus, and it attacks a diverse range of hosts such as fruitless mulberry, grape, nightshade, rose, and walnut.

Description

The adult female has a thin, round scale covering about 2 mm across. The body color beneath the cover is reddish and shows through the scale covering. The exuvium is located centrally or just off-center. The male scale covering is gray and elongate.

Field Biology

Female scales give birth to young that remain under the scale covering for 1 or 2 days before emerging as crawlers. Crawlers seek a favorable site to settle, insert their mouthparts, and begin feeding. The female molts twice before becoming mature. Male and female development are similar until after the first molt, when the male covering becomes elongate rather than round. The male passes through a prepupal, pupal, and winged adult stage. There are two or three generations per year, and any stage in the life cycle may be found at any time of the year.

Damage

All parts of the olive tree can be infested, but only on rare occasions are treatments needed. California red scale does not discolor fruit, which distinguishes its damage from that of the olive and oleander scales. However, infested fruit is worthless and must be culled before processing (color plate 15.19).

Monitoring and Control

Depending on the climate, growing season, and treatment for other pests, biological control can be effective against California red scale in some areas of the state, though not in the San Joaquin Valley. Red scale can be monitored by examining fruit, twigs, and leaves, or pheromone traps. If treatments are required, time applications against the first-generation crawlers in June or the second generation in late July and August. For more information about California red scale, see *Integrated Pest Management for Citrus, 2nd Edition* (University of California Statewide Integrated Pest Management Project. 1991. Oakland: Agriculture and Natural Resources, Publication 3303).

OLIVE MITE

The olive mite, *Oxyenus maxwelli* (K.), is a native of the Mediterranean region and is now found throughout the world's olive-growing regions. Of California's olive cultivars, Ascolano is the most susceptible, followed by Sevillano, Manzanillo, and Mission.

Description

Olive mites are tiny, four-legged eriophyid mites with yellowish to orange bodies (color plate 15.20). Females are broadest at the front of the body and taper to the rear. They are tiny, about 140 to 160 micrometers long, and difficult to see without a microscope or at least a 20×-power lens.

Field Biology

Olive mites overwinter as adults in bark crevices. Egg laying begins in late winter or early spring and continues until summer. Sudden periods of relative humidity below 20 percent and high temperatures cause high mortality. The mite estivates in various stages of development during summer and resumes activity again in fall until cold weather.

Damage

Olive mite is normally found on the surfaces of immature terminal olive leaves. Usually it causes no damage; when present in large numbers on young leaves, it silvers them and causes longitudinal curling, but this does not damage the tree or its productivity. In spring, the mites collect on the developing inflorescence, and high density populations can cause pistil abortion and subsequent crop losses. Dead and discolored floral buds, bud drop, blossom blast, and inflorescence abscission are also symptoms of bud damage associated with olive mite.

Monitoring and Control

Treatment is not recommended unless fruit set and crop have been below normal for several years and large numbers of mites are found. However, if poor cropping has occurred several years in a row, examine shoot tips and developing bloom for the presence of olive mites. If high density populations occur on developing inflorescence, insecticide treatment is recommended.

WESTERN FLOWER THRIPS

The western flower thrips, *Frankliniella occidentalis* (Pergande), is widely distributed throughout western North America. It has a very wide host range, including over 139 species of plants in California alone. Western flower thrips is attracted to olives during bloom. Ascolano is most susceptible although other cultivars can be injured.

Description

Western flower thrips adults are tiny insects, about 1 millimeter long, with two pairs of fringed wings. Adults vary in color, from white to yellow with slight brown spots on top of the abdomen, to yellowish with an orange thorax and brown abdomen, to completely dark brown. Different color forms predominate according to the time of year.

Eggs are opaque and kidney shaped and are inserted in the parenchyma cells of leaves, flower parts, and fruit. First-instar nymphs are opaque or light yellow, turning golden yellow after the first molt. Upon completing development, nymphs drop to the ground and pupate in protected places. Pupae are soft bodied, with visible wing pads.

Field Biology

Adults overwinter in weeds, grasses, and other sites within or outside the orchard. In early spring, they deposit eggs in shoots, buds, and flower parts of host plants. Eggs hatch in 5 to 15 days, depending on temperatures. Nymphs feed on developing leaves, fruit, and shoots. After completing their development, nymphs drop to the ground where they molt twice before emerging as adults. Populations usually peak in May or June. As wild areas dry up, thrips migrate to cultivated areas, including olive orchards, where additional generations are produced. There are five to six generations of western flower thrips per year.

Damage

Because flower thrips migrate to olive groves from adjoining areas after they dry up in spring, trees near drying grain fields or near dry weeds within the orchard are most susceptible to damage. Although thrips feed on leaves and tender shoots, most damage is caused when they feed on fruit. Damaged fruit is scarred and dimpled and must be culled before processing (color plate 15.21).

Monitoring and Control

There are no insecticides registered for thrips control on olives, but infestations can be prevented culturally. Avoid disking orchard ground vegetation while trees are in bloom. Open areas adjacent to groves should be disked as early as possible to prevent thrips development and migration to olive trees.

BRANCH AND TWIG BORER

The branch and twig borer, *Polycaon confertus* (LeConte), attacks a number of fruit and nut trees in California, but grape, madrone, and oak are its preferred hosts. Damage to olive is generally limited to areas adjoining these preferred hosts. It seldom causes economic injury.

Description

The adult branch and twig borer is a slender brown beetle about 13 to 20 millimeters long (color plate 15.22). The body is round, with the head and thorax narrower than the body. Larvae are "C" shaped, white, and covered with fine hairs.

Field Biology

The adult lays eggs in dead and dying wood of many native and cultivated trees and shrubs outside the orchard. The larvae bore into the heartwood of the host and feed until development is complete. Pupation occurs inside infested wood, and adults emerge early in spring. Adults fly to nearby trees, where they bore into branches and twigs, causing a characteristic injury. There is one generation per year.

Damage

Adults bore into the axil of small twigs and branches or into the base of buds. Small branches die, and injured branches frequently break off at the holes made by these beetles. Borer damage is sporadic and not usually of economic importance.

Monitoring and Control

Branch and twig borers can be minimized by burning all infested wood inside and around the orchard to destroy developing larvae. There are no chemical controls for this pest.

AMERICAN PLUM BORER

On occasion the American plum borer, *Euzophera semifuneralis* (Walker), infests olive trees. This borer also attacks a number of other cultivated fruit and nut trees and ornamental plants.

Description

Adult moths have gray forewings with brown and black markings and a wingspan of about 18 millimeters. Eggs are oval and white when first laid, then turn a dull red shortly thereafter. Eggs are laid singly or in small clusters, usually in cracks or bark crevices. Young larvae are white with large, dark-brown heads. Mature larvae are about 25 mm long and vary in color from dusky white, to pink, to dull green. Pupae are olive green when first formed, becoming dark brown before emergence.

Field Biology

American plum borer overwinters as either immature or mature larvae, depending on the olive region. Mature larvae pupate in early spring, and adult moths emerge in April and May. There are multiple generations in California. In late fall, larvae construct loose silken cocoons under bark scales, at the entrance to or near feeding sites in which they overwinter.

Damage

The larvae attack the soft, spongy callus tissue that occurs at graft unions, tree wounds, and in galls caused by the olive knot bacterium. They can continue to feed into normal tissue, girdling limbs, which may be weakened or killed. Most damage is caused to new grafts.

Monitoring and Control

The borer can be detected by the brownish frass and webbing at feeding sites. No control treatments have been developed for this insect on olive.

BLACK VINE WEEVIL

The black vine weevil, *Otiorhynchus sulcatus* (Fabricius), has been recorded from more than 80 host plants. It has long been a serious pest of grape in Europe and of strawberries and ornamentals (especially container-grown plants) in the western United States. Occasionally it attacks olives, primarily in the San Joaquin Valley.

Description

Adult black vine weevils are oblong, about 10 mm long, and dark-brown to black, with a somewhat roughened surface (color plate 15.23). The body is covered with dense, short, light-colored hairs with small patches of yellow hairs on the "elytra" or hard front wings. A long, broad snout projects from the front of the head.

The legless larvae are about 10 mm long when mature; the body is dirty white with a brownish head.

Field Biology

Black vine weevils overwinter as larvae in the soil. Pupation takes place inside earthen cells in the soil, and adult females emerge in March in the San Joaquin Valley and begin laying eggs from 2 to 4 weeks after emergence. The black vine weevil is parthenogenetic (i.e., there are only females, no males). After eggs hatch, young larvae work their way into the soil, where they feed on roots until the following spring. There is one generation per year.

Damage

Damage caused by larval feeding on grape roots in parts of Europe has been described as severe. Little is known about the impact of larval feeding on olive roots, however. Feeding by adults is what most concerns growers in California. Adult black vine weevils are nocturnal: they hide beneath loose bark, in debris, or in other protected places during the day and move up the tree to feed at night. They primarily feed on leaves, and heavy infestations can cause considerable leaf loss. Adults feed along the leaf margin, causing a characteristic notched appearance.

Monitoring and Control

Because adults hide under loose bark and debris at the base of the trees during the day, they are difficult to detect. In grape, tree wraps placed around trunks can be used to detect the presence of adult weevils. There is no specific recommendation for controlling black vine weevil in olives. In grapes, insecticides applied to the trunks and the base of the trunk after adult emergence and before egg laying begins have been effective. Baited insecticides spread near the trunk has also been effective to control the weevil in other crops.

16

Nematodes of Olive

M.V. McKENRY

Nematodes are microscopic, true roundworms; plant-parasitic nematodes are those that derive their nutrition directly from plants. Of concern to olive growers are nematodes that feed on olive roots and increase to high population levels. Almost no nematode pathogenicity data are available for olives. Therefore, based on experience with other crops, the three nematode genera of particular concern are root lesion nematodes (*Pratylenchus* spp.), citrus nematode (*Tylenchulus semipenetrans*), and root knot nematodes (*Meloidogyne* spp.).

Growers should expect variability in nematode damage and incidence, depending on soil texture and seedling or rootstock variability. Unthrifty trees in localized areas of the orchard are among the most obvious symptoms of nematode damage. To determine whether nematodes are present, a soil sample must be taken for nematode analysis.

ROOT LESION NEMATODES

Several species of root lesion nematode can occur in olive orchards. It is important to know which species of root lesion nematode is present when attempting to diagnose a field problem as nematode related.

Pratylenchus vulnus

A species that commonly damages olive, causing poor growth and dieback of small branches, is *Pratylenchus vulnus*. Young trees planted in infested soil frequently fail to make satisfactory growth and are dwarfed or stunted. Larger roots of infected trees have symptoms of longitudinal cracking of the root cortex, and the area underneath these cracks is darkened and necrotic. Necrotic lesions are typical of root lesion nematode attack, and nematodes are normally present in root tissue immediately adjacent to the dead area. Nematodes also attack and frequently kill small feeder roots.

This nematode is more prevalent in the warmest regions of California, but it may be found in northern olive producing regions. Its favored hosts are most woody perennials including walnut, rose, almond, stonefruit, and grape.

Pratylenchus penetrans

Another root lesion nematode that can occur in olive orchards is *Pratylenchus penetrans*. It has a very wide host range including roots of woody perennials, clovers, and grasses. It is most common in the cooler climates of the northern United States and the northern half of California, but it also occurs south of the California delta region, especially at higher elevations on crops such as cherry and apple. Generally speaking, Northern California olive growers deal primarily with *P. penetrans,* whereas growers in the southern San Joaquin olive district deal primarily with *P. vulnus.* The extent of damage by these two nematode species is unknown.

Pratylenchus neglectus

A third root lesion nematode, *Pratylenchus neglectus*, occurs in orchards on roots of grasses and weeds but probably does not feed on olive roots.

CITRUS NEMATODE

The citrus nematode, *Tylenchulus semipenetrans*, attacks olive roots in localities where trees are adjacent to, or planted on land previously occupied by, citrus or grape. Its effects on olive tree growth and production are largely unknown, but infected root systems are characterized by considerable disintegration of small feeder roots. Infested olive orchards respond to nematicide treatment with increased flower development and subsequent yield. Trees infected with citrus nematode can be expected to lack vigor and have a thin foliar canopy.

Host species for the citrus nematode include citrus, grape, persimmon olive, and Marianna 2624 plum. It can be prevalent in a wide variety of soils including those with 50 percent or more clay particles. This nematode occurs in olive orchards of Southern and Northern California. An impressive characteristic of this nematode is its ability to develop to very high population levels.

ROOT KNOT NEMATODES

Root knot nematodes, *Meloidogyne* spp., sometimes attack olives, causing the formation of galls, or knots, on the roots; heavily infected roots cannot perform normal functions. Infected trees may have reduced vigor and show symptoms of decline.

There are no methods to control root knot nematode infestations on roots of established olive trees. Preplant soil fumigation and use of nematode-free planting stock are the best methods to avoid future nematode injury to young trees. A clonal olive rootstock, Allegra, developed and patented by the University of California, shows high resistance to *Meloidogyne* spp. in laboratory tests. All own-rooted olive cultivars grown in California are susceptible to this root knot nematode.

These nematodes are very common in California and are especially problematic in sandy soils south of the delta region. At least two *Meloidogyne* species, *M. incognita* and *M. javanica*, have been shown to dramatically reduce growth of seedlings in inoculation experiments.

SOIL SAMPLES

Soil samples taken from the planting site for examination in a professional laboratory help show which nematode species are present. This information is needed to make decisions about soil fumigation and rootstock selection. High nematode populations are common in soils previously planted to woody crops, and preplant fumigation is recommended for those cases.

Some laboratories collect samples, or growers may collect their own (consult your local University of California Cooperative Extension office for the nearest commercial analytical laboratory). Growers who collect samples should make sure the laboratory will process them as soon as they are received. Processing usually takes 1 to 2 weeks. Laboratory reports should be kept as part of the permanent orchard history.

Timing of Sample Analysis

Sampling can be done any time of year. It is best to sample when the soil is moist, preferably within 1 week after rainfall or irrigation. Take samples to a depth of 36 inches (91 cm) using a soil auger, a sampling tube (Viehmeyer, Oak Field, or the like), or a shovel. The amount of root collected with a sampling tube is much smaller than with a soil auger.

Sample Collection

To collect samples, visually divide the orchard site into sampling blocks that represent differences in soil texture, drainage patterns, and cropping history. Take a separate sample for each block so problems unique to that block can be identified. A sample for nematode analysis consists of about 1 quart (1 L) of soil taken from a mixture of 5 to 20 subsamples. Nematodes are harder to detect when soil has been fallow or recently planted in nonhost crops such as cereal grains. In these situations, taking as many as 20 subsamples from several locations increases the likelihood of detecting the presence of any nematode.

In an established orchard, separate subsamples should be taken for comparison from around trees that show symptoms and around adjacent, healthy-looking trees. Subsamples should include feeder roots when possible and should be taken in zones that are frequently wetted at the edge of the tree canopy.

For each sample, collect subsamples at various depths from 6 inches to 3 feet (15 to 91 cm). Thoroughly mix the subsamples in a bucket, and take 1 quart (1 L) as a representative sample for the sampling block. Pour the soil and roots into a durable plastic bag or other moisture-proof container, seal it tightly, and keep it in the shade. Label each bag with your name and address, location of the orchard, sample block, soil type or texture, cropping history (crops for last several years, current crop, anticipated crop), and notable symptoms; this information is critical for a meaningful analysis. More than one sample from each sampling block improves the precision of the estimate and the information on nematode distribution in the field, but processing samples is costly.

Any diagnosis of nematode samples must distinguish between the three root lesion nematode species. Send or deliver the samples to the laboratory as soon as possible using a cardboard box insulated with newspaper or, in summer, a styrofoam ice chest. If any delay occurs, keep the samples in a cool place, 40° to 55°F (4° to 13°C).

Damage thresholds have not been established for the different nematode pest species in olive. If soil samples indicate that root knot, root lesion, or citrus nematodes are present, and the land to be planted has a crop history of woody perennials or broadleaf plants, the soil needs to be fumigated before planting.

SOIL FUMIGATION

Nematode pests cannot be eradicated completely over a large area. Nematode populations rebuild gradually over time, and no postplant eradication treatments are available. Preplant soil fumigation allows an orchard time to develop a healthy root system that can ultimately withstand or tolerate future nematode damage.

The quantity of chemical applied is only one factor that determines the effectiveness of soil fumigation. Equally important is soil moisture content, soil texture, and soil temperature. Each of these must be considered before fumigation. Tree stumps and old roots that are larger than $1/2$ inch (1.3 cm) in diameter harbor nematodes and protect them from fumigation; these sources of protection must be removed before fumigation.

The best time to fumigate is usually from September until mid-November, but can vary regionally and with soil texture; greater flexibility is possible in sandiest soils. Soil conditions that are less than optimal result in a faster repopulation by nematodes and can reduce the extent of protection from 6 years to 6 months.

17

Diseases of Olive

BETH L. TEVIOTDALE

OLIVE KNOT

Since ancient times, olive knot, caused by the bacterium *Pseudomonas syringae* pv. *savastanoi* (Smith 1908) (Young, Dye, and Wilkie 1978), has afflicted olive trees. The disease occurs wherever olives are grown and probably was brought to California on cuttings in the last half of the nineteenth century. Olive knot does not kill trees, but it does reduce productivity by destroying twigs and branches, and fruit from infected trees may have off-flavors. All cultivars are susceptible, and damage can be severe when weather favors disease.

Symptoms

Rough galls (knots) are usually ½ to 2 inches (1.3 to 5 cm) in diameter and develop on twigs and small branches at wounds including leaf and blossom scars, freeze injury sites, pruning cuts, and wounds that occur during mechanical harvest or other orchard operations (color plate 17.1). They occasionally form on leaves and fruit or in rifts made where shoots emerge from branches; galls on branches or trunks may grow quite large. Galls interfere with transport of water and sugars, causing defoliation and death of twigs and branches. The disease is restricted to the aboveground parts of the tree and does not affect root tissues.

Disease Cycle

The bacteria survive in galls and reproduce inside them all year. During rains, they are extruded to the gall surface and are readily washed about. Infection rarely occurs without moisture. Rain especially favors olive knot, but wet, humid conditions also promote healing of leaf scars. In the relatively dry climate of California where spring rains are often infrequent and last only a few hours, leaf scars remain susceptible for about 9 days. The bacteria may also be carried by pruning shears and other equipment. Insect transmission of olive knot has not been reported in California.

Olive knot bacteria enter and establish infections only in wounded tissue, not in natural openings such as stomata and lenticels. The most commonly colonized wounds are leaf scars; thus, periods of heavy leaf fall present the greatest threat of infection. Infection of cracks in bark caused by freezing injury can cause severe damage, as well. It is often the olive knot infection, not the freeze injury itself, that causes the greater harm.

Temperature is not a limiting factor in disease development. The optimal temperature for pathogen growth is 72° to 75°F (22° to 24°C), with a maximum of 90°F (32°C) and a minimum of 40° to 50°F (4° to 10°C). Most natural infections in California happen during the rainy season between October and June; however, knots develop when the tree is actively growing, in spring and early summer. Therefore, infections established in late fall are not noticeable until spring, but spring infections produce galls within 10 to 14 days.

Control

Olive knot is difficult to control. Prevention is the only reliable strategy. Applications of copper-containing bactericides to protect leaf scars or other injuries minimize disease, but they must often be repeated to protect new wounds as they appear. A minimum of two applications is usually necessary: one in fall before winter rains begin, and another in spring when most leaves are shed. Copper can injure trees in areas of low rainfall.

Careful pruning is helpful, during the dry season, to remove galls that are the sources of bacterial inoculum. The material Gallex kills galls, but application is costly in time and labor, and it is appropriate only for infections on limbs or trunks.

OLIVE LEAF SPOT

Olive leaf spot, peacock spot, and bird's eye spot are all names for the same disease caused by the fungus *Spilocea oleaginea* (Cast.) Hughes. Worldwide, it is known as olive leaf spot; in California, it is usually referred to as peacock spot. The disease occurs in all olive-growing regions of the state. Cultivars vary in susceptibility, but all are subject to infection. Outbreaks are sporadic, and the disease may take several years to become serious enough to cause alarm.

Symptoms

Leaves, fruit, and fruit stems can be attacked, but lesions are observed most often on the upper leaf surfaces. Lesions first appear as small, sooty blotches $^1/_{16}$ to $^1/_4$ inch (2 to 6 mm) across; these later become muddy-green to black spots (color plate 17.2). Some lesions develop a yellow halo and remind people of the eye spot on a peacock's tail feathers; hence, the common names peacock spot and bird's eye spot. Many lesions can occur on a leaf. Most infected leaves fall prematurely, which weakens and kills small wood and eventually reduces productivity. New infections are first seen in late winter and early spring; by summer, most affected leaves have fallen, leaving partially defoliated shoots with healthy leaves on the tree. The disease is usually most severe in the tree's lower part and north side. Old lesions become crusty and whitish and seldom produce many conidia.

Disease Cycle

Not all infected leaves fall, and the fungus survives on those that remain on the tree. These holdover lesions produce very few conidia during summer, and in fall, the lesion margins expand, and a new crop of conidia is produced. In Spain, young leaves were found to be very susceptible in spring. Many young leaves infected in spring remained symptomless until fall when they became the main sources of inoculum through fall and winter.

The conidia are picked up and spread by moving water, which is why the lower parts of trees are most commonly infected. Lateral spread is very limited, and even adjacent trees may exhibit vastly different amounts of disease.

Conidia germinate only in the presence of free moisture, and germination, infection, and mycelial growth proceed readily over a wide range of temperatures, 70°F (21°C) being optimal. Most infections take hold during the coldest part of the California winter season; temperatures above 86°F (30°C) restrict germination of the spores. Infections established in winter take longer to become visible as lesions than do those initiated in spring.

Inoculum buildup appears to play a major role in the severity of olive leaf spot. It may take several years for this disease to cause economic loss.

Control

Olive leaf spot is controlled by a copper-containing fungicide applied once in late fall before winter rains begin. A second application is of questionable value; if used, it must be applied before mid-January. Later treatments, as recommended for olive knot, offer no protection against olive leaf spot in California.

PHYTOPHTHORA ROOT AND CROWN ROT

Root and crown rot of olive trees occurs but is not a common or serious problem in California. The disease is caused by any of several species of *Phytophthora*, a soilborne, fungus-like organism. At present, *P. citricola* and two unidentified species of *Phytophthora* have been isolated from olive trees with symptoms of root and crown rot. *P. dreschleri* is highly virulent in olive in greenhouse tests.

Symptoms

Phytophthora-infected trees exhibit reduced growth, have thin canopies, and eventually die. If the disease progresses rapidly, trees may expire in 1 or 2 years. Root systems of infected trees are discolored, but the mycelium of the *Phytophthora* fungus cannot be seen by the unaided eye. If infection has progressed to the crown, a juncture between healthy, white bark and dark, diseased tissue is apparent.

Disease Cycle

Phytophthora species require free moisture in the soil to produce mobile zoospores, and these need free moisture to invade olive root tissue. Consequently, root and crown rots produced by *Phytophthora* are associated with heavy soils and prolonged periods of high soil moisture (color plate 17.3). The fungi live independently in the soil and survive long periods of dryness as oospores. Each species has its own particular requirements of temperature, moisture, nutrients, and host susceptibility.

Control

Water management is the basis for control of Phytophthora root and crown rot. Cultural practices that avoid prolonged saturation of soil, such as planting on berms, shortening irrigation time, and improving water penetration, lessen root rot. No chemicals are available to control this disease, and resistant olive rootstocks have not been identified.

ARMILLARIA ROOT ROT

Armillaria root rot, also called oak root fungus, is a serious disease of many tree crops but not of olive in California. The pathogen, *Armillaria mellea* (Vahl.) Quel., is a soilborne fungus.

Symptoms

Infected trees have slowly thinning canopies and appear weak. This symptom often develops first on one side of the tree and then progresses over several years to involve the whole tree. The bark and outer wood of the upper roots and crown show discoloration. Distinctive, white, fan-shaped sheets of fungal mycelium, called plaques, are located between bark and wood (color plate 17.4). Rhizomorphs—flat, stringlike structures of white mycelium with a protective, dark, rubbery coating—are sometimes found on the surfaces of infected roots. These, however, are often difficult to find and can be confused with small roots.

DISEASE CYCLE

Armillaria mellea resides in dead wood, such as old tree roots, and can survive for decades if not subjected to desiccation. The rhizomorphs usually grow along the root surface but may also grow away from the root into the soil. A healthy, growing root is invaded by coming in contact with an infected root or by way of root grafts. The slow, circular pattern of spread through the orchard, from tree to tree, reflects this means of dispersal. Trees with large root systems, such as oak, that are infected by *A. mellea* leave many sources of inoculum distributed throughout the soil profile.

Control

Preplant removal of roots remaining after infected plants are discarded, followed by deep fumigation, can slow the progress of the disease, but fungal eradication has not been achieved. No olive rootstocks are resistant, and infected trees usually cannot be cured.

DIPLODIA CANKER

Diplodia canker is found in olive orchards in the Sacramento Valley and probably occurs elsewhere. It does not cause direct harm to the tree, but it can aggravate damage resulting from olive knot disease. Details of the epidemiology of Diplodia canker are unknown, and there is no recommended method for controlling the disease.

Symptoms

The fungus, a species of *Diplodia*, invades olive knot galls and progresses into the twig to form an elliptical canker (color plate 17.5). The canker girdles and kills small shoots or branches, exacerbating the damage caused by olive knot. Diplodia canker is not known to infect wood greater than ½ inch (13 mm) in diameter.

VERTICILLIUM WILT

The most serious economic disease of olive in the southern San Joaquin Valley's olive-growing region is Verticillium wilt. Caused by the soilborne fungus *Verticillium dahliae* Kleb., it kills many young and mature trees each year.

Symptoms

Leaves on one or more branches suddenly collapse and die soon after the first warm weather of summer. Dead leaves and bloom (in the case of early spring death) remain on the tree, indicating the branches that have been infected (color plate 17.6). Internally, there is often little or no discoloration of the vascular tissues that is seen in other *Verticillium*-infected plants. Trees die after repeated attacks over several years. Infections increase with tree age as root systems enlarge and explore larger volumes of contaminated soil.

Disease Cycle

Verticillium dahliae is found in many agricultural soils around the world. It has a wide host range and is a pathogen of many crops grown in California, including cotton, melon, pepper, pistachio, stone fruit, and tomato. It is also found in the lower San Joaquin Valley in association with indigenous, particularly solanaceous, weed species.

The fungus survives for many years in soil as microsclerotia, which are dark, multicelled structures the size of small grains of sand. Microsclerotia are formed inside infected plants and are released into the soil as plant tissues decay. They remain quiescent until a plant root grows within a few millimeters, stimulating them to germinate and penetrate the root. Once inside the plant, the fungus grows into water-conducting elements, the current year's xylem; this disrupts the plant's water transport system and causes wilt and subsequent death. Many microsclerotia must participate in infection to cause disease.

Most *V. dahliae* infections occur in cool, moist soil during late winter and spring before high temperatures prevail. As temperatures rise, infections decrease until soils cool in late summer or early fall, and then another round of infections can occur. During hot summer months, the fungus dies out in the upper parts of the plant and becomes difficult to isolate, although disease is apparent. When cool and moderate spring temperatures persist or summers are mild, Verticillium wilt is extremely common.

Control

No reliable method of control has been developed. Soil fumigation is effective in nurseries but is not reliable for established plantings. Site selection for new plantings should be based on crop history and an assessment of the inoculum level (number of microsclerotia) in the soil. Land previously planted to *Verticillium*-susceptible crops is likely to harbor high counts of microsclerotia. Inoculum levels can be determined by soil analysis, available through private laboratories. Solarization, which entails covering the soil between established trees with plastic sheeting in the affected area for several weeks during the summer to raise soil temperature and destroy fungi, has provided inconsistent control. A resistant rootstock is not available although some tolerance has been reported in the cultivar Ascolano.

18

Weed Management in Olives

CLYDE L. ELMORE

Weed management in an olive orchard should reduce the negative impact of weeds on trees, prevent buildup of hard-to-control weeds, and reduce plant debris around the base of the tree for ease of harvest. Weed management is most critical in young orchards and around the base of all trees. Permanent cover crops or sod cultures between the tree rows may be desirable in an olive orchard, particularly on sloping ground. Cover crop root systems, especially those of annual grasses, can penetrate plow pans and improve water percolation in many soils. Plants can provide a firmer soil surface than cultivated soil for better year-round access in the orchard. They also help reduce soil erosion and soil surface sealing.

If not properly managed, weeds can create problems in an orchard. They can compete with trees for water, nutrients, and sunlight, especially in newly planted orchards and on shallow soils. Young orchards infested with weeds may take longer to come into production. Weeds are less competitive with trees when the orchard is 3 to 4 years old and has become established, but many weeds—especially such perennials as bermudagrass, dallisgrass, field bindweed, and johnsongrass—can still lower orchard productivity. Harvesting is more difficult when weeds have been left in the orchard. In addition, if weeds are not mowed closely before harvest, they may be a hazard to workers.

Weed-infested orchards can enhance the activities of other pests by providing shelter or overwintering sites for insects, rodents, and snakes. When winter vegetation (such as wild oat, mustard, and radish) dries, these weeds can also create a fire hazard. Vegetation around the base of trees provides cover for rodents that may girdle trees.

GROWTH HABITS

Plants found in an olive orchard can be grouped as annuals, biennials, or perennials. Annuals germinate, grow, flower, and produce seeds in one season. The cycle may be completed during several months at any time of the year, depending on the weed species, but most annuals are classified generally as winter or summer annuals. In California's mild climate, certain annuals can behave as biennials or short-lived perennials; an example is cheeseweed (little mallow). Biennials, such as bristly oxtongue, complete the life cycle in two growing seasons, producing vegetative parts in the first season and flowers and seeds in the second. Perennial weeds live 3 years or longer, often dying back in winter and regrowing in spring from underground parts.

MANAGEMENT GUIDELINES

Management differs for each orchard and depends on the weed species, soil type, irrigation method, amount of control desired for the growth of the trees, and the appearance of the orchard. For example, winter annuals are least troublesome because there is usually enough moisture during winter to support both trees and weeds. These can be managed in spring by cultivating, mowing, or using herbicides. However, summer annuals, biennials, and perennials require stricter management. Perennial weeds should be removed outright to reduce competition with trees, especially for water use.

Site Preparation

Weed management starts before the orchard is planted. Control annuals by disking or by applying postemergent herbicides. Control perennials before trees are planted in a new orchard. This reduces competition and avoids potential injury to young trees from herbicides. Control bermudagrass, dallisgrass, and johnsongrass with repeated discing and drying during summer (if the site is not irrigated); seedlings can be controlled after the orchard is planted. Field bindweed can also be reduced using this method, but it is best controlled by irrigating to produce a vigorous plant and then treating with glyphosate or 2,4-D, followed in 10 days by discing and drying the soil. Field bindweed is not completely controlled with any method, but seedlings can be managed with cultivation or contact herbicides.

Management in New Orchards

Weed management is most critical in new plantings. Weeds around young trees compete for nutrients, water, and light. Weedy orchards may take 1 to 2 years longer than those that are weed free to become economically productive.

Some growers prefer to manage weeds without herbicides for the first 1 or 2 years after planting. This usually requires hand-weeding around trees several times during spring and summer, as well as cultivating between tree rows. It may be feasible to use polypropylene or polyester mulches around young trees to reduce annual weeds. It is preferable to cultivate before weeds have gone to seed. Many of these orchards are converted to nontillage after the second year, controlling weeds by mowing or with herbicides. Tillage with disks cuts the tree roots around the base of the trees and can also allow pathogens an entry point at the cut from the disc.

To control weed seedlings, pre-emergence herbicides can be applied after planting trees, either in a square or circle around each tree (at least 4 to 6 feet [1.2 to 1.8 m] across) or as a strip treatment down the tree row. Weeds between the tree rows can be controlled by mowing or discing. Mowing may be required 4 to 8 times during spring and summer, whenever weeds are 6 to 8 inches (18 to 20 cm) tall. Discing is frequently required after each irrigation. It is important to note that discing wet soil can create hardpan, which reduces water penetration.

Management in Established Orchards

In established orchards, there are many options for weed control. These include the methods discussed above for new orchards plus other herbicides that can be safely used on established trees. Options include (1) discing or mowing between rows, with hand-weeding around trees; (2) discing or mowing between rows, with a basal square or circle of herbicide around each tree; (3) strip treatment with herbicides down the tree row (color plate 18.1); and (4) total reliance on herbicides. Total reliance on herbicide treatments can mean either applying pre-emergence materials across the whole orchard floor with follow-up postemergence spot treatments or chemical mowing (using low rates of postemergence herbicides three to four times during the year to suppress vegetation) between rows with strip treatments down the row.

Certain disadvantages are associated with a total reliance on herbicides. No single herbicide controls all annuals; combinations of herbicides, sequential treatments, or pre-emergence plus postemergence combinations are needed to maintain a weed-free orchard. In orchards on slopes, soil erosion can be a problem if soils are bare. In some soils, compaction and development of a thin, silty surface layer, which impedes water infiltration, may become a problem. Light, shallow cultivating or scratching the soil surface may remedy this.

Pre-emergence herbicides do not control established perennials. These weeds spread rapidly in the absence of annuals; this is particularly true of bermudagrass, field bindweed, and nutsedge. Some pre-emergence herbicides control only certain groups of plants, leaving the tolerant ones to propagate. For example, simazine controls broadleaved weeds but not crabgrass or witchgrass, and oryzalin controls grasses but leaves unharmed common groundsel, sow thistle, fleabane, and some other weeds (table 18.1).

USE OF HERBICIDES

Herbicides are used to control specific weeds that are or can become a problem in an orchard. They may be used in strips, around the bases of trees, or on the entire orchard floor. Select herbicides and time their applications with care.

Pre-emergence Herbicides

Pre-emergence herbicides are sprayed on the soil to control germinating weed seeds. They must be moved by water (rainfall or irrigation) into the top 1 to 3 inches (2.5 to 7.6 cm) of soil where weed seeds germinate. One of the herbicides, napropamide, must be incorporated within 1 week by rainfall or irrigation; others can stay on the soil surface and wait for the water to incorporate them. Some cannot be mechanically incorporated without weed control being reduced. Herbicide labels state how soon the herbicide must be incorporated after application or whether incorporation is advisable. Examples of pre-emergence herbicides are diuron (Karmex), isoxaben (Gallery), simazine (Princep), oryzalin (Surflan), oxyfluorfen (Goal), and napropamide (Devrinol).

Oxyfluorfen also has postemergence foliar activity on certain young, established weeds and is more effective against young annual broadleaves, including cheeseweed, than against annual grasses and perennials. None of the other listed pre-emergence herbicides control existing weeds.

Pre-emergence herbicides can control weed emergence from several weeks up to a year, depending on annual rainfall, the solubility of the material, soil

Table 18.1. Weed susceptibility to herbicides

	Preemergence herbicides						Postemergence herbicides					
Weed species	Diuron (Karmex)	Isoxaben* (Gallery)	napropamide (Devrinol)	oryzalin (Surflan)	oxyfluorfen (Goal)	simazine (Princep)	Glyphosate (Roundup)	Clethodim* (Prism)	oxyfluorfen (Goal)	paraquat (Gramozone)	Sethoxydim* (Poast)	Fluazifop* (Fusilade 2000)
Annual grasses												
Annual bluegrass	C	P	C	C	P	C	C	C	N	C	N	N
Barnyardgrass	C	N	C	C	N	P	C	C	N	P	C	C
Crabgrass	C	N	C	C	N	P	C	C	N	C	C	C
Jungle rice	C	N	C	C	N	P	C	C	N	P	C	C
Lovegrass	C	N	C	C	N	P	C	C	N	C	C	C
Sprangletop	C	N	C	C	N	P	C	C	N	P	C	C
Wild barley	C	N	C	C	N	P	C	C	N	C	C	C
Wild oats	P	N	C	P	N	P	C	C	N	C	C	C
Witchgrass	P	N	C	C	N	P	C	C	N	P	C	C
Annual broadleaves												
Brass buttons	C	—	C	P	C	C	C	N	C	C	N	N
Cheeseweed	P	—	P	P	C	P	P	N	C	P	N	N
Chickweed	C	C	C	C	P	C	C	N	P	C	N	N
Cudweed	C	C	C	P	C	C	C	N	P	P	N	N
Filaree	C	C	C	C	C	C	P	N	P	P	N	N
Fleabane	C	P	P	N	P	C	C	N	P	P	N	P
Groundsel	N	C	P	P	C	C	C	N	C	C	N	N
Henbit	C	C	N	C	C	C	C	N	C	C	N	N
Horseweed	C	P	P	N	P	C	C	N	N	N	N	N
Knotweed	C	—	C	C	C	C	C	N	P	P	N	N
Pigweed	C	C	C	C	C	C	C	N	C	C	N	N
Prickly lettuce	C	C	C	P	C	C	C	N	P	C	N	N
Puncturevine	P	—	P	C	C	P	C	N	P	C	N	N
Purslane	C	C	C	C	C	C	C	N	P	C	N	N
Shepherd's purse	C	C	P	P	C	C	C	N	C	C	N	N
Sowthistle	C	C	C	P	C	C	C	N	C	C	N	N
Speedwell	P	—	C	C	C	C	C	N	—	C	N	N
Spurge	C	C	N	P	C	P	C	N	P	C	N	N
Starthistle	C	—	P	N	C	C	C	N	C	C	N	N
Perennial grasses												
Bermudagrass	N	N	N	N	N	N	C	C	N	N	P	P
Johnsongrass	N	N	N	N	N	N	C	C	N	N	P	P
Dallisgrass	N	N	N	N	N	N	C	—	N	N	P	P
Perennial broadleaves												
Blackberry	N	N	N	N	N	N	C	N	N	N	N	N
Curly dock	N	N	N	N	N	N	P	N	N	N	N	N
Dandelion	N	N	N	N	N	N	P	N	N	N	N	N
Field bindweed	N	N	N	P(seed)	N	N	P	N	N	N	N	N
Nutsedge	N	N	P	N	N	N	P	N	N	N	N	N

C = controlled; P = partially controlled; N = not controlled
*Nonbearing trees only

properties, frequency and method of irrigation, weed species, and dosage applied. Prolonged moist conditions around low-volume emitters promote the breakdown and leaching of herbicides. Splitting a pre-emergence treatment into two applications (with the same total dosage) can prolong control, particularly in areas with heavy rainfall, in orchards on sandy soils, in orchards treated in early fall, or in orchards with a heavy growth of summer annuals. Split applications can be made by using one-half to two-thirds the amount of chemical in fall and the remainder the following spring.

A given dosage of pre-emergence herbicide is more phytotoxic to plants in sandy soils or soils low in organic matter than in soils high in clay or organic matter. Herbicides also leach from the surface of sandy soils more readily than from clay soils, which allows weeds to grow above the herbicide. In orchards on sandy soils, split treatments give longer residual control and are safer for trees.

Because pre-emergence herbicides can persist in soil for a few months to 1 year, their use should be discontinued 1 to 2 years before removing an orchard. Where a tree must be replaced, backfill untreated soil around the roots of the new tree to avoid damaging the tree itself.

Postemergence Herbicides

Postemergence (foliar-applied) herbicides are used on young, established weeds or (in the case of glyphosate) on rapidly-growing, flowering perennials.

The two types of postemergence herbicides differ in their mode of action. Contact herbicides kill only the parts of the plant that are actually sprayed; good coverage and wetting are therefore essential. An example is paraquat. A single spray kills susceptible annuals; retreatment is necessary if regenerating perennials are present or if annuals re-establish themselves from seed. A contact herbicide is most effective when applied to seedlings or young weeds, because it is easier to get good coverage and less material is needed.

Translocated herbicides (glyphosate, fluazifop, clethodim, and sethoxydim) do not require thorough coverage because the material is transported from the sprayed part to the rest of the plant, including its roots, growing points, and storage structures. They are, therefore, more effective in killing perennials than are contact herbicides. Because different herbicides work in different ways and on different weeds, herbicide combinations are sometimes desirable, such as oxyfluorfen plus glyphosate for control of a broad spectrum of annual grass and broadleaf weeds.

Herbicides and application rates are chosen according to the weed species present, soil type, irrigation method, and age of trees. No single herbicide registered for olives controls all weed species; in many instances, combinations or sequential applications of different herbicides provide better control than one compound alone. It is crucial to follow all label precautions carefully. Table 18.2 is a list of currently registered herbicides in olive orchards. For an update contact your county's University of California Cooperative Extension Farm Advisor, Pest Control Advisor, or County Agricultural Commissioner.

COVER CROPS

In some orchards, cover crops are planted rather than using resident (weed) vegetation as a cover crop. These cover crops can be winter annual, fall-seeded, cereal crops, such as wheat, oat, cereal rye, and barley, or winter annual Blando bromegrass, Zorro fescue, and subterranean clovers. These are seeded into a prepared seedbed during late September through mid-November as winter cover. The latter plants to not have to be seeded annually if mowed in January or early February and then allowed to regrow and seed in April and May. Mowing after the seeds mature ensures seeds for the next season. These cover crops should be combined with a strip treatment down the tree row so that the plants do not grow around tree trunks. For more information on cover crops, consult *Covercrops for California Agriculture* (Oakland: University of California Division of Agriculture and Natural Resources, Publication 21471).

Table 18.2. Herbicides registered for use in olives

Herbicide	Pre-emergence	Postemergence	Tree age*
diuron	x		bearing*
napropamide	x		nonbearing and bearing
oryzalin	x		nonbearing and bearing
oxyfluorfen	x	x	nonbearing and bearing
simazine	x		bearing*
glyphosate		x	bearing*
paraquat		x	nonbearing and bearing
clethodim		x	nonbearing
fluazifop		x	nonbearing
isoxaben	x		nonbearing
sethoxydim		x	nonbearing

* Tree age and size restrictions may apply; check label for specifics.

MONITORING

Monitoring to determine which weed species are present is essential for selecting a weed management program, especially for selecting the proper herbicides. It should be done three times a year: in November, February, and May.

In November, after the first rains have begun, look for winter annual seedlings in the tree row to determine whether a pre-emergence treatment was adequate. Also, check the ground cover for perennial seedlings. In February, the full spectrum of winter weeds should be present. If a few species were not controlled, note them for possible changes in next season's treatment. This happens when the pre-emergence herbicides used in the tree row are ineffective against some weeds in the orchard. If weed growth is heavy, consider a postemergence treatment. By May or June, summer annuals have germinated. Monitoring at this time reveals whether a pre-emergence treatment was effective against summer annuals and what species of perennials are present.

When tillage is the main method of weed control, monitoring before tilling allows the grower to treat perennials with the correct translocated herbicide so that the equipment will not spread the stems or underground parts of the plant.

Records are essential in weed management. Weed survey information collected over several years is valuable in identifying changes in weed populations and in planning weed control programs. A sample format for recording weed data is given in figure 18.1. Perennials deserve special attention because they are more difficult to control; it is useful to sketch a map of the orchard and mark where they occur. These records should be part of the permanent orchard history.

Weed records can be stored on computer using a form similar to figure 18.1 to record the species found in individual orchards, the herbicides used, and whether or not control was achieved. Species can also be categorized by year or, for perennials, by location in the orchard. Knowing which weeds are present and their susceptibility to registered herbicides allows the grower to select effective herbicides for the following season. A scale from 1 to 5 can indicate the level of infestation: 1 = very few weeds; 2 = light infestation; 3 = moderate infestation; 4 = heavy infestation; 5 = very heavy infestation. Weed species in treated and untreated areas, as in strip weed control, should be recorded separately.

ORCHARD LOCATION _____   CONTROL METHODS _____

CONTROL DATES _____

COMMENTS _____

	NOV _____		FEB _____		MAY _____	
	% of total weeds		% of total weeds		% of total weeds	
ANNUAL GRASSES	treated	untreated	treated	untreated	treated	untreated
annual bluegrass						
barnyardgrass						
crabgrass						
sprangletop						
wild barley						
wild oat						
_____						
_____						
_____						

ANNUAL BROADLEAVES

	treated	untreated	treated	untreated	treated	untreated
cheeseweed (mallow)						
clovers						
groundsel						
filaree						
fiddleneck						
knotweed						
lambsquarters						
mustards						
pigweeds						
puncturevine						
purslane						
_____						
_____						
_____						
_____						
_____						

PERENNIALS

	treated	untreated	treated	untreated	treated	untreated
bermudagrass						
dallisgrass						
johnsongrass						
curly dock						
field bindweed						
nutsedge						
_____						
_____						

Figure 18.1. Sample form for recording weed species.

19

Spray Application Principles and Techniques for Olives

JOHN E. DIBBLE

Olive trees grow differently than deciduous fruit trees. The result is a heavy, dense foliage, mostly on the periphery of the tree. This natural density resists spray penetration and may cause poor coverage within the tree canopy and top center. Essential to good spray coverage, then, is a pruning program that opens up the tree. A pest control program that uses spray chemicals as well as beneficial insects is far more likely to be successful when olive trees have been periodically pruned. There are also other benefits of pruning such as increasing light inside the tree (which discourages scale infestations) and increased production.

For properly pruned trees, the prerequisites for successful high-volume or low-volume spray coverage are the same: evaluation of tree size and spacing, calibration of equipment, and proper calculation of the materials needed. When these prerequisites are met, the pesticide can be applied satisfactorily by either method so that it effectively hits the target pest. Chemical failure or insect resistance is too often blamed when the problem is really poor coverage.

HIGH- VERSUS LOW-VOLUME APPLICATION

High-volume (dilute) sprays are defined as those that deliver 350 to 800 gallons per acre (gpa) (3,276 to 7,488 L/ha) of solution. Spray applications at these volumes usually result in spray runoff. Low-volume (concentrate) applications apply 20 to 100 gallons per acre (187 to 936 L/ha) of spray solution and no runoff or drip usually occurs. Spray rates as low as 15 gallons per acre (140 L/ha) (called extra-low-volume or high-concentrate sprays resulting in a mist) and mid-volume sprays (150 to 300 gpa [1,404 to 2,808 L/ha]) that result in slight drip have also given satisfactory results in other fruit tree crops.

California test studies and grower evaluations show that coverage and control in most tree crops are reduced when sprayer speeds exceed 2.5 miles per hour (4.2 km/hr) for dilute spray and 2 miles per hour (3.2 km/hr)

for concentrate. Failures in complete tree coverage are most easily seen when comparing effectiveness of scale control on the inside and tops of the tree. To be effective, concentrate spraying is necessarily more exacting in its requirements than dilute. High air velocity, a narrow range in small droplet size, and proper travel speed are essential for good coverage and control when using concentrate sprays. In other words, the sprayer must move slowly enough (remain adjacent to the tree long enough) to penetrate the overall tree canopy.

Coverage

Spray coverage from a dilute application usually shows a "washy" spray pattern that completely covers surfaces but does not necessarily provide better pest control than the "stippled" pattern from a concentrate application, the latter being uniformly deposited for satisfactory control. The type of spray deposit in each case is a result of the spraying techniques. The total number of gallons of spray per acre is not necessarily the critical factor in obtaining proper spray coverage and pest control. Careful evaluations of most tree crops show that concentrate applications can give coverage equal to dilute; furthermore, fungicides and various chemical plant additives can also be satisfactorily applied as concentrates.

In the case of hard-to-control scale insects, there are frequently more failures on fruit and nut trees with dilute than with low-volume treatments. The greater volume of spray emerging from the dilute sprayer often gives the operator a false sense of satisfactory coverage. However, this high volume of spray does not compensate for a too fast speed of travel, poor nozzling, or a badly directed air pattern. Nozzle wear, in particular, occurs rapidly with the use of wettable powders and takes place regularly in both concentrate and dilute sprayers. This factor may be ignored more often by operators of dilute sprayers simply because they have a large number of nozzles, and checking nozzle wear is time consuming. Nozzle wear affects droplet sizes and gallons-per-minute discharge; it is often mistakenly compensated for by increasing travel speed, which only compounds the problem.

Correct Nozzling

All sprayer applications, from dilute to high concentrate, overspray the bottom half of the tree. With improperly calibrated sprayers, such spray chemical deposits in the bottom of the tree can be four to five times greater than in the top half. This overspraying is due in part to the height and location of the sprayer in relation to the tree's height and configuration. The imbalance can be largely corrected through proper nozzling. This is accomplished by adjusting the gallons per minute discharge of the spray, as well as the nozzle placement, so that approximately two-thirds of the spray is emitted from the top half of the nozzle manifold. This adjustment can be made on most sprayers by putting large nozzle tips at 1, 2, 10, and 11 o'clock on the spray manifold, medium tips at 3, 4, 8, and 9 o'clock, and small tips at 5, 7, and 12 o'clock (fig. 19.1). Air discharge can also aid coverage if it is adjusted to approximately the same configuration.

Adjustment of air discharge is done quite easily if the sprayer has adjustable air vanes in the fan housing. If not, reconfiguration of the air discharge opening may be necessary by installing air vanes, narrowing or widening the air discharge outlet, or moving nozzles and plumbing out of the air stream area. Air speed measured at the fan housing discharge (one method of measurement is done by using a rebuilt airplane air speed gauge) can give air velocity differences or deficiencies from the top to bottom of the air discharge outlet in miles per hour. Air volume and velocity is very difficult to control and measure once it leaves the sprayer. Therefore, it is best to evaluate its performance by the use of a food dye added to the spray, plus target cards placed high and low inside, as well as on the periphery of, the tree. Water sensitive paper can also be used without using a dye. Obviously, since air is the

vector for the spray it plays a very important role in the proper distribution of a pesticide.

In dilute spraying, runoff and dripping from branch to branch helps to counteract somewhat the effects of improper adjustment, but for maximum coverage, correct nozzle calibration is necessary. Although the overspraying that occurs in dilute applications protects the careless operator to some degree, in low-volume spraying there is no such allowance. It is, therefore, good practice for all sprayer operators to ensure proper nozzling, the correct speed of travel, accurate calculation of the amount of spray needed per acre, and careful measurement of insecticides.

TYPES OF EQUIPMENT

Dilute (High-Volume) Spraying

The general configuration and basic function of dilute air-carrier sprayers are well known to growers. These sprayers are available in many styles and sizes, but they all perform in basically the same way.

This type of spray application has been used by olive growers for many years. Although the advent of the air-carrier dilute sprayer greatly reduced problems caused by the old high-pressure handgun sprayers, it has not solved all coverage problems. Both systems use large volumes of water. The handgun's poor coverage resulted mostly from human fatigue, while poor coverage with the air-carrier sprayer often results from improper nozzling and travel speed.

Drawbacks of the high-volume system include the frequent need to refill with water and handle the pesticide (usually 1 to 2 times/acre [3 to 5 times/ha]). Many such sprayers also have a large number of nozzles, increasing the potential for plugging and wear. Usually larger than low-volume concentrate sprayers, dilute units can also be more awkward to handle, and they may create greater soil compaction and maintenance problems. On the plus side, in applying large volumes of water, dilute sprayers produce large droplets that help counteract the effects of wind. The greater volume of water does not necessarily mean, however, that spray reaches higher or deeper into the foliage.

Concentrate (Low-Volume) Spraying

Concentrate spray is commonly applied using older dilute sprayers with a modified pump pressure and spray manifold. This adaptation is not always successful. Newer models of dilute sprayers are designed to convert easily for concentrate spraying. These can be

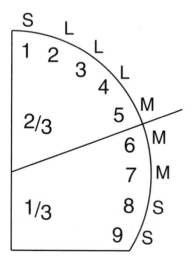

Figure 19.1. Most desirable general division of nozzle tips.

adjusted down to the desired 100-pound spray pressure at the manifold, have air velocity capabilities of 100 to 160 miles per hour (161 to 257 km/hr), and feature a second or multipurpose manifold that accommodates the smaller, hollow-cone, disk-type nozzles used for concentrate applications.

A third group of low-volume sprayers is specifically designed for concentrate applications. Most use the same kind of nozzles, pressure, and air velocity rate used to adapt dilute sprayers. Others use low-pressure systems to move the spray liquid to special nozzles where a high-velocity (160 to 220 mph [257 to 354 kmh]) air discharge shears the spray liquid into small droplets. In all cases, a narrow range of small droplet sizes is desired for concentrate spraying. This group of sprayers cannot usually deliver spray rates above the concentrate or semiconcentrate range.

Most concentrate spray applications made commercially are in the 25- to 100-gallons-per-acre (gpa) range. Interest in the high-concentrate range of 5 to 25 gpa is rising, as it requires the fewest fill trips and stops, but it may never enjoy wide use in olive groves, given the form and density of the trees. Although not used extensively on olives, low volume sprays are a common practice in California and the Pacific Northwest deciduous tree fruit areas. The same would be true, but to a lessor degree, of the possible pesticide reduction per acre with concentrate applications.

Sprayer Selection

Growers should always check the performance of any sprayer system depending on their particular needs and request a demonstration in their orchard. Depending on the severity of pest problems, growers may want a larger unit with a bigger fan or greater tractor horsepower (to operate a power take-off sprayer). This would allow the equipment to direct greater amounts of air into particularly dense or tall trees, as well as into widely spaced rows. After affordability, growers should also consider the convenience and complexity of the equipment's operation and maintenance.

Concentrate Advantages

Because low-volume spraying is increasingly popular in nondeciduous tree crops, the advantages of concentrate spraying are discussed here even though its use is limited in olive groves at this time. Low-volume applications can permit the use of equipment that is smaller, initially less costly, and often more easily and cheaply maintained than the equipment used for dilute applications. (Power take off [PTO] units are even more economical than engine-powered units.)

Savings in time per spray operation are notable with the low-volume method: there is less downtime because there are fewer refills. Using a 400-gallon (1,514-L), low-volume sprayer calibrated for 40 gallons per acre (374 L/ha), 10 acres (4 ha) can be sprayed between fills. In a 30-foot (9.1-m) row planting at a travel speed of 1.8 miles per hour (2.9 km/h), coverage takes a little over 9 minutes per acre (22 min/ha) (6.5 acres per hour [2.6 ha/h]), resulting in approximately 1.5 hours of continuous spraying for each 10 acres (4 ha).

Low-volume spraying on fruit trees can be as effective as dilute while using less chemical per acre—up to 25 to 30 percent less. This reduction, though not always advisable, is possible primarily because of the efficiency of the technique, and there is hardly any of the spray runoff from the tree that occurs in dilute applications. Deposition of the numerous small and relatively uniform droplets from low-volume applications is highly efficient and can frequently equal that of dilute applications, even at the lower rate.

In addition, the total spray water used per acre with low-volume applications is reduced by 75 to 90 percent from that used in dilute spraying. Transporting less water weight through the orchard means reduced soil compaction, even more desirable when soil is wet.

In summary, low-volume sprays can be as effective as high-volume sprays in reducing pest populations to an acceptable level, providing the olive trees are opened up by pruning. Scale control, of particular concern to olive growers, poses no greater problem than that of other pests whose control requires complete and uniform spray coverage. The number of gallons of spray per acre does not appear to be a major factor for effective coverage and control.

DRIFT PROBLEMS

The drift of minute chemical droplets can be hazardous to people, animals, and wildlife and can contaminate adjacent crops. Pesticides can be carried by air drift or water runoff, and drift cannot be entirely eliminated from ground applications. A certain number of tiny droplets, produced by all types of nozzles and application techniques, tend to become airborne and drift downwind. As a spray application rate comes down in spray gallonage per acre, it must come down in droplet size to produce the droplet surface area required for good coverage. Potentially, then, the low-volume technique poses a greater drift hazard due to its lighter spray. Although a great many of these very small droplets are subject to drift, it has been generally reported to amount to no more than 2 to 3 percent of

Table 19.1. Example for nozzle chart (showing gallons per minute at 150 psi)

Nozzle size (psi)	50	100	150	200	250
2			1.0		
3			1.2		
5			1.9		
8			2.1		
10			2.5		
15			3.0		
25			3.5		

Table 19.2. Orchard sprayer calibration chart for sprayer traveling at 2 miles per hour (mph)

Gallons per minute (gpm) discharge necessary from each side of sprayer for 50 to 600 gallons per acre (gpa) at different row spacings

	Row spacing (ft)						
gpa	18	20	22	24	28	30	45
50	1.8	2.0	2.2	2.4	2.8	3.0	4.5
100	3.6	4.0	4.4	4.8	5.6	6.0	9.0
150	5.4	6.0	6.6	7.2	8.4	9.0	13.5
200	7.2	8.0	8.8	9.6	11.2	12.0	18.0
250	9.0	10.0	11.0	12.0	14.0	15.0	22.5
300	10.8	12.0	13.2	14.4	16.8	18.0	27.0
350	12.6	14.0	15.4	16.8	19.6	21.0	31.5
400	14.4	16.0	17.6	19.2	22.4	24.0	36.0
450	16.2	18.0	19.8	21.6	25.2	27.0	40.5
500	18.0	20.0	22.0	24.0	28.0	30.0	45.0
550	19.8	22.0	24.2	26.4	30.8	33.0	49.5
600	21.6	24.0	26.4	28.8	33.6	36.0	54.0

Formulas Useful for Calibrating Spray Applications in Orchards

gallons per minute (gpm) (for one side of sprayer) $= \dfrac{gpa \times mph \times \text{row spacing (ft)}}{1{,}000}$

gallons per acre (gpa) $= \dfrac{\text{gpm (for 1 side)} \times 1{,}000}{\text{row spacing (ft)} \times mph}$

miles per hour (mph) $= \dfrac{\text{gpm (for 1 side)} \times 1{,}000}{gpa \times \text{row spacing (ft)}}$

acres per hour $= \dfrac{12 \times mph \times \text{row spacing (ft)}}{100}$

speed of travel (expressed as tree spaces passed per minute) $= \dfrac{\text{mph (desired)} \times 88}{\text{tree spacing (ft)}}$

number of trees per acre $= \dfrac{43{,}560 \text{ (square feet per acre)}}{\text{row spacing} \times \text{tree spacing}}$

EXAMPLE: $\dfrac{43{,}560}{30 \times 30} = 48$ trees per acre

the total volume of spray. Also, because of the mechanical design of most low-volume sprayers, air volume (the amount of air) is low, so its force does not usually extend much past tree height, which would expose spray droplets to potential drift. Nevertheless, high-volume spray applications tend to cast spray far above tree height, where smaller droplets are susceptible to drift.

Most damage by pesticide drift is done within the specific farm area of application. However, more extensive damage can result from the transport of chemicals through direct water contact, from soil-water runoff from treated fields, and from high-level airborne drift. Pesticide drift can also produce excessive residues on nearby crops, rendering them unfit for the retail market or for animal fodder. Confining chemicals to their intended field target and reducing losses from chemical drift onto nontarget areas are objectives that must be met more effectively than ever if agriculture is to continue using many pesticide chemicals.

SAFETY

The dangers and precautions involved in spraying are similar for all application techniques. Operators should keep in mind that the chemical is most concentrated in the container and that the material may still be highly concentrated in the tank. Guided by label and law, they must wear protective clothing, depending on the compound used—including a spray-protecting hat (if required), footwear, gloves, and an approved respirator—during and between spray runs, and especially when loading, for their greatest protection.

Low-volume spraying is frequently applied using less toxicant per acre than high-volume spraying, a factor in its favor. The operator also handles the actual pesticide or containers only once every 5 to 10 acres (depending on gallons per acre and tank capacity) rather than usually every acre, as with high-volume sprays. Furthermore, the operator is not subjected to drenching by the spray, nor is the cover crop or ground saturated with runoff.

SPRAYER CALIBRATION

The principles involved in the proper calibration of an air-carrier orchard sprayer are relatively simple and have already been described generally. Following are some formulas the sprayer operator will find useful when calibrating, as well as detailed, step-by-step procedures, and an example. Refer to tables 19.1, 19.2, and 19.3 as work through the example. Figures 19.1 and 19.2 provide a visual nozzle setup, and figure 19.3 is a general sprayer calibration worksheet to be used in the field.

Table 19.3. Orchard sprayer calibration charts for three different spray rates per acre

Gallons per minute discharge necessary from each side of sprayer at different speeds and planting distances

mph	18	20	22	24	28	30	45
			Row spacing (ft)				
			100 gpa				
1.00	1.80	2.00	2.20	2.40	2.80	3.00	4.50
1.25	2.30	2.50	2.75	3.00	3.50	3.75	5.63
1.50	2.80	3.00	3.30	3.60	4.20	4.50	6.75
1.75	3.15	3.50	3.85	4.20	4.90	5.25	7.88
2.00	3.60	4.00	4.40	4.80	5.60	6.00	9.00
			400 gpa				
1.00	7.2	8.0	8.8	9.6	11.2	12.0	18.0
1.25	9.0	10.0	11.0	12.0	14.0	15.0	22.5
1.50	10.8	12.0	13.2	14.4	16.0	18.0	27.0
1.75	12.6	14.0	15.4	16.8	19.6	21.0	31.5
2.00	14.4	16.0	17.6	19.2	22.4	24.0	36.0
2.25	16.2	18.0	19.8	21.6	25.2	27.0	40.5
2.50	18.0	20.0	22.0	24.0	28.0	30.0	45.0
			500 gpa				
1.00	9.00	10.00	11.00	12.00	14.00	15.00	22.50
1.25	11.25	12.50	13.75	15.00	17.50	18.75	28.13
1.50	13.50	15.00	16.50	18.00	21.00	22.50	33.80
1.75	15.75	17.50	19.25	21.00	24.50	26.25	39.38
2.00	18.00	20.00	22.00	24.00	28.00	30.00	45.00
2.25	20.25	22.50	24.75	27.00	31.50	33.75	50.63
2.50	22.50	25.00	27.50	30.00	35.00	37.50	56.2

Calibration Procedures for Orchard Air-Carrier Sprayers

Information

Known:
1. gpa (gallons per acre)
2. psi (sprayer pressure at manifold)
3. mph (miles per hour)
4. number of nozzles/side
5. row spacing

Unknown:
1. gpm needed
2. nozzle sizes and placement
3. simple measurement for speed

Example

Known:
1. gpa = 400
2. psi = 150
3. mph = 2
4. number of nozzles/side = 9
5. row spacing = 30 × 30 ft

Unknown:
1. gpm/side = $\dfrac{\text{gpa} \times \text{mph} \times \text{row spacing}}{1{,}000}$

$= \dfrac{400 \times 2 \times 30}{1{,}000} = \dfrac{24{,}000}{1{,}000}$

= 24 gpm/side

2. nozzle sizes and placement

If there are 9 nozzles per side and 24 gpm are needed,

24 ÷ 9 = 2.7 gpm/nozzle

However, the best arrangement is to obtain ⅔ gpm from the top half of the manifold and ⅓ from the bottom half; therefore, different size nozzles should be used (fig. 19.1). In the example here, medium-size nozzle tips that discharge approximately 2.7 gpm are selected along with smaller and larger ones that will discharge a total of 24 gpm (fig. 19.2). Use the correct nozzle chart for your sprayer nozzles—select nozzles that best fit the needed smaller and larger category as per the example chart (table 19.1). After setting up the same nozzle arrangement on both sides of the sprayer, the calibration is complete. Sprayer calibration charts show the gallons per minute discharge necessary for different row spacings traveling at 2 miles per hour and spray rates at various travel speeds (tables 19.2 and 19.3).

3. speed of travel (using tree spaces as measuring units and desiring 2 mph)

1 mph = 88 ft/min

$\text{spaces/min} = \dfrac{2 \text{ mph} \times 88 \text{ ft/min}}{30 \text{ ft tree spacing}}$

$= 176 = 5.9$ trees passed per minute at 2 mph

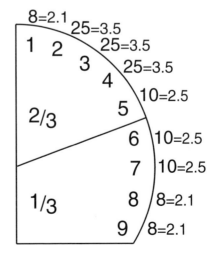

Figure 19.2. Specific desirable arrangement of nozzle tips to discharge total of 24 gpm.

FILL IN (based on your spray operation)
    A. Tree row spacing (in feet):
    B. Gallons of spray desired per acre (gpa):
    C. Speed of travel selected in orchard (mph):

CALCULATE (using orchard sprayer calibration chart if speed of travel is 2 mph; otherwise,
        using following formula)
    A. Gallons per minute (gpm) necessary per sprayer side

$$\text{gpm} = \frac{\text{gpa} \times \text{mph} \times \text{tree row spacing}}{\times 1{,}000} = \underline{\hspace{4cm}}$$

    B. ⅔ of gpm (for top half of manifold) = _____
    C. ⅓ of gpm (for bottom half of manifold) = _____

CHECK (with a pressure gauge)

    Your sprayer pressure at the manifold = _____

SELECT (your proper nozzling)
    A. Obtain a nozzle chart for your type of nozzle tips (orifice sizes). Refer to the column indicating the same pressure (psi) at which your sprayer operates. Working with only one side of your sprayer, first select tips for the top half of the manifold that total approximately ⅔ of the gpm discharge for one side. The balance (⅓) of gpm discharge should come from the nozzles on the bottom half of the manifold. Preferably these nozzle tips should not all be the same size but rather arranged so that those in the 2, 3, and 4 position are the largest; those in the 5, 6, and 7 position are the medium size; and those in the 1, 8, and 9 position are the smallest. This is done to conform to the trees' height and width, the distance the spray must travel, and the density it must penetrate. If your sprayer has more or fewer nozzles than the nine in the example, adjust the gpm per nozzle accordingly, but maintain the ⅔ and ⅓ relationship. In each case, the total gpm discharge of all nozzles should equal the amount calculated.

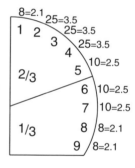

    B. Now set up the same nozzle arrangement on the other side of your sprayer.

CALCULATE (the speed of travel)
    A. Check your desired speed in the orchard by traveling the required number of spaces in one minute.

$$\text{Tree spaces/min} = \frac{\text{mph} \times 1\,88}{\text{tree spacing (ft)}} = \underline{\hspace{3cm}}$$

VERIFY (speed against other measures)
    A. Spray out an acre or part of an acre of trees with plain water to check the pattern as well as the total gallons per acre (gpa) output. If the spray pattern needs to be adjusted based on your observed penetration and deposit, rearrange the nozzles accordingly. For example, the larger nozzles may need to be moved up or down on the manifold to better conform to tall or to low, bushy trees.

Figure 19.3. Orchard sprayer calibration worksheet.

20

The Olive Harvest

LOUISE FERGUSON, KAREN KLONSKY, AND GEORGE C. MARTIN

All crops are harvested when they are judged to be horticulturally mature, a stage of development that meets an agreed-upon standard established in the marketplace. For the California processed olive fruit, horticultural maturity occurs about 4 months before physiological maturity. This early harvest allows olive fruit to be processed according to the California black-ripe or green-ripe methods to achieve defined industry standards.

Grower payment for processed olives is based on total tonnage and individual olive fruit size composition after cullage (see chapter 21: Grading Canning Olives); however, size and weight have not been directly used by the olive industry to determine the timing of harvest. When to pick is generally determined by visual and physical factors that have been demonstrated to correlate with maximum tonnage and optimal fruit size. An olive is considered mature if it exudes a characteristic white juice when squeezed (color plate 20.1). The color range considered ideal for picking extends from an even pale green with a minimum of whitish spots (lenticels) through a straw color. A red blush is permissible on Manzanillo, Mission, and Sevillano olives early in the season, but color is considered undesirable late in the season (color plates 20.2, 20.3, 20.4, 20.5, and 20.6).

WHEN TO HARVEST

Olive harvests have customarily begun in mid-September, peaked in mid-October, and finished in mid-November. The primary reason for delaying harvest early in the season is to accrue value through weight and size. The primary reason for accelerating harvest late in the season is to decrease losses due to overripeness, drying wind, and cold damage. Clearly, the traditional method of determining when to harvest olives has been inexact. Generally it has resulted in a too-early rather than too-late harvest. Overripe fruit is usually more obvious to the grower because of fruit appearance and value lost.

From their analysis of the components of value in an olive harvest, University of California researchers have generated a method for determining optimal crop value. The components of crop value are shown for 3 years of crops in figure 20.1: the upper portion of each graph shows the crop by size category on each harvest date, and the lower portion depicts the net value of the crop and its total weight on each harvest date. The two components of olive crop value are the weight and size of the crop; however, the weight of the total crop changes little through the harvest season. Therefore, weight has essentially no relationship to crop value. Also, as figure 20.2 demonstrates, individual olives, within their size classification, do not change weight significantly over the harvest season. This is constant despite tree crop load. Olive sizes, however, particularly the total percentage in the standard canning categories of medium, large, and extra large, are closely related to the crop's net value. In all instances shown, crop value is greatest when these three sizes reach their maximum total cumulative percentage.

The second half of the research, determining when this optimal crop value occurs, produced the following procedure for determining when to harvest:

1. Beginning in mid-September, take daily samples from three olive trees (100 randomly selected olives from each tree), in each representative area of the orchard.

2. Determine the total percentage of standard medium, large, and extra-large olives present in the samples.

3. When 50 percent of the olives are within those categories, and the percentage is increasing at the rate of 3 to 5 percent per week, picking should begin within 1 week and last no longer than 2 weeks.

A 14-day period in mid-October has been identified as the period when olive fruit quality and yield combine for greatest profit. Harvest before or after this period results in substantial losses in income (fig. 20.3).

Growers eager to take advantage of this information have been frustrated by the difficulty in completing a

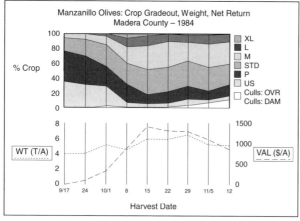

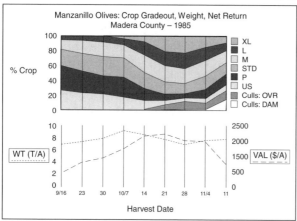

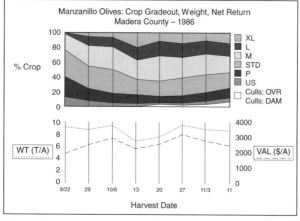

Figure 20.1. The components of olive crop value: (top half) percent of the crop by fruit size and (bottom half) the relationship of weight (ton/acre) to value ($/acre) through the harvest season.

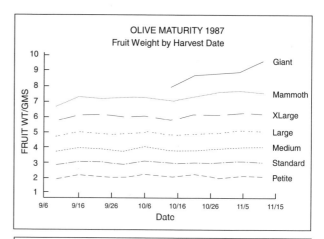

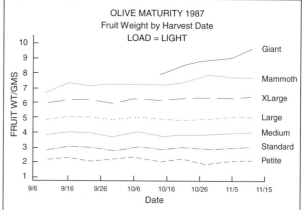

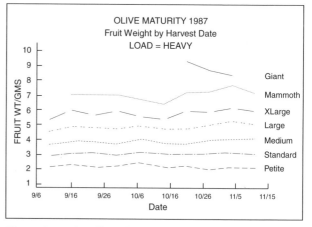

Figure 20.2. The effect of harvest date on individual olive fruit weight within size grades on trees with moderate, light, and heavy crops.

harvest in a 14-day period. The best laborers can harvest 1,000 pounds (454 kg) of olives per day. Thrifty orchards average about 3 tons per acre (6.8 metric t/ha) of fruit; thus, in this example 12 worker-days are required to harvest an acre. In California, the defined economic unit is an orchard whose size can support and be managed by a family of four. For olive, this is

about 100 acres (40.5 ha). An orchard that size would require 25 days for 48 workers to harvest. These estimates mean that harvest for the 100-acre (40.5-ha) orchard would exceed the period for maximum return by at least 11 days. Many growers are able to complete harvest in about 21 days, but they still lose much crop value.

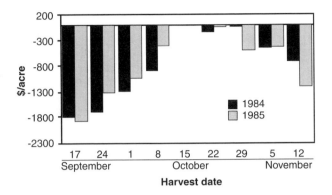

Figure 20.3. Percent of total crop income lost per acre when harvest occurs before and after the optimal time. Maximum crop value is shown for October 15. (Adapted from Sibbett et al. 1986.)

HAND HARVEST

Hand harvesting is the more expensive of the harvest options (table 20.1) due to labor costs. In the first few years after planting, olives are harvested by hand from the ground; in time, ladders must be used. In both cases the method of olive removal is the same. The fruit are removed by sliding the cupped, gloved hand down the shoot in a milking action. The shoot is placed so that fruit fall into the picking bag. When the bag is full, the fruit are dumped into standard orchard bins that hold 1,000 pounds (454 kg). This process can result in considerable fruit and tree damage. Fruit damage occurs from using a rough technique, dropping fruit from great distances, and including debris with the fruit. Tree damage results from leaves being torn off with the fruit. At each leaf scar, olive knot bacteria can enter.

Ladder use presents another problem for hand harvesting (fig. 20.4). Pickers are less likely to harvest fruit from upper limbs that extend beyond 14 feet (4.3 m). In addition, the increasing likelihood of laborers falling from ladders makes 14 feet (4.3 m) the maximum safe harvesting height. Ladder maintenance is recommended, and weakened ladders should be discarded.

Table 20.1. Example of hand harvest costs

Tons per acre	Costs per ton ($)	Costs per acre ($)
<1.5	$275	$413
1.5	225	338
2.0	225	450
2.5	200	500
3.0	200	600
3.5	200	700
4.0	175	700
5.0	175	875

Figure 20.4. Traditional hand harvest on large trees.

Growers should assume that laborers do not know how to use a ladder safely. Thirty minutes of safety instruction with each new crew is time well spent in terms of decreasing injuries to the work force.

The lack of available labor for handpicking in the United States makes it less likely that olive growers can achieve optimal harvest by hand. Research in California shows that mechanical devices that position workers in the orchard (such as on picking platforms) do not increase hand harvest rates. These devices improve the picking speed of only the slowest workers; the best workers may be slowed down because the picking aid moves at the rate of the slowest picker. Unless picking crews are well matched, motivated workers work better without the harvest aid.

MECHANICAL HARVEST

There is great interest in mechanical harvesting among olive growers in the United States. Chief among the pre-

Figure 20.5. Tree shaker used to harvest olives from large Mission trees.

dictable reasons are the high cost and the scarcity of labor. To avoid both of these problems, a few olive growers have been motivated to convert to mechanical harvesting. Thus far, two methods of mechanical harvesting have been investigated: trunk shaking and canopy-contact harvesting. Development of the former has been largely abandoned. Development of the canopy-contact harvester started in 1996 and is ongoing.

Trunk-Shaking Mechanical Harvesters

Trunk shakers were the first mechanical harvesters used commercially in California. The goal is to conduct vibration from where the machine grips the tree to the point of fruit attachment (fig. 20.5). The amount of energy reaching the fruit is reduced by such factors as moisture in the wood, internal and external damping forces, bark characteristics, and the natural frequency of the fruit and stem. The shaking energy delivered to the tree is a function of stroke (length) and frequency (motions per unit of time). Researchers have established an ideal stroke-frequency index for many crops, including olive. If the parameters they describe are applied, 60 to 80 percent of the olives can be shaken

from the tree with minimal tree and fruit damage. However, the 20 to 40 percent remaining on the tree after shaking means lost income for 2 years. There is reduced income for the current year and reduced flowering and fruiting for the following year due to the effects on alternate bearing. It has not proven economically feasible to have pickers glean after shake harvesting as the remaining olives are spread throughout the tree. For these reasons trunk shake harvest has not been widely adopted in California.

Pruning for Trunk Shaking Harvesters. In their natural growth habit, olive trees extend, in a weeping fashion, cascades of long, pendulous limbs that bear fruit at their extremities. For mechanical harvest, lower branches must be removed to make space for attaching the shaker clamps. Without a clear view of the trunk or scaffold limb, the bark is damaged when the clamp is attached or detached. In the main tree structure, scaffold limbs should be at an angle of 45° or less (that is, more upright) as acute-angled limbs transmit energy more efficiently than do more horizontally oriented limbs. Crossover limbs absorb energy and must be removed. Dead limbs and those with overly dense twigs should be thinned out. For details on pruning, see chapter 9: Pruning Mature Bearing Olive Trees.

Canopy-Contact Mechanical Harvesters

Evaluation of canopy-contact mechanical harvesters began in 1996. This type of mechanical harvester uses direct canopy contact, similar to grape, blueberry, and coffee harvesters, to remove the olives. It consists of a single or multiple, vertically-mounted, cylindrical heads with radiating rods approximately 3.5 feet (1.1 m) in length. The head is mounted on a mobile unit above a catch frame (figs. 20.6 and 20.7). As the harvester moves forward at .5 to 1 miles per hour (.8 to 1.6 km/h), the radiating rods engage the tree branches and passively rotate the head. A rotating counter weight at the top of the head produces a 12-inch (30.4-cm) horizontal whipping motion in the distal tip of the radiating rods. It is this horizontal whip of the rods perpendicular to and against the hanging olive branches that removes the olives. Initial trials established that harvester efficiency is directly dependent on fruit accessibility. Four years of field trials have established that, if the radiating rods contact the bearing canopy, the harvester can remove 90 percent of the fruit. Fruit on the top of the tree, on the rounded leading and trailing edges of the canopy, and in the tree skirt below 3 feet (.9 m) is the most difficult to remove.

Pruning for Canopy-Contact Harvesters. Thus far hedgerowed or pyramidal trees appear to be the best shape for the canopy-contact harvester. Trees that can present maximum bearing surface to the harvester with minimal harvester head manipulation and maximum harvester speed are best for this type of harvester. Theoretically, it appears the ideal tree for the canopy-contact harvester is a hedgerow no more than 14 feet (4.2 m) tall, with a skirt 3 feet (.9 m) above the ground and a canopy width of 12 feet (3.6 m). It has not been established whether a flat or pyramidal top is best. As with all tree crops, but particularly so with an evergreen tree that bears on 1-year-old shoots, hedging, and, particularly, topping, decrease crop the year of pruning. There is a slight thinning effect as fruit size in topped and hedged trees is improved the year of pruning. However, this improvement in fruit size is not sufficient to replace normal thinning. The yield-decreasing effects of mechanical pruning, and fruit size compensation, dissipate in subsequent years if the mechanical pruning is not repeated. The hope is that the decreases in pruning and harvest costs will compensate for the yield loss produced by mechanical pruning. The effects of skirting the tree at 3 feet (.9 m) have not been established. The interior canopy must be hand pruned to remove thicker wood that will be broken by the harvester.

Thus far it appears that mechanically topping and lightly hedging in alternate years are sufficient for the

Figure 20.6. Large single head mechanical harvester (Ag Rite).

Figure 20.7. Catch frame and one of three heads on a mechanical harvester (Korvan).

canopy-contact harvester. This type of mechanical harvester is equally efficient at removing fruit from a tree that was hedged the current or prior years. Data has not been developed, but it appears that skirting is needed annually. As with hand pruning, mechanical pruning should be done in May or June, after rains have ceased and chemical thinning is completed.

Mechanical pruning may interact with alternate bearing. Mechanical pruning in another alternate-bearing species (pistachio) suggests it is better to mechanically prune entering the low crop year of the 2-year cycle. This is because less crop is then removed over the 2-year alternate-bearing cycle.

ECONOMICS OF THE OLIVE HAND HARVEST

Hand harvesting currently accounts for 45 to 65 percent of the total cash production costs for olive. As crop size increases, so does the total harvest expense; however, the larger the crop, the lower the harvest cost per ton. Excessive brushy growth, dead limbs, heavy weed growth, smut from black scale infestations, and rough ground add to harvest expense. Cost projections for mechanical harvesting have not been developed.

Maximizing yield does not necessarily create the greatest overall profit. Heavy tonnage is commonly associated with small fruit size and alternate bearing. Though delaying harvest to increase size pays off with certain crops, the delay usually results in too many black fruit, as well as frost damage. The desire for marketable product must be balanced with that for overall yield.

POSTHARVEST CONSIDERATIONS

Picked fruit begins to lose moisture immediately. When harvested in hot, sunny weather, fruit should be set in the shade while waiting to be hauled away. Unshaded fruit becomes sunburned and is graded as cull. Rough handling causes bruises and a reduction in grade. Ideally olives should be graded and storage or processing begun within 24 hours of picking.

REFERENCES

Sibbett, G. S., M. W. Freeman, L. Ferguson, D. Anderson, and G. Welch. 1986. Timing Manzanillo harvest for maximum profit. Calif. Agric. 40:19–22.

21

Grading Canning Olives

LOUISE FERGUSON AND GENE WELCH

Upon delivery to the processor, all canning olives are graded by licensed state inspectors to ensure that established standards are uniformly enforced. Inspection procedures are specified by Federal Marketing Order 932 and administered by the California Olive Committee. The inspection service is maintained by a cooperative agreement between the U.S. Department of Agriculture's Agricultural Marketing Service and the California Department of Food and Agriculture's Division of Inspection Services and Fruit and Vegetable Quality Control (Federal-State Inspection Service). Processors pay the state for this service.

Returns to growers are based on total weight and quality of olives within each size classification. The inspector's job is to ensure that weighing and sizing are correctly done, either personally or, more usually, by the processor's personnel. However, it is the inspector who is accountable to the California Olive Committee for proper implementation of procedures and accuracy of dates, weights, counts, and records of the same. The California Department of Food and Agriculture *California Fresh Olive Inspection Circular* (1987) details the procedures and documentation required of olive inspectors.

The initial inspection request each season generally requires a minimum of 48 hours notice. If there has been a cessation of processing during the season, 24 hours notice is sufficient for resumption of inspections. Before grading any lot, the inspector verifies its identity and confirms that it is consistent with accompanying documentation—generally a weighmaster's receipt, company receipt, or Weight and Grade report (form COC-3).

STEP 1: DETERMINING OLIVE CONDITION

The first step in grading olives is to determine whether they are "natural condition olives" or "canned-ripe olives of the tree-ripened type." The former are freshly harvested olives, generally in field bins, but they may be in water or a preserving solution. The latter are pack-

aged, but not oxidized, olives of advanced maturity. If lots are combined before inspection, they must be accompanied by a Lot Combining Authorization (form COC-23) to certify grower authorization. Generally, growers combine lots for a single inspection if they are of the same variety and are delivered within a 24-hour period. Individual lots from different growers are also combined if all of the above requirements, including grower authorization, are met but no individual grower's contribution weighs more than 500 pounds (227 kg).

STEP 2: VERIFYING VARIETY

The second step is to verify the olive variety and, therefore, the variety group. The division of the five commercial varieties into the two groups shown in table 21.1 is based on size. Group I olives are generally much larger than Group II olives and constitute a much smaller proportion of total production. The dates of color break are based on historical observation.

STEP 3: REMOVING IMMATURE AND OVERRIPE CULLS

The third step, removing immature and overripe culls, is done before size grading. Growers should start picking Mission and Manzanillo (Group II) when they have no more than 20 percent immature fruit, and Sevillano

Table 21.1. Olive varieties and color break: early and late season

	San Joaquin Valley	Sacramento Valley
Group I		
Ascolano	Oct. 15–25	—
Barouni	—	—
Sevillano	Oct. 22–27	Oct. 20–25
Group II		
Mission	Nov. 5–10	Oct. 5–10
Manzanillo	Oct. 16–21	Oct. 20–25

and Ascolano (Group I) when they have no more than 15 percent immature fruit. Picking should stop when more than 10 percent of the fruit is overripe. An olive is considered immature if it does not produce the characteristic white exudate under moderate finger pressure (see color plate 20.1). An olive is considered overripe if its skin coloration—deep purple or black in the early season, red through black in the late season—penetrates the olive meat. Penetration of skin color into the fruit usually does not occur before October 1. There are additional maturity characteristics specific to individual cultivars.

Group II olives (Mission and Manzanillo) should have an even, pale-green color with a minimum of whitish lenticels visible. For Manzanillo, pale green to straw color is acceptable (color plates 20.2, 20.3, 20.4, 20.5, and 20.6). During the first half of the season, a light red blush covering less than 50 percent of the olive surface is permissible; later than that it is undesirable. Mission olives are still considered optimal when dark red through the first half of the season, but not later. The break between the early and late season for Mission is October 5 through 10 in the Sacramento Valley and November 5 through 10 in the San Joaquin Valley. For Manzanillo the break is October 20 through 25 in the Sacramento Valley and October 16 through 21 in the San Joaquin Valley.

In Group I, Ascolano are optimal when they are evenly pale green, with a minimum of whitish spots, through a straw color. Sevillano are optimal when straw colored. During the first half of the season, blush is permissible if it is limited to the shoulder of the stem end; no blush is permissible during the second half of the season. Ascolano olives should be picked starting when they are pale green and the lenticels have disappeared, on through their straw-colored phase.

Olives may be culled for reasons. These include machine or hail damage, *Parlatoria* or other scale damage, mutilation, wrinkling, being dropped or ground fruit, deformation, split pits, highly developed color, contamination, and frost damage.

- Machine damage is caused by trucks, tractors, and spray equipment as it moves through the grove after fruit set. Where young fruit is bruised, dimples or brown scar tissue forms, making the olives unacceptable for processing as whole or pitted fruit.

- Hail-damaged fruit resemble machine-damaged fruit but are present throughout larger parts of the tree and may constitute as much as 60 percent of the crop. Processors generally agree to separate and salvage as much fruit as possible; if separation is not possible, they generally pay a price based on petite fruit and use the olives for chopped or sliced fruit.

- Infestations of *Parlatoria* no longer appear to be a serious problem; however, when scale is attached to the stem end of the olive fruit, the fruit is culled.

- Fruit mutilated in picking, loading, or hauling is culled.

- Wrinkled fruit with evidence of sustained water stress will not recover and is culled. Fruit recovered from the ground is also in this category.

- Fruit deformed as a result of insect stings early in development or as a result of boron deficiency, which causes monkey face, is routinely culled.

- Fruit with split pits is culled. This is more common on own-rooted Sevillano and can be as high as 30 percent of harvested fruit.

- Mission or Manzanillo fruit with highly developed color early or late in the season is culled. This indicates higher oil content that produces oily scum in canned product.

- Fruit damaged by frost shows surface blisters and spots on the stylar end 3 days after freezing, indicating freeze damage around the pit. This fruit is culled.

- Fruit on which illegal chemicals have been used is culled.

- When varieties are mixed within a single bin, the fruit present in the lesser percentage is judged cull. When the mixture is even, the entire bin is culled.

STEP 4: SIZE GRADING

This is the most important of the four steps. Sampling procedures are designed to ensure representative samples from each lot. Procedures vary depending on how a lot is delivered and whether a sample grader is available.

Sampling

Lug Boxes. When sampling lots arrive in lug boxes, the number of lugs to be sampled is determined as detailed in table 21.2. For Mission and Manzanillo, a minimum of ½ pound (.23 kg) should be drawn from each lug for lots of over 100 lugs; fewer than 100 lugs requires a ¾-pound (.34-kg) sample from each lug. A minimum of 1 pound (.45 kg) is required for Ascolano, Sevillano, and other large varieties. Inspectors randomly sample lugs from all rows within each layer of a lot.

Bins. When the lot arrives in bins, the number of bins to be sampled is determined as in table 21.3. The inspector determines the specific sampling bins by first pulling the required number of numbered bin cards from a shuffled bin selector deck of cards. Then starting at the left front top corner (driver's side) of a bin stack, the inspector counts counterclockwise in the top layer until complete, then the second layer when complete, and so on. A minimum of 40 pounds (18.2 kg) is drawn from each bin.

Whether delivered in lugs or bins, the selected sample must be reduced with a splitter, which halves the sample until specified weights are reached. The objective is to ensure that olives from all sources are represented in the final sample in the same proportions as in an unreduced sample. Sample sizes designated as workable are shown in table 21.4.

Table 21.2. Size and number of samples for olives delivered in lug boxes

Variety	Lot size in lugs	Number of lugs in sample	Sample size (lb)	Sample size (oz)
Ascolano	≤50	10	10.0	160
and	51–100	15	15.0	240
Sevillano	>100	20	20.0	320
Mission	≤50	10	7.5	120
and	51–100	15	7.5	120
Manzanillo	>100	20	10.0	160

Table 21.3. Size and number of samples for olives delivered in bins

Variety	Lot size in bins	Number of bins in sample	Minimum sample size (lb)	Minimum sample size (oz)
Ascolano	1	1	10.0	160
and	2–4	2	15.0	240
Sevillano	5–11	3	20.0	320
	12–22	4	20.0	320
	23–39	5	20.0	320
	40–50	6	20.0	320
Mission	1	1	7.5	120
and	2–4	2	7.5	120
Manzanillo	5–11	3	10.0	160
	12–22	4	10.0	160
	23–39	5	10.0	160
	40–50	6	10.0	160

Table 21.4. Example of reduction by splitting (lb)

	Manzanillo	Sevillano
Number drawn	48	104
First split	24	52
Second split	12	26

Using an Automated Grader. For fruit run over an automated sample grader, three methods of sampling are acceptable. First, a sample can be sheared off the conveyor belt with a board as field containers are dumped. Second, a small amount of olives may be dropped from the bottom of the hopper as field containers are dumped. In either case, the size of the sampling conduit cannot be changed during sampling. Finally, hand sampling can be done for field containers, but not for undumped bins.

In all of these methods, care is taken to produce a representative sample that reflects the entire lot. However, a processor may also size-grade entire lots by sampling whole bins. In this case the entire lot's identity must be preserved until inspection is completed.

Grading the Sample

Once a sample has been selected, or the entire lot has been submitted, the olives are run over a sample grader and the numbers of olives per pound in each size category are counted. In this procedure, therefore, both size and weight of individual olives matter. If the olives meet the ranges designated by U.S. Standards and Marketing Order sizes, the lot is passed. In the case of lug, bin, shear board, hopper, and hand samples, the graded sample is viewed as representative of the entire lot. However, when the entire lot is sampled by bin, individual bins—containing one size—may fail to achieve average count ranges per pound; in that case the specific bins, and adjacent bins, are resampled until they do. This means the entire lot does not have to be regraded. If average count-per-pound ranges are not achieved, the grower is notified that entire lots of the sample variety group with a similar deficiency will not be certified.

Olives that do not meet standards are reported on the Obligation Credit form (form COC-5). This designates that the olives cannot be used for canning. Both growers and processors have the right to complain about the inspection service, inspectors, and specific inspection results. Complaints about the service or its employees should be addressed to the state inspection service or the California Olive Committee. In the case of a disputed grade sheet, Certificate 303, the appeal for reinspection is made to the state inspection service. The appeal inspection should be done as soon as possible, on a sample twice as large as the original.

2 2

Processing California Olives

B. S. LUH, LOUISE FERGUSON, ADEL KADER, AND DIANE BARRETT

Olives grown in California are processed into black-ripe (99 percent) or California-style green and Spanish-style green olives (less than 1 percent). The method used is pickling—the process of adding an edible acid, generally lactic or acetic acid in the form of vinegar—to a food. The acidification preserves the olive without fermentation. The history of pickling olives extends into antiquity, and the methods of preparing and pickling fruits and vegetables presumably originated in Asia as early as 300 B.C.

OLIVE COMPOSITION

Chemical Composition

As a representative example, Mission olives are typical of a wide range of olive cultivars. Their composition is given in table 22.1.

Ripe Mission olives contain 20 to 25 percent oil, Manzanillo olives 16 to 18 percent, and Sevillano and Ascolano cultivars less than 15 percent. The fatty acid content of olive oils varies somewhat by cultivar, maturity, and growing area. Generally, they are as follows: stearic acid (18:0), 2.0 to 2.7 percent; oleic (18:1), 70.5 to 78.4 percent; linoleic (18:2), 7 to 12 percent; linolenic (18:3), 0.4 to 0.8 percent; palmitic (16:0), 9 to 12 percent; palmitoleic (16:1), 0.71 to 0.76 percent; arachidic (20:0), 0.42 to 0.55 percent; and ecosanoic (20:1), 0.24 to 0.46 percent.

Oleuropein

Unpickled olives are very bitter due to the presence of the glucoside compound oleuropein. The bitterness is destroyed by treatment with a dilute base (alkali) at room temperature. Removing the excess base does not cause a return of the bitterness. Commercial processing destroys oleuropein by treatment with a 1 to 2 percent lye solution at room temperature prior to canning.

Pigments

Anthocyanins are the major pigments in olives. The most prevalent anthocyanins in ripe olive fruits are cyanidin-3-glucoside and cyanidin-3-rutinoside. During olive development, anthocyanins increase rapidly until reaching a maximum, then decrease as the fruit becomes overripe. Light greatly influences pigment formation, and fruit ripened in light normally develops 10 times more anthocyanins than fruit ripened in darkness.

STORAGE OF FRESH OLIVES

Fresh olives picked at the mature-green or fully-ripe (black) stages can be stored between harvest and processing for a few days to a few weeks, depending on storage conditions. Storage can be used to maintain quality and safety of fresh olives and to extend the processing season while maintaining an orderly flow to the processing plant. Storage conditions and duration can greatly influence the quality of the fresh olives at the time of processing and of their processed products, including oil. Quality attributes of fresh olives include size, color, and freedom from defect (such as mechanical damage, shrivelling, surface blemishes, scale and other insect injuries, and chilling injury) and decay. Initial sorting of fresh olives to remove those with serious defects or decay, as well as leaves and twigs, is the first step in successful storage.

Table 22.1. Composition of Mission olives

Ripe Mission olives	Moisture	Oil	Total sugars	Protein	Mannitol	Water soluble solids	Alcohol-precipitable solids
Before pickling	55.0	21.4	4.6	1.65	4.40	13.1	0.47
After pickling	63.4	26.4	0.10	1.56	0.94	7.2	0.43

Chilling Injury

The optimal storage temperature range is 41° to 45°F (5° to 7°C) because lower temperatures can cause chilling injury of green olives and higher temperatures accelerate ripening as indicated by changes in skin color and flesh softening (fig. 22.1). A relative humidity of 90 to 95 percent is recommended to minimize water loss from fresh olives. Black olives can be stored at 36° to 41°F (2° to 5°C) because they are less susceptible to chilling injury than green olives. Cooling fresh-green olives to 41°F (5°C) and black olives to 36°F (2°C) using forced-air cooling before storage and maintaining good air circulation within the storage room are strongly recommended to maximize the benefits of refrigerated conditions between harvest and processing.

The incidence and severity of chilling injury in fresh olives depend on temperature and duration of storage as well as the cultivar and ripeness stage. A comparison of sensitivity to chilling injury among mature-green olives of four cultivars (color plate 22.1) revealed that Sevillano was the most susceptible, followed by Ascolano, Manzanillo, and Mission (least susceptible). Symptoms of chilling injury include internal browning, which begins in the flesh around the pit and radiates outward toward the skin as time progresses. Skin browning indicates an advanced stage or greater severity of chilling injury. Chilling injury can be a major cause of deterioration when fresh olives are stored before processing for longer than 2 weeks at 32°F (0°C), 5 weeks at 36°F (2°C), or 6 weeks at 38°F (3°C).

Respiratory Heat and Ethylene Accumulation

Respiration rates of fresh olives range between 5 to 10 milliliters of carbon dioxide per kilogram per hour for mature-green olives and 10 to 20 milliliters carbon dioxide per kilogram per hour for black-ripe olives at 41°F (5°C). Respiration rates increase two- to threefold for every 18°F (10°C) increase in fruit temperature. The accompanying heat production (2200 to 4400 Btu/ton [.9 metric t]/day at 41°F [5°C]) must be included in calculating the refrigeration load required to maintain the olive temperature during storage. Effective air circulation throughout the olives within the storage room is critical to preventing respiratory heat accumulation in any area within the stored olives since this heat can accelerate deterioration of the fruit.

Fresh olives produce very small quantities of ethylene (less than .1 microliters per kilogram per hour by mature-green olives and .3 to .5 microliters per kilogram per hour by ripe black olives kept at 68°F [20°C]). These rates decrease with lowering of temperature. Exposure to ethylene above 1 part per million can hasten loss of green color and softening of mature-green olives. Thus,

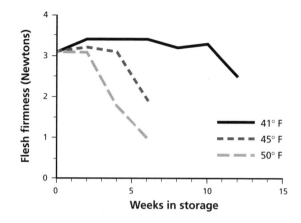

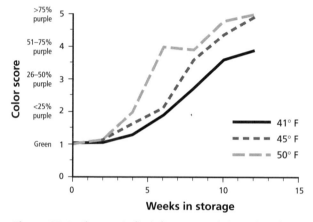

Figure 22.1. Changes in flesh firmness and skin color of Manzanillo olives during storage at three temperatures for 12 weeks

to keep the ethylene concentration below this level, ethylene-free air should be introduced into the storage room, and sources of ethylene, such as ripening fruits and propane-operated forklifts, must be avoided.

Storage Potential

Black-ripe Manzanillo and Ascolano olives can be stored at 41°F (5°C) for up to 4 weeks whereas Mission and Sevillano olives can be stored for up to 8 weeks at 41°F (5°C) while maintaining good fruit and oil quality. Differences in storage potential of these four cultivars are related to rates of softening and decay incidence (fig. 22.2).

Exposure to carbon dioxide levels above 5 percent aggravates chilling damage if olives are kept below 45°F (7°C) while 2 percent oxygen atmospheres can be beneficial in maintaining green color and flesh firmness in olives kept at 41°F (5°C) or higher temperatures. Exposure to oxygen concentrations below 2 percent can cause off-flavors in both green and black olives. Under

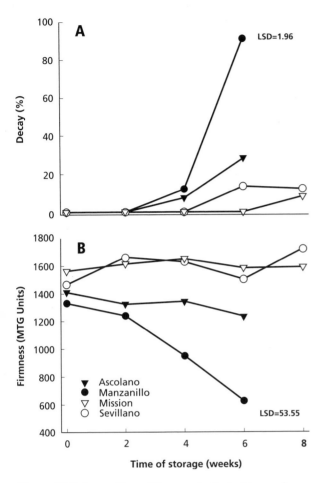

Figure 22.2. Intercultivar differences in the incidence of decay (A) and softening rate (B) of olives picked at the black-ripe stage and stored at 41°F (5°C) (Agar et al. 1998).

an optimally controlled atmosphere of 2 to 3 percent oxygen and 0 to 1 percent carbon dioxide, fresh-green olives can be stored for up to 12 weeks at 41°F (5°C) or 9 weeks at 45°F (7°C), while fresh black olives can be kept in good quality (of fruit and oil) for 4 weeks at 36°F (2°C) to 41°F (5°C); decay incidence was the main factor in determining storage potential.

HOLDING AT THE PROCESSING FACILITY

During harvest, most processing plants do not have enough vats to process all the olives available. Therefore, much of the crop is stored until pickling vats become available. Almost all olive storage today is done in a relatively-dilute, acidulant solution that includes an antimicrobial agent rather than in the traditional salt brine. Olives for premium product are always processed by July of the following year. However, olives can be

stored in acid for up to 3 years; in general, these olives would be used as generic, sliced product.

Holding in Salt-Free Solution

Because it is difficult to dispose of waste brines without contaminating the soil or water, an alternative method for storage has been perfected that uses an acidulant solution containing 0.67 percent lactic acid, 1.0 percent acetic acid, 0.3 percent sodium benzoate, and 0.3 percent potassium sorbate. Sorted, size-graded olives are placed in open-top redwood tanks 5 feet (1.5 m) high and 6 feet (1.8 m) across, of 2.5-ton (2.3-metric t) capacity, with a slatted false head fixed in place. The olives and the false head are covered with the solution, and then polyethylene sheets (6 millimeters thick) are spread over the solution and secured with pliable slats nailed to the inside of the tank. A wax compound (for example, Sealtite) forms an airtight seal between the plastic and the inside of the tank.

No fermentation occurs in this system, unlike in brine storage. The flavor of olives kept in salt-free storage is as good as or better than that of the same cultivars processed from salt storage. The flavor and texture of Sevillano olives are improved, lacking the characteristic strong flavor and woody texture of brine-stored Sevillano olives. Shrivel, always a problem with Ascolano and Sevillano olives stored in salt brine, is virtually eliminated, and so, therefore, is the step of passing the olives over a needle board. More than 90 percent of California olives are now stored by the salt-free method.

Holding in Brine

The traditional method of storage in sodium chloride brine uses paraffin- or plastic-coated concrete tanks or wooden tanks of a 20-ton (18-metric t) capacity. The initial brine contains 5.0 to 7.5 percent salt, or about 20° to 30° salometer. (A saturated solution of sodium chloride, 26.5 percent salt, reads 100° salometer.) At intervals of one to several days, salt or saturated brine is added so that the brine is gradually strengthened to 30° to 36° salometer (7.5 to 9 percent salt); the brine is kept at this concentration for the first 3 months of storage. Added salt or brine must be mixed thoroughly into the tank by means of a circulating pump. As the weather becomes warmer, the brine should be strengthened to 40° salometer. Ascolano and Sevillano olives require an initial brine of 15° salometer to avoid shriveling, and the final salometer reading should be maintained at 30° to 32°.

Holding tanks are located outdoors, where sunlight prevents the growth of putrefactive microorganisms. A mild lactic acid fermentation takes place that helps preserve the fruit until processing. The lactic acid content in the brine may reach .4 to .45 percent in 4 to 6 weeks. It is important that olives be kept under the brine. The head must have openings that allow circulation by pump when salt or saturated brine is added.

If the salt concentration is too low or the acidity insufficient, bacterial softening in the olives is apt to occur due to the growth of bacteria of the *Escherichia coli* and *Enterobacter aerogenes* group. These bacteria cause gas blisters in the olives and are responsible for what is termed *Fisheye spoilage*. At the first sign of spoilage, the brine should be fortified to an 8 percent concentration and acidified with .5 percent lactic or .25 percent acetic acid.

Delay in placing the olives in brine after harvest may cause nailhead, a condition in which small depressions form beneath the skin. These depressions persist in the pickled product and are thought to be caused by bacterial action, as colonies of bacteria are found in them. Nailhead is avoided by pickling olives promptly after harvest or storing them promptly in brine.

The pink yeasts associated with softening of olives—*Rhodotorula glutinis* var. *glutinis*, *R. minuta* var. *minuta*, and *R. rubra*—produce polygalacturonases that cause a slow softening of olive tissue. Commercial control of these yeasts is not difficult when anaerobic conditions are provided. Otherwise, processors must remove the yeast film from the brine surface manually, by skimming or by flagellation.

Other Holding Methods

Chemical salts other than sodium chloride are partially successful in holding olives for several months without spoilage. Ammonium nitrate brines can be used for periods of up to 15 weeks; however, it is difficult to remove the salt completely during preparation for canning.

CALIFORNIA-STYLE BLACK-RIPE OLIVES

The industrial-scale processing of California-style black-ripe olives is laid out in figure 22.3. California-style black-ripe olives can be made from either fresh or stored olives. Generally, the olives are size graded before being loaded into tanks for lye treatment.

Loading

Size-graded olives are placed in paraffin- or plastic-coated cement tanks of a 10- to 20-ton (9- to 18-metric t) capacity. The tanks usually have dimensions of 10 × 5 × 2½ feet (3 × 1.5 × 0.8 m) deep. Redwood tanks can

also be used. The tanks are supplied with four overhead pipelines containing water, dilute lye, dilute brine, and compressed air. Air for aeration and stirring is distributed by perforated pipes at the bottom part of the tank. The tanks are equipped with outlets for discharging spent lye, brine, and wash water.

Lye Treatment

In the pickling process, olives are subjected to two to six applications of .5 to 1.5 percent lye (sodium hydroxide) solution at temperatures of 50° to 70°F (10° to 21°C), depending on the cultivar. Also, when fruit has been stored longer and ambient storage temperatures have been high, lower temperatures and weaker lye concentrations are required in processing.

A more dilute lye is applied when previous storage time in brine was long. The greater the number of lye applications and the shorter the duration of each one, the better the color will be. Lye treatments help natural phenolic compounds in olives to oxidize and polymerize, forming a black pigment. Proper lye treatment and exposure of olives to air, or aerating olives in water between lye treatments, develops the black color.

In most processing plants, the first lye treatment is allowed to penetrate about one-fourth of the distance into the flesh, determined by using a drop of phenolphthalein in 95 percent alcohol as an indicator on the cut surfaces of olives or by noting discoloration of skin and flesh. Each subsequent lye application penetrates another one-fourth of the distance to the pit. In some plants, the first three or four lye treatments last only long enough for the lye to barely penetrate the skins of all olives.

Color formation is most rapid at a pH of 8.0 to 9.5. Color retention is better in olives pickled in solutions made with hard water probably because calcium salts aid color fixation. Calcium chloride greatly improves color retention when added in low concentration (.1 to .5 percent) to storage solutions before pickling, to lye solutions, or to the water bath between lye treatments.

The effects of harvest maturity on the pectin and texture of canned black olives have been studied. As the maturity of Sevillano olives advances from a green-straw color to bluish, purple-red, and then to dark black, firmness gradually decreases. Olives harvested at a green-straw color have a firm texture after canning.

Lye Removal

Lye is removed by changing the water in the pickling tanks at least twice daily and stirring it frequently by means of compressed air or paddles. If the wash water is stirred continuously, it is possible to remove the lye

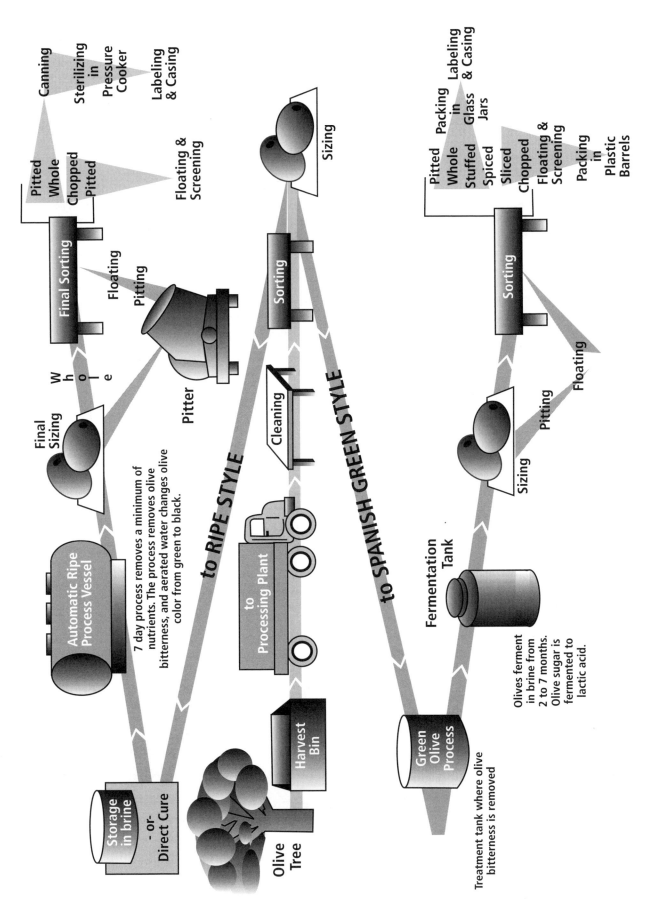

Figure 22.3. Processing sequence of California style black-ripe and Spanish green style olives.

in 3 to 4 days. In several plants, the wash water is replaced with 10° to 12° salometer brine after leaching in water for 2 to 3 days.

CURING IN DILUTE BRINE

When all the lye is removed by washing, olives are stored in dilute brine for about 2 days, first in 3°, then in 6°, and finally in 10° salometer brine (2.5 percent salt). Longer storage is undesirable because bacterial growth, texture breakdown, and other microbial troubles may arise. It is at this time that ferrous gluconate at a concentration of .1 percent (P/V) is added to fix the color. Aeration must be avoided during this time. Usually, only 24 hours is required to fix the color.

Cured olives are sorted on a conveyor belt to remove those that show a mottled color at the blossom end. Broken and soft olives are sent to the oil mill. Olives to be pitted are put through an automatic pitter at this time. Pitted olives are canned in the same manner as unpitted ones.

Canning

The pH value of olives at the time of canning greatly affects color retention during canning and subsequent storage; a pH of 7.0 to 7.5 appears to be most favorable.

Well-pickled olives are packed by weight into cans with a protective C-enamel, which prevents bleaching of the olive color after canning. The most commonly used can sizes are No. 300 (300 × 407 mm), Buffer (211 × 304 mm), Picnic (211 × 400 mm), No. 1 Tall, and No. 10. For chopped or sliced olives, 4-ounce (113-g) cans are used.

After filling, a brine of 8° to 10° salometer (2 to 2.5 percent salt) is added. The cans are exhausted at 199° to 205°F (93° to 96°C) for 5 minutes to reach 170°F (77°C) or higher; then they may be rebrined and sealed at 170°F (77°C) in a double seamer. An alternative practice is to add hot brine at 205°F (96°C) to the cans, followed by sealing at 170°F (77°C) in the double seamer. If the olives are cold, it is advantageous to seal with steam injection at 5 pounds per square inch (.35 kg/cm²). Another variation of this procedure is to add a salt tablet and hot water at 205°F (96°C) to each can, followed by double seaming with steam injection.

Olives in No. 300 cans are heat processed at 240°F (116°C) for 60 minutes in a nonagitating retort or at 250°F (121°C) for 50 minutes. For glass containers, the process is 70 minutes at 240°F (116°C). The California State Board of Health requires that a temperature-chart record of every retort load of canned olives be made

available to the inspection service. Records of the double-seam inspection, fill weight, and temperature-time recording chart must be kept on each lot (coded with numbers) and be available to the inspection service.

Olives packed in water in glass jars must be sterilized in a retort with superimposed compressed air. Otherwise, the pressure that develops in the jar during processing forces off the lids.

Spoilage

Spoilage in California ripe olives during processing is characterized by the softening and ultimate sloughing of skin and tissue from the olive. Spoilage can be controlled by reducing the washing period from the customary 4 to a maximum of 3 days. Microorganisms associated with spoilage include some gram-negative pectinolytic bacteria (*Enterobacter aerogenes, Escherichia intermedia, Paracolobactrum aerogenoides, Aeromonas liquefaciens,* and *Achromobacter*).

CALIFORNIA-STYLE GREEN-RIPE OLIVES

For the processing of canned, green-ripe olives, ripe Manzanillo, Mission, and Sevillano olives of pink or straw-yellow color are subjected to successive treatments of a 1.25 to 2.0 percent lye solution at 61° to 70°F (16° to 21°C) until the lye reaches the pits. To avoid darkening between treatments, the olives are never exposed to air. The process may take 24 to 30 hours; the end point is indicated when a drop of phenolphthalein indicator (1 percent in 95 percent ethyl alcohol) turns red on the cut surface of an olive.

When lye penetration is complete, the lye solution is removed quickly and replaced with cold water to leach out excess lye. The leaching water is changed every 4 to 6 hours during a 24- to 30-hour period. Some packers add .25 percent hydrochloric acid to the washing water to neutralize the last trace of lye. Prolonged washing and undue exposure of fruit to air may result in an undesirable darkening. Olives are then stored in dilute brine for 2 to 3 days, first in 3°, then in 6°, and finally in 10° salometer brine (2.5 percent salt) and then canned in 2.5 percent brine as described previously for black-ripe olives.

SPANISH-STYLE PICKLED GREEN OLIVES

Pickling of green olives is a minor industry in California as the foreign product is more cost competitive. Sevillano, Manzanillo, and Barouni are popular cultivars for green pickling although the Mission cultivar is also used to some extent. Olives for pickling are allowed to reach full size but are picked before they have begun to darken. Fruit are graded for size and placed promptly in shallow paraffin- or plastic-coated concrete pickling vats.

Lye Treatment

Dilute lye solution (1.25 to 1.75 percent) is applied at 54° to 70°F (12° to 21°C). The alkali is allowed to penetrate three-fourths of the way to the pit in 8 to 12 hours. Round redwood vats, each holding 7 to 8 tons (6.3 to 7.3 metric t) of size-graded olives, may also be used for lye treatment.

Removing the lye solution before it penetrates to the pits leaves a small amount of untreated bitter flesh, which contributes to the flavor of the pickled olives. One drop of phenolphthalein indicator solution is applied to the cut surface of an olive to show the depth of lye penetration into the flesh.

After the lye treatment, olives are washed with cold water for 24 to 36 hours; the water is changed every 4 to 6 hours. After washing, the treated flesh of the olive should respond only faintly to the phenolphthalein color test.

Fermentation

Washed, lye-treated olives are transferred to 50-gallon (189-L) oak barrels or 180-gallon (681-L) chestnut barrels. To fill the containers, the heads are removed. After filling, the heads are replaced and the hoops driven into place with a mechanical hoop driver or a hand hoop iron. Brine of 11 percent salt (approximately 44° salometer) is added through a side bung to fill the barrel. Due to the problem of shrivelling with Sevillano olives, it is customary to start with a 20° to 30° salometer brine, and then to add salt daily or every other day until the brine reads 30° salometer.

The favorable temperature range for fermentation is 75° to 80°F (24° to 27°C). Some olive-processing plants in California now ferment green olives in closed red-wood tanks, each holding several tons. Steam pipes beneath the tanks can maintain a favorable temperature, or tanks can be stored in a heated room. The total acid, expressed as the lactic acid content of the brine, should be 0.8 to 1.2 percent. In California, a small amount of glucose or sucrose is added to the barreled olives after fermentation has proceeded for several weeks. Total acidity, pH, and salometer readings of the brine are monitored frequently.

The pH should be 3.8 or less when fermentation starts. Fermentation may be completed in 3 to 4 weeks or may take as long as 1 year, depending on the tem-

perature, salt concentration, and number of lactic acid bacteria present. Control measures should be carefully integrated to maintain optimal brine temperature and concentration, to ensure the presence of lactic acid bacteria in the brine, and to add enough glucose or sucrose to the brine so that the right acidity is produced. Most processors do not use pure cultures of lactic acid bacteria as starters, but instead take 1 or 2 quarts (0.9 or 1.9 L) of brine per 50-gallon (189-L) barrel from a barrel of the current season in active fermentation.

Many processors perform all steps—lye treatment, washing, brining, and fermentation—in tanks of 10- to 20-ton (9- to 18-metric t) capacity made from paraffin- or plastic-coated concrete, glass fiber, plastic, or stainless steel. The bulk fermentation process is more economical than barrel fermentation in terms of labor cost, but it requires supervision by trained personnel to avoid losses from acute microbial spoilage.

Under favorable conditions, lactic acid bacteria, some yeasts, and some gas-forming bacteria of the *Enterobacter aerogenes* group grow fairly well. Eventually, the lactic acid bacteria predominate.

Packing

Pickled olives are destemmed and size graded, if this was not done earlier, then sorted on a conveyor belt to remove defective, blemished, and off-color olives. Defective olives may be made into minced olives or relish. Pickled olives should be free of fermentable sugar and have a total acidity above .75 percent (.75 g lactic acid per 100 g). Other desirable qualities include a uniform, yellow-green color, a crisp texture, and a pleasant flavor and aroma.

Sorted olives are packed carefully, often in glass jars in a definite pattern. Packed jars are then filled automatically with water or brine, then emptied to rinse off any adhering sediment. The jars are then filled with brine of 28° salometer. Some packers may acidify the brine with .2 to .5 percent lactic acid if the olives are below the optimal acidity. Jars are then sealed in a capping machine. Table 22.2 gives the industry-suggested drained weight of different canning styles.

Although it is not customary, it is advantageous to pasteurize bottled olives at 140°F (60°C) or to use hot brine at 175° to 180°F (79° to 82°C). This will prevent sedimentation from bacterial growth.

Spoilage

Occasionally, barrels of olives develop an off-odor and off-flavor, termed Zapatera spoilage. This spoilage is characterized by a penetrating, unpleasant odor in fermenting olives. In the early stages, the odor is usually

Table 22.2. Suggested drained weight of olives (% of fill weight)

Trade type, style, and size	Content of containers			
	≤250	251–500	501–2,000	2,001–10,000
Green olives*				
Whole and stuffed				
>300 fruit/kg	65	65	68	70
150–300 fruit/kg	60	62	66	68
<150 fruit/kg	55	60	64	65
Pitted				
>150 fruit/kg	50	55	60	60
<150 fruit/kg	45	50	55	55
Halved	45	50	50	50
Sliced	50	55	55	55
Broken	80	85	90	90
Chopped (minced)	90	95	95	95
Black olives in brine				
>300 fruit/kg	65	68	70	70
150–300 fruit/kg	55	60	65	65
<150 fruit/kg	50	58	60	60
Black olives in dry salt†	50	58	60	60
Whole and stuffed				
>300 fruit/kg	52	54	57	60
150–300 fruit/kg	50	52	57	60
<150 fruit/kg	48	50	55	58
Pitted				
>150 fruit/kg	40	44	45	45
<150 fruit/kg	38	42	44	44
Halved	45	50	55	55
Sliced	45	50	55	55
Broken	80	85	85	85
Chopped	90	90	90	90

Source: FAO/WHO Codex Alimentarius Committee 1971.

*Olives that do not require heat sterilization for preservation.

†Olives that require heat sterilization for preservation.

described as cheesy or sagey, but as deterioration progresses it becomes a foul, fecal stench.

Under California conditions, Zapatera spoilage, unlike butyric fermentation, occurs when lactic acid fermentation is allowed to cease before the brine pH has dropped below 4.5. A continuous loss of acidity (or rise in pH) as the spoilage progresses begins only at pH values above 4.2. Hence, maintaining pH values below 4.2 is advisable.

Whereas normal brines contain acetic and lactic acids, suspect and spoiled samples contain additional acids. Propionic acid occurs most frequently, followed by butyric acid; succinic, formic, valeric, caproic, and caprylic acids have also been found. These latter volatile acids, together with butyric acid, are partly responsible for the odor of Zapatera spoilage. The lactic and acetic acids furnish energy for the bacteria—two species of the genus *Propionibacterium* and several species of *Clostridium*—that appear to cause Zapatera spoilage.

If the start of lactic fermentation in olives is delayed unduly, the continued high pH permits various butyric

acid bacteria to grow, producing butyric odor and flavor and making the olives inedible. Either inoculation with lactic cultures or initial acidification prevents butyric spoilage.

Yeasts and bacteria of the *Enterobacter* group may cause Fisheye spoilage. Acidification of the brine with lactic acid and using a higher initial salt content (44° salometer or higher) in the brine discourage this type of spoilage.

STUFFED OLIVES

To prepare stuffed olives, pickled and fermented green olives are pitted, either by hand or with high-speed automatic pitters. The pitted olives are stuffed with strips of red pimento previously preserved in heavy brine. Small onions and almond meats are also used. The stuffed olives are barrel fermented for several weeks in 30° salometer brine before packing. Occasionally, stuffed, Spanish-style green olives in bottles show gas formation and spoilage. To prevent this, the pimento must be properly treated in brine to remove the sugars before stuffing.

Stuffed olives are packed in the same manner as Spanish-style pickled green olives, described in the previous section.

GREEK-STYLE NATURALLY RIPE OLIVES

Greek-style olives are made from olives picked when they are purple or black. The fruit is put into wooden or concrete tanks of a 1- to 20-ton (.9- to 18-metric t) capacity that are coated with paraffin or plastic paint. These are covered with brine of about 40° salometer (10 percent salt). Salt is added from time to time to maintain this brine concentration. Fermentation occurs through the action of lactic acid bacteria and yeasts. When fermentation is completed, the olives are graded for size and color and packed in fresh brine in tin containers or paraffin-coated barrels of about a 300-pound (136-kg) capacity. They may also be packed in vinegar brine to be used as an appetizer.

In an alternative method, olives are picked when overripe, placed in baskets, and washed with water. After 2 to 3 days, the olives are removed and placed in fresh baskets in alternate layers with solid salt. By this means, the natural wrinkles become more pronounced, and the partially dried product keeps well due to the high salt concentration.

The fermentation of Greek naturally ripe olives in brine is thought to be due to the activity of a mixed flora composed of coliform, yeast, and possibly *Lactobacillus* species. The total acidity of the brine is usually less than .5 percent. Sometimes a layer of molds, yeasts, and bacteria forms over the surface of the brine, causing removal of sugar and acids and thereby increasing the pH of the brine. This spoilage may also result from the growth of clostridia, propionic acid bacteria, and possibly sulfate-reducing organisms. Softening is another type of undesirable change.

As no lye treatment is used in the preparation of this product, bitterness and other fruit components are only partially and slowly leached into the brine. The degree of blackening depends on, and is favored by, high pH values. Under certain conditions, naturally ripe black olives undergo complete lactic fermentation, developing a total acidity as high as 0.8 to 1.0 percent. The product can be kept in brines of moderate salt content.

GRADES AND STANDARDS FOR PROCESSED OLIVES

Food standards are the body of rules directly governing foodstuffs, whether they are issued by official, semiofficial, or factory authority. The U.S. Department of Agriculture (USDA) grade standards for processed olives are voluntary, and therefore not required by federal law for olive processors and distributors. The standards are widely used, however, as an aid in wholesale trading because the quality of a product affects its price. The USDA grade is sometimes, but not always, shown on processed vegetables in retail stores. The justification for establishing food standards is threefold: (1) to prevent the transmission of disease, (2) to limit the sale of unsatisfactory products, and (3) to simplify the marketing of foods.

Canned Table Olives

Table olives are prepared from sound, clean, and sufficiently matured fruit classified according to trade type (in which both the stage of ripeness and the processes undergone are taken into account).

Trade Types. Processed olives fall into five main trade types:

1. Green olives in brine: treated green olives (bitterness eliminated by treatment with lye) and untreated green olives

2. Olives turning color in brine: treated olives turning color and untreated olives turning color

3. Black olives in brine: treated black olives, untreated black olives, and naturally shriveled black olives

4. Black olives in dry salt: treated black olives in dry salt, untreated black olives in dry salt, and pierced black olives in dry salt

5. Other trade types: bruised olives, treated split olives, untreated split olives, treated olives darkened by oxidation, and specialties

Styles. Whole olives may be offered in one of the following styles:

1. Whole: olives of natural shape from which the pit has not been removed, with or without the stem attached

2. Whole stoned (pitted): olives of natural shape

3. Whole stuffed: whole stoned olives stuffed with suitable products, such as pimento, onion, almond, celery, or anchovy

4. Halved: whole stoned or stuffed olives that have been split into two approximately equal parts along or perpendicularly to the fruit's major axis

5. Quartered: stoned olives split into four approximately equal parts

6. Sliced: stoned or stuffed olives sliced into parallel segments of fairly uniform thickness

7. Chopped or minced: small pieces of random shapes and sizes

8. Broken: olives that have broken while being stoned or stuffed

Sizes. Table olives may or may not be size graded. Whole olives should be size graded according to the number of fruit in one kilogram or hectogram. When the unit is a kilogram, the size range is expressed in steps of 10 olives up to size 150/160, 20 from this up to size 200/220, and 30 up to size 370/400; above 400 per kilogram, the steps are 50 olives. When the weight unit is the hectogram (not shown here), the range is expressed in steps of 1 olive up to size 15/16; 2 olives from this up to size 20/22, and 3 olives up to size 37/40; above 40 olives per hectogram, the steps are 5 olives (table 22.3).

Table 22.3. Olive size counts

Count designations			
Per kilogram	Per pound	Per kilogram	Per pound
400/450	181/223	140/150	64/68
370/400	167/181	130/140	59/64
340/370	154/167	120/130	54/59
310/340	141/154	110/120	50/54
280/310	127/141	100/110	45/50
250/280	114/127	90/100	41/45
220/250	100/114	80/90	36/41
200/220	91/100	70/80	32/36
180/200	82/91	60/70	27/32
160/180	73/82		
150/160	68/73		

Source: FAO/WHO Codex Alimentarius Committee 1971.

Description of Trade Types of Table Olives

Green Olives in Brine. These are prepared from green olives harvested while still ripening (before full ripeness is attained but after fruit has reached its normal size). Green olives are firm, sound, resistant to slight finger pressure, and without marks other than the natural pigmentation. The color of the fruit may vary from clear green to straw yellow.

Green olives treated in brine are then treated with lye, stored in brine, and preserved by natural lactic fermentation or partial natural fermentation. This may be followed by pasteurization, sterilization and pasteurization, the addition of preserving agents, refrigeration, or a combination of these processes.

Green olives untreated in brine are placed directly in brine and preserved by natural fermentation.

Olives Turning Color. Olives turning color are rose, wine rose, or brown in color. They are harvested before complete ripeness is attained and may or may not have been subjected to lye treatment. Treated olives turning color are obtained from fruit treated with lye solution, preserved in brine, and heat sterilized. Natural olives turning color are preserved in brine and are ready for consumption.

Black Olives in Brine. Black olives in brine are firm, smooth, and glossy skinned. Owing to their methods of preparation, they may have slight depressions. The color varies according to production region and time of harvesting, from reddish black through violet-black, deep violet, yellowish black, to deep chestnut. Natural black olives retain a more pronounced fruity taste than treated black olives and may be slightly bitter.

Treated black olives are come from firm and practically ripe fruit treated with lye. After natural oxidation, they are preserved by one or a combination of the following: brine, sterilization or pasteurization, or a preserving agent.

Natural black olives are prepared from firm fruit harvested when fully ripe or slightly before full ripeness is attained. They are placed directly in brine and preserved by means of one or a combination of the following processes: brine, sterilization or pasteurization, or a preserving agent.

Naturally shriveled black olives are obtained from olives harvested when fully ripe, after they have become shriveled on the tree. They are placed directly in brine.

Black Olives in Dry Salt. These have a shriveled or furrowed appearance, although the skin is intact. Natural black olives in dry salt retain a slightly bitter taste and a more pronounced fruity flavor than treated black olives in dry salt.

Treated black olives in dry salt are obtained from firm, practically ripe fruit. After a slight lye treatment, they are preserved in alternating layers of olives and dry salt or by sprinkling dry salt over the olives.

Natural black olives in dry salt are made by placing fully ripe olives immediately in alternating layers with dry salt or by sprinkling dry salt over the olives.

Naturally shriveled black olives in dry salt are obtained from fruit harvested when fully ripe, after they have become shriveled on the tree. They are preserved in alternating layers of olives and dry salt or by sprinkling dry salt over the olives.

Pierced black olives in dry salt are obtained from fruit harvested when fully ripe. After the skin has been pierced, they are preserved in alternating layers of olives and dry salt or by sprinkling dry salt over the olives.

Other Trade Types. These include bruised olives, split olives, and treated olives darkened by oxidation.

Bruised olives are obtained from whole fruit, fresh or previously treated in brine. They are subjected to a process whereby the flesh is bruised or crushed and the stone left whole and untouched within the fruit. They may be treated in weak lye to remove bitterness and are preserved in brine, sometimes spiced. There are three types of bruised olives: bruised fresh olives, bruised treated olives, and fermented green olives turning color.

Treated split olives are obtained from green olives, olives turning color, or black olives split lengthwise after treatment in a lye solution. They may be preserved in a vinegary brine, with or without the addition of olive oil and possibly aromatic substances.

Untreated split olives are obtained from green olives, olives turning color, or black olives split lengthwise. They may be preserved in a vinegary brine, with or without the addition of olive oil and possibly aromatic substances.

Treated olives darkened by oxidation are obtained from olives not yet fully mature. The bitterness has not been removed by lye treatment, but they have been darkened by oxidation. They are packed in brine and preserved by heat sterilization.

Qualitative Classification of Trade Types

The following descriptions are adapted from the Standard of the International Olive Oil Council, applicable to table olives for delivery to international trade. More detailed tolerances are given in the Standard. Table olives ready for consumption are classified as first class, standard class, or market class. Stuffed olives may be prepared only from first- or standard-class (green) olives.

First-Class Olives. Olives in this class must be prepared using fruit of suitable ripeness, of one sole variety, and having the organoleptic characteristics of this variety in the highest degree. First-class olives must be very uniform in color, taste, appearance, texture, and size. Provided that the general good appearance is not impaired, first-class olives may have very slight variations in color, shape, and firmness of flesh—if these slight variations do not upset the general uniformity—and very slight superficial damage, hardly visible to the naked eye, in the form of scratches or scalds, or that caused by insects or physical knocks. In the case of whole olives stuffed with pimento, very slight defects of color or very slight imperfections in the consistency or placing of the stuffing are permissible.

A tolerance of 10 percent not possessing the required first-class characteristics but having those required for classification as standard class is permissible, excluding such olives admitted into the standard class though in fact belonging to the market class.

Batches of table olives (including stuffed olives) meeting the requirements for the first class, but containing no fruit benefiting from tolerances of size or quality and packed in containers of less than 2.5 kilograms and of perfect appearance, may be offered on the international market under the description "extra."

Standard-Class Olives. Olives in this class must be prepared using fruit of suitable ripeness, of one sole variety, and having the organoleptic characteristics of that variety. Standard-class olives ready for consumption must be very uniform in color, taste, appearance, texture, and size. Provided that their general appearance is not affected, standard-class olives may have slight variations in color, shape, and firmness of the flesh—if those slight variations do not upset the general uniformity—and slight superficial damage in the form of scratches or scalds or that caused by insects or physical knocks. In

the case of whole olives stuffed with pimento, slight imperfections of color or slight imperfections in the consistency or placing of the stuffing are permissible.

A tolerance of 10 percent of olives lacking the required standard-class characteristics but having those required for classification as market class is permissible.

Market-Class Olives. Olives in this class must be prepared using fruit of suitable ripeness, of one sole variety, and having the organoleptic characteristics of that variety. They are prepared from fruit that cannot be included in the higher classes but that nonetheless meet the minimum quality requirements of goods recognized as sound, fair, and marketable according to international trade practices.

Provided that they do not in any way affect the nature of the product, olives with the following defects or blemishes are allowed: variations of color, shape, firmness of the flesh; defects in the specific flavor of the fruit; damage in the form of scratches or scalds or that caused by insects or physical knocks; and olives not meeting the general specifications for ripeness.

REFERENCES

Agar, I. T., B. Hess-Pierce, M. M. Sourour, and A. A. Kader. 1998. Quality of fruit and oil of black-ripe olives is influenced by cultivar and storage period. J. Agric. Food Chem. 46:3415–3421.

FAO/WHO Codex Alimentarius Committee. 1971. Proposed draft standard for table olives. Econ. Comm. for Europe Committee on Agricultural Problems. Rome: Food and Agriculture Organization.

Fernandez, A. G., M. J. Fernandez Diez, and M. R. Adams. 1997. Table olive production and processing. London: Chapman Hall.

Kader A. A., G. Nanos, and E. L. Kerbel. 1990. Storage potential of fresh Manzanillo olives. Calif. Agric. 44(3):23–24.

Luh, B. S., and J. G. Woodroof. 1988. Commercial vegetable processing, 2nd ed. New York: Van Nostrand Reinhold.

Olias, J. M., and J. M. Garcia. 1997. Olive. In S. Mitra, ed)., Postharvest physiology and storage of tropical and subtropical fruits. Wallingford: CAB International.

Woodroof, J. G., and B. S. Luh. 1986. Commercial fruit processing, 2nd ed. Westport, CT: Avi Publishing.

2 3

Olive Oil Production

PAUL VOSSEN

The present author wishes to acknowledge the contributions of G. S. Sibbett and Joseph H. Connell, authors of Olive Oil Production in the first edition of this manual.

HISTORY

The Spanish missionary padres were the first to make olive oil in California in the late 1700s. They brought with them cuttings of their Mission variety that is believed to have been a seedling selection developed in the New World. In the late 1800s, approximately 80 varieties were introduced into California from Europe and North Africa, primarily for oil production. The first commercially produced olive oil in California came from the Camulos oil mill in Ventura, established in 1871. By 1885, California olive growers were producing oil from approximately 2,000 acres of oil varieties planted in coastal and mountain foothill areas. The California olive oil industry was short lived, however, due to significant price decreases in the early 1900s. There was a resurgence in olive oil milling during World War II, but after the war growers could no longer compete economically with seed oils or imported olive oils. After this decline, few California oil producers remained.

In the early 1900s, a canning process was developed to produce the California-style, firm, black olive, and a new planting boom started, but this time with table instead of oil varieties. Since 1945, California's olive oil industry has primarily been a salvage operation utilizing unharvested or cull fruit from the table olive industry to produce oil. The vast majority of the oil produced today continues to be made in this way from Manzanillo, Ascolano, Mission, and Sevillano varieties.

In the late 1980s, a new demand for olive oil in the high-quality, "gourmet sector" prompted the planting of numerous small orchards, a few large orchards, and the development of several new olive oil mills, primarily in the North Coast counties. Since many of these orchards are just coming into production, they are producing only about 25 percent of California's olive oil, though this is expected to increase. Many old, abandoned orchards of European varieties or seedlings of unknown origin have also been rejuvenated in order to harvest and process the fruit for oil.

The estimated acreage devoted exclusively to olive oil in 2003 was approximately 4,000 acres of specialty oil varieties with several hundred more acres still non-bearing. Another 1,000 to 2,000 acres of Mission and other varieties are in a semi-abandoned state in old North Coast and Sierra Foothill plantings and are also harvested specifically for oil. In years with low prices paid for table fruit, interest in oil production increases, so more table fruit is harvested specifically for oil.

WORLD OLIVE OIL PRODUCTION AND CONSUMPTION

The average annual world production of olive oil for 1996–1997 to 1999–2000 was 2.351 million metric tons, or about 750 million gallons per year. (Olive oil weighs 7.61 pounds per gallon and there are 2,205 pounds per metric ton.) On the average, world consumption is about equal to production. A holdover from year to year assures a steady supply because the range in production is highly variable, mostly due to the influence of rainfall in the dry-farmed production areas. Olive oil is a commodity on the world market representing about 3 percent of all liquid food oils produced. European, North African, and Middle Eastern countries produce 99.5 percent of the world's olive oil and consume most of it, as well. Production is expected to increase over the next few years due to increases in plantings primarily in Spain, Australia, and Argentina (table 23.1).

Although California produces an average of about 110,000 tons (99,770 metric t) of olives on 34,000 acres (13,760 ha), most of this is table fruit and production varies year to year. An estimated 10,000 tons (9,070 metric t) of traditional table fruit varieties and newly

Table 23.1. World olive oil production and consumption

Country	Average production (% of world) (1996/1997–1999/2000)	Total acres of olives (1998–1999)	Average consumption (% of world) (1996/1997–1999/2000)	Average per capita consumption (L) (1996/1997–1999/2000)
Spain	35.72	5,989,704	22.85	15.0
Italy	23.67	3,536,000	30.40	13.5
Greece	17.37	2,535,246	10.53	26.1
Tunisia	7.20	3,800,000	2.30	10.0
Turkey	3.97	2,174,480	3.29	1.3
Syria	3.77	1,000,750	3.76	6.0
Morocco	2.48	1,111,900	2.29	2.0
Portugal	1.66	1,307,000	2.93	7.8
Argentina	0.40	86,480	<1.00	0.2
USA	<0.10	37,000*	6.48	0.6
Other	3.66	1,661,515	15.17	—
World	100	23,206,075	100	—

Sources: International Olive Oil Council 2001, Author survey 2002.
*Estimate of fruit production for oil only is 3,000 acres.

Table 23.2. California extra virgin olive oil production (gallons)

96–97	97–98	98–99	99–00	00–01	01–02	02–03
123,000	200,000	250,000	236,000	135,000	350,000	400,000

Source: Author survey.

Table 23.3. Sources of U.S. olive oil imports; U.S. production; U.S. exports and consumption (millions of gallons)*

	1994	1995	1996	1997	1998
Imports from					
Italy	28.1	25.0	23.7	34.7	34.6
Spain	4.0	4.1	3.9	5.3	6.4
Turkey	1.8	3.7	1.9	3.6	2.8
Greece	1.4	1.2	1.0	1.4	1.3
Morocco	0.0	0.2	0.7	1.0	1.1
Tunisia	0.5	0.5	0.0	0.4	0.5
Other countries	0.7	0.7	1.4	0.9	1.1
Total imports	36.5	35.4	32.6	47.3	47.8
U.S. production	0.1	0.1	0.1	0.2	0.3
U.S. exports†	1.7	2.7	3.0	2.7	2.3
U.S. consumption	34.9	32.8	29.5	44.4	45.2

Source: USDA Economic Research Service 1999.
*This data is no longer being collected.
†These figures include repackaged imported oils.

planted oil varieties have been harvested for oil each year over the last few years, producing an average of about 200,000 gallons (691 metric t) of extra virgin olive oil per year. That is less than 0.1 percent of the world's olive oil and less than 1.0 percent of the olive oil consumed in the United States.

There are currently 13 processing mills for olive oil in California, ranging in size of production from 4,000 to 100,000 gallons (14 to 345 metric t) each. There are also several very small mills that each process less than 1,000 gallons (3.5 metric t) per year. Production in 2002–2003 was 400,000 gallons (1,375 metric t), and in 2001–2002 it was 350,000 gallons (1,203 metric t). In 1999–2000, cumulative production was approximately 236,000 gallons (814 metric t) of extra virgin grade olive oil, compared to 250,000 gallons (863 metric t) in 1998–1999, 200,000 gallons (690 metric t) in 1997–1998, and 123,000 gallons (in 1996–1997 (table 23.2).

The United States imported 47.3 million gallons (163,244 metric t) of olive oil in 1997 and slightly more in 1998, which was about a 35 percent increase over the 3 previous years. Most of olive oil imported by the United States comes from Italy. The International Olive Oil Council (IOOC) Trade Standard designates as "Country of Origin" the country in which the product undergoes substantial processing. Since Italy imports olive oil from many countries and processes it, the actual country where the olives are grown may not be known unless the bottle indicates an appellation of origin or country where the fruit was specifically grown. U.S. exports are mostly repackaged imported oils (table 23.3).

The per capita consumption of olive oil is 26.1 liters in Greece, 15.0 liters in Spain, and 13.5 liters in Italy. In the United States, it is 0.6 liter. Traditionally, consumption has been very low in most countries outside the Mediterranean region; however, it has been increasing moderately in recent years. Consumption in Europe, Canada, Australia, Japan, Saudi Arabia, France, Portugal, Great Britain, Germany, and the United States continues to rise at a steady rate. The United States currently ranks fourth in the world, consuming 6.5 percent of the world's olive oil, up from 4.6 percent in the 1990s (table 23.1).

PRODUCING OLIVES FOR OIL

Generally, the cultural practices required for oil olive production are the same as those used for table olives, especially pruning, fertilization, irrigation, and pest and disease control. The main differences between growing table olives and oil olives are cultivar selection, crop load management for fruit size, harvest maturity, and harvest handling. Table olive cultivars are usually larger with a lower concentration of oil. Some dual-purpose cultivars, such as Mission and Picual, are both large enough for traditional table fruit and have a very high oil content. The Manzanillo table olive is also known for its high-quality oil production.

Fruit size is not a primary concern in oil olives so fruit thinning is not practiced; however, alternate bearing is likely mitigated with thinning in heavy crop years. Table olives are harvested at the green-ripe stage while oil olives are harvested at a more mature stage of ripeness, making them easier to remove from the tree with mechanical harvesters. Table olives must not be bruised in any way during harvest while oil olives do not need to be handled quite so delicately as long as they are processed quickly.

The primary objective when growing olives for oil is to produce an optimal annual oil yield (gallons of oil per acre) with suitable quality and at a low enough cost to earn a profit. Site, cultivar, cultural practices, and especially harvest influence oil yield, quality, and costs.

Climate for Oil-Producing Olives

Climate has some influence on the fatty acid composition of olive oil (palmitic, linoleic, oleic, etc.). The content of polyphenols (water soluble flavor components in the fruit) can also be different in one area compared to another. This can have a dramatic effect on flavor. No research data has been collected, however, that includes direct comparisons of climatic influences on olive oil quality in different regions of California.

Oil olives are usually harvested at maturity (purple skin-green flesh) in November, December, and January. Frost injures fruit and begins a rapid decomposition and oxidation process, rendering the fruit unsuitable for high quality oil. Therefore, sites with a high probability of frost prior to maturity should be avoided. Most of the new oil varieties have not been adequately tested in California to determine their frost susceptibility, but large differences in cold tolerance have been observed in Europe.

Olives grown for oil need long, hot, dry summers to produce fruit with maximum oil content. At the same time, the trees need irrigation water to maintain fruit turgor late in the season in order to avoid shriveling and excessive dehydration. Shriveled fruit produces low quality oil.

Oil Cultivars

High-quality, extra-virgin olive oils are usually made from varietal blends in order to balance good flavor components with a stable shelf life. Oil quantity and quality are highly dependent on the variety. It has taken centuries for the best oil varieties in the world to develop reputations for fruit yields, oil content, flavor, stability, maturity date, and ease of harvest.

Most olive cultivars range in oil content from 10 to 35 percent of fresh weight at full maturity. It is not usually profitable to grow varieties exclusively for oil that have an average oil yield of less than 20 percent, or approximately 40 to 45 gallons (138 to 155 kg) of oil per fresh ton (.9 metric t) of fruit (early harvest table olives typically yield less than 20 gallons of oil per ton).

Of the major olive cultivars grown in California (Manzanillo, Sevillano, Ascolano, Mission, and Barouni), Mission contains the highest percentage of oil in the fruit (see Producing Oil in chapter 1: History and Scope of the Olive Industry). Each of the varieties has unique flavor components, and the quality of oil made from these cultivars can be excellent. Oils made from the Manzanillo, Ascolano, and Sevillano cultivars are recognized as very fruity oils with unique olive-fruitiness flavors. Mission is primarily used for blending since it has little fruitiness when harvested ripe and is very bitter and pungent when harvested too green. The fruitiness characteristics of most of the table varieties are unfamiliar, however, especially when compared to internationally-known oil varieties with tradition, name recognition, and marketing history. Varietal standards and recognition for olive oil varieties is similar to those of wine varieties in the world.

Flavor components within each cultivar come from the water-soluble flavenoids, phenols, polyphenols, tocopherols, and esters that make up the bitter flavor of fresh olives. These compounds are naturally occurring antioxidants that extend oil shelf life by reducing rancidity, and they are also the source of the fruity and aromatic character of the oil. High polyphenol content oils that have a long shelf life (up to 2 years) are somewhat bitter when first made, and can cause a temporary burning sensation in the back of the throat when swallowed (pungent or peppery). Oils with short shelf lives (about 1 year) may be very fruity when first made, but their flavor diminishes, and they turn rancid more quickly.

Single varietal oils are usually not as complex as blended oils and do not possess a balance of fragrance, soft mouth appeal, and full-bodied flavor. Blending offers the opportunity to mask astringency, add longevity to low polyphenol oil, and create depth.

The most prominent oil varieties in the world are listed in table 23.4. Thousands of other varieties exist, but most are confined to small regional areas. Many prominent varieties, along with their companion traditional pollenizer and blending varieties, have been introduced into California in the past few years. Regional adaptability of these oil varieties within California is not known. In fact, little is known worldwide regarding the performance of different oil varieties outside their traditional growing regions. What many California growers have done is to try and match their variety choices with similar Mediterranean climatic regions, market popularity, and flavor appeal.

There are many myths surrounding oil quality. In many oil producing regions, there are specific varieties, growing techniques, and processing methods used that,

Table 23.4. Primary world olive oil cultivars and several California table varieties for comparison

Cultivar	Oil content (gal/ton)[a]	Cold hardiness	Fruit size	Polyphenol content[b]	Pollenizer varieties[c]
Arbequina	25–40	hardy	small	low	self compatible
Aglandau	30–40	hardy	med.	med.	self compatible
Ascolano	15–25	hardy	large	med.	Manzanillo, Mission
Barnea	30–40	unknown	med.	med.	self, Manzanillo, Picholine
Barouni	18–20	hardy	large	med.	Manzanillo, Ascolano, Mission
Bosana	35–45	unknown	med.	high	Tondo de Cagliari, Pizze Carroga
Bouteillan	35–45	hardy	med.	med.	Aglandau, Melanger Verdale
Chemlali	40–50	unknown	very small	high	self
Coratina	40–50	hardy	med.	very high	self, Cellina di Nardo, Ogliarola
Cornicabra	40–50	hardy	med.	very high	self compatible
Empeltre	35–45	sensitive	med.	med.	self compatible
Frantoio	30–45	sensitive	med.	med.-high	Pendolino, Moraiolo, Leccino
Farga	30–40	hardy	med.	med.	Arbequina
Hojiblanca	20–30	hardy	large	med.	self compatible
Kalamon	30–40	moderate	large	med.	Mastoides
Koroneiki	40–50	sensitive	very small	very high	Mastoides
Leccino[d]	25–35	hardy	med.	med.	Frantoio, Pendolino, Moraiolo
Manzanillo	30–40	sensitive	large	high	Sevillano, Ascolano
Maurino[d]	35–40	hardy	med.	high	Lazzero, Grappolo
Mission	35–55	hardy	med.	high	Sevillano, Ascolano
Moraiolo[d]	35–45	sensitive	small	very high	Pendolino, Maurino
Pendolino[d]	25–35	hardy	med.	med.	Moraiolo, Frantoio, Leccino
Picholine	35–40	moderate	med.	high	self, Aglandau
Picual	40–55	hardy med.	very	high	self, Picudo
Picudo	35–50	hardy	large	low	Picual, Hojiblanca
Sevillano	10–20	hardy	very large	low	Manzanillo, Mission, Ascolano
Taggiasca	30–45	sensitive	med.	low	self

Sources: Barranco, Fernandez-Escobar, and Rallo 2001; Barranco et al. 2000; Cimato et al. 1997; Tous, Romero, and Barranco 1993; Griggs et al. 1975.

[a]Oil content is given in gallons of oil per ton of mature ripe fruit (some purple-black color on the fruit skin). Yield per ton varies with fruit maturity, moisture content, and extraction system.

[b]Oils with high polyphenol content have longer shelf life and are generally more bitter and pungent.

[c]Most olive varieties are somewhat self-incompatible. They usually set a better crop with cross-pollination, especially under adverse weather conditions.

[d]Leccino, Maurino, Moraiolo, and Pendolino are self-sterile.

in most cases, have developed from information passed down from one generation to the next. Very little testing has been done to compare varieties between regions or between countries. In some cases, quality is defined by the particular experiences of a regional people. It also depends on the use of the oil. (See Olive Oil Grades and Standards and Sensory Evaluation of Olives, below.)

Cultural Practices for Oil Olives

Effects of Soil. Studies on the effects of fertilizer in Spain and other Mediterranean countries have shown that the nutrient content of soil has very little influence on oil quality or lipid composition unless nitrogen is excessive, which can cause a reduction in oil quality. The predominant effect of soil is on water-holding

capacity, with subsequent influences on yield and quality of oil. In general, the polyphenol content of non-stressed (irrigated) olives is slightly lower than dry-farmed trees. However, carefully monitored irrigation is necessary in California to maintain fruit turgor in the late season so that fruit will not shrivel and dehydrate excessively. Shriveled fruit produces low quality oil. Irrigation can also increase total yields.

Pruning. Pruning has been demonstrated to have no influence on oil composition or quality parameters. The central leader system of forming the tree may have some advantages for better fruit harvest, but it is more difficult to maintain and comes into bearing later in some varieties. The bush system attempts to keep the trees low for hand harvest, but hard pruning to limit tree size in olive trees often promotes excessively vigorous vegetative growth. The open-center pruned olive tree is still the most common tree form used, and most studies have shown that pruning every other year works well. Because fruit size is not a factor for oil olives, trees can be pruned less than those producing table olives, especially in the smaller wood.

Alternate bearing should be managed as best as possible (see chapter 8: Flowering, Pollination, Fruiting, Alternate Bearing, and Abscission and chapter 9: Pruning Mature Bearing Olive Trees). The best overall oil yields are obtained from moderate crops of 3 to 6 tons per acre (6.7 to 13.4 metric t/ha) produced on an annual basis. Late harvesting, leaving the fruit on the trees past December, also causes lighter cropping the following year due to competition with flower development.

Fruit Maturity

After variety, fruit maturity has the strongest influence on oil flavor characteristics and quality. Just as with any fruit, ripe olive fruit has a very different flavor than immature, green, olive fruit. The International Olive Oil Council defines fruitiness in olive oil, however, as the natural fruit flavor components from ripe or unripe olives. Both are acceptable and positive oil attributes (color plate 23.1).

Immature Fruit. Deep-green, firm, and immature fruit produces oil with an unripe-fruit, grassy, and vegetative characteristic. It is usually very bitter and pungent due to the high content of polyphenols and other flavor components. The oil is very green in color from the high chlorophyll content. It is more difficult to extract oil from firm olives since the oil containing vacuoles within the cells are not as easily ruptured.

Veraison. As the olive fruit matures from green to yellow-green it starts to soften, and then the skin turns red-purple in color. This is called veraison, just as in wine grapes. At this point the fruit still contains most of the polyphenols as it begins to develop some of the ripe-fruitiness character and is generally regarded to be at its peak. Oils made from fruit harvested at this stage of maturity obtain close to the maximum amount of oil per dry weight basis, maximum quantity of polyphenols, some ripe fruity character, some bitterness, and some pungency.

Black Fruit. As the olive fruit further matures the purple color of the skin turns black, and the flesh blackens all the way to the pit. With flesh coloration, the polyphenol and chlorophyll content of the fruit declines and the carotenoids increase. Oils produced from these late harvest fruits are golden in color, less bitter, less pungent, and less stable. They are often described as sweet oils.

Maturity Index. Harvesting should take place when the majority of the fruit are at the optimal stage of maturity depending on the variety and style of oil desired for the market. Since not all of the fruit in an orchard or even on a single tree ripen uniformly, a maturation index test based on fruit color was developed by olive researchers to help determine when to harvest for consistency each year.

For the maturity index determination, approximately 2 to 3 pounds (0.9 to 1.4 kg) of fruit are harvested from several trees, high, low, and from all sides. The fruit is mixed uniformly and 100 olives are picked from the sample at random and arranged according to eight color stages with the following number designation and description.

0   Deep-green skin color

1   Yellow or yellow-green skin color

2   Yellow-green with less than ½ of fruit with reddish spots and violet skin color

3   Red to purple skin color on more than ½ of the fruit

4   Light purple to black skin color with white-green flesh color

5   Black skin color and violet flesh color less than ½ way to the pit

6   Black skin color and violet flesh color almost to the pit

7   Black skin color and dark flesh color all the way to the pit

Maturity index =

$$[(0 \times N_0) + (1 \times N_1) + (2 \times N_2) + (3 \times N_3) + (4 \times N_4) + (5 \times N_5) + (6 \times N_6) + (7 \times N_7)] / 100$$

where N = number of fruit in each numerical classification (0–7)

A maturity index of 2.5 to 4.5 is usually used for most olive oils, depending on the variety and desired flavor characteristics of the oil.

The best-quality oil comes from olives matured to at least the red-ripe stage. Fully-mature, black fruit yield sweeter oils with little or no bitterness or pungency, but during harvest, they are soft and easily damaged. Immature olives that are green or straw colored are sometimes processed because of the unique flavor that less mature fruit impart to oil. The present trend is to harvest earlier to achieve an oil with a green color, some bitterness, and pungent character. However, there is a maze of choices for harvest date, depending on the desired type of oil, long-term stability of the oil, and color. For example, with low polyphenol content varieties, a 1-month delay in harvest can cause a 4-month loss in oil stability due to the drop in polyphenol content.

Later harvest usually yields a better percentage of oil per ton of fruit, so processors and growers are often interested in harvesting as late as possible to augment oil quantity. The olive tree manufactures and stores oil in the fruit throughout the season, but the rate of oil storage flattens and stops just before maturity due to low light intensity and cool temperatures, providing no real gain in oil content. Olives naturally lose moisture in the maturation process, so the perceived rise in oil content, late in the growing season, is actually a loss of fruit moisture. At a maturity index of 3.0 to 5.0, olives have reached their maximum oil content.

Oil Olive Harvest

While olives are on the tree, the oil inside the fruit is in perfect condition (low acidity level, flavorful according to variety, and nonoxidized). Changes that influence quality occur during and after harvest. Harvest methods vary with regard to how much damage they do to the fruit. Hand harvest is the best, but very expensive. If done properly with the right equipment, mechanical harvest can be almost as good and much less expensive. The key is to not break the fruit skin in any way and to process the fruit within a few hours.

Mechanical harvesting of fruit is essential to economically rationalize oil olive production in California. Future olive orchards must be planted and pruned to accommodate mechanical harvesting of some type. (See chapter 20: The Olive Harvest.)

High-density plantings (approximately 400 trees/acre [988 trees/ha]) using tree shakers to super-high density plantings (approximately 900 trees/acre [2223 trees/ha]) using compact varieties and over-the-row harvesters are in the early stages of experimental evaluation. A new vibrating-finger harvester for large trees is also being studied as an alternative to shakers for mechanical fruit removal. These systems may be available in the near future to reduce harvest costs.

HANDLING FRUIT PRIOR TO MILLING

Postharvest handling has a major effect on olive oil quality. Olives left in bins for long periods at ambient temperature before processing ferment and mold; the resulting defective oil is of low value and must be refined to remove the disagreeable flavor. Wet, warm fruit is much more likely to ferment than dry fruit. Olives should be transported in shallow bins to prevent smashing bottom fruit, and the bins must have ventilation holes.

If possible, fresh olives should not be stored but rather harvested, transported to the processing plant, and processed immediately. If storage is necessary, olives should be kept cool by harvesting in the morning and placing them in the shade or in cold storage at 41°F (5°C) with 90 to 96 percent relative humidity. Oil olives keep well with little quality deterioration for up to 15 days in cold storage if the fruit is in perfect condition. Warm fruit in large (1,000-lb [454-kg]) bins must be forced-air cooled rapidly to bring the fruit temperature down close to the storage temperature. Fruit quality can be maintained for longer periods with controlled atmosphere storage at 3 percent CO_2 and 5 percent O_2.

Fruit should be classified and separated by quality prior to shipment to the mill since most mills do not have the capacity to grade fruit. Fruit with defects should be processed separately from good fruit because even a very small portion of bad fruit (color plate 23.2) can ruin a large quantity of good oil. Ground fruit or fruit that has been damaged should never be included with high-quality fruit.

PROCESSING OLIVES INTO OIL

Olive oil readily takes on odors and flavors. Therefore the oil mill must be kept perfectly clean and odor free. The mill facility should be made of materials that are easily cleaned so that small quantities of spilled oil or processing wastes are not allowed to ferment or oxidize and produce rancid or disagreeable odors.

Washing and Leaf Removal

The purpose of preliminary washing is to remove any foreign material that could damage machinery or contaminate the oil—primarily rocks, soil, leaves, and twigs. Only olives that have been harvested from the ground, require removal of spray residues, and so on need to be washed. If olives are crushed in a hammermill, the extra moisture from the wash-water can cause extractability problems because an emulsion forms between the oil in the fruit and the added water.

Polyphenol content is lower in washed olives. Oil sensory ratings for washed olives is usually affected negatively, and washed olives generally have a lower bitterness rating, pungency, and less fruity flavor. Wash water is also often dirty and has a good chance of passing flavors into the oil, so clean water should be used to rinse the fruit after washing (color plate 23.3). It is also important that no fruit remains stuck in the bins and hoppers at the processing plant as it can ferment and ruin the oil.

Milling

The objective in crushing the olives is to break the cells of the fruit and release the oil for extraction. Four primary types of machines are used to crush olives: the stone mill, hammermill, disc mill, and a pitter machine that removes the pits while smashing the pulp.

Stone Mills. This is the oldest type of milling apparatus and consists of a stone base and upright millstones enclosed in a metal basin, often with scrapers and paddles to spread the fruit under the stones and to circulate and expel the paste (color plate 23.4). The slow movement of the stone crushers does not heat the paste and results in less emulsification, so the oil is easier to extract from the paste. This method has been almost completely abandoned in Spain and Greece but is being used in parts of Italy specifically to produce a more coarse paste and reduce excess bitterness in strong-flavored varieties. There are a few stone mills operating in California.

The disadvantages of this method are the bulky machinery, its slowness of operation, its high cost, and its inability to be continuously operated. The stones are also more difficult to clean, and the slow milling time can increase oxygen exposure and paste fermentation. However, some small-scale producers prefer this method. Hammermills in most large operations have replaced stone mills because of their greater efficiency.

Hammermills. This method generally uses a metal body with blades inside that rotate at high speed, smashing the olives against and through a metal screen (color plate 23.5). The major advantage of metal crushers is their speed and continuous operation, which translate into high output, compact size, and low cost. They are also much easier to clean and maintain. Their disadvantage is due to the speed of crushing, which causes more emulsification and leads to a longer mixing period needed to achieve a good oil extraction.

Oil produced from a hammermill is generally greener, more bitter, and more stable since the skins are broken up into finer particles. Extra care must be taken when green fruit or fruit from very strong flavored varieties is milled with a hammermill since it can produce a very fine paste, making an excessively bitter and pungent oil.

The emulsification problem is overcome by malaxation for slightly longer. The size of the hammermill mesh screen should be adjusted as the season progresses and the fruit becomes riper and softer. A smaller mesh screen is needed to produce a finer paste from firm olives. This improves the breakup of the oil cells. As the fruit ripens, the cells break up and oil release is more rapid; therefore, a larger mesh screen can be used, and a more coarse paste can be worked.

Disc Mills. This method offers an alternative to working the olive paste. The disc mill has a stationary plate, or disc, with several protruding knives molded into it (fig. 23.1). An opposing disc with protruding knives slices the fruit into a paste as it rotates with the fruit entering into the middle. The disc mill produces a paste that is coarser and less emulsified than a hammermill, yet is continuous and easier to clean and maintain than a stone mill.

Figure 23.1. Disc mill opened to show both sets of protruding knives.

Pitter Mills. These are machines that remove the olive pits as they smash the fruit against stainless steel rods that are spaced about 1 to 2 millimeters apart. The fruit is pushed against the rods from the inside with a rapidly rotating auger (fig. 23.2). The fruit pulp breaks up into a paste as it is pushed between the rods, and the pits remain behind. There are only a few of these machines currently operating in the world and the technology is too new to know of its advantages and disadvantages. Early indications are that the paste and oil produced from pitted fruit is somewhat less oxidized and less bitter.

Mixing of the Olive Paste (Malaxation)

Malaxation is a slow mixing of the paste at approximately 15 to 18 revolutions per minute in a jacketed warming tank. It prepares the paste for separation of the oil from the pomace (color plate 23.6) and is particularly important if the paste was produced in a hammermill. The mixing process optimizes the amount of oil extracted through the formation of larger oil droplets and a reduction of the oil-water emulsion. Optimally, the malaxator is designed to assure thorough mixing, leaving no portion unmixed. The paste is slowly stirred for 20 to 90 minutes. Paste produced in a stone mill requires less malaxation time. Difficult pastes produced from high moisture content olives require longer malaxation times. Water should never be added to the malax-

Figure 23.2. Opened pitter mill with stainless steel rods. Paste is forced through rods from the inside. Olive pit on outside shows distance between rods.

ation process unless the paste is so dry it will not flow.

The temperature of the paste during malaxation is very important. It should be warm (77° to 86°F [25° to 30°C], which is still cold to the touch) to improve the viscosity of the oil and extractability. Temperatures above 86°F (30°C) can cause problems such as loss of fruit flavors, increase in bitterness and astringency, and a cooked flavor.

Sometimes it is difficult to get good oil extraction from certain pastes, and it is usually because the olives have too much moisture. A paste moisture content of about 45 to 50 percent is easily worked, but extraction from paste with a moisture content of greater than 50 percent is more difficult. Difficult pastes have the following characteristics:

- The past is very fluid and watery-looking with crushed pits easily visible.

- During malaxation the paste sticks to the mixing paddles, the paste color remains constant, and little visible oil is seen separating from the paste.

- In selective filtration separators, very little oil is extracted.

- In press systems, pressure must be advanced very slowly or the paste squirts out from between the mats, the juice (fruit-water and oil mixture) obtained is emulsified, and the pomace strongly adheres to the filter mats.

- In horizontal centrifugation systems, the oil and wastewater contain too much solid material, the oil produced is dirty and emulsified, and the waste products have an abnormally high quantity of nonextractable oil left in them.

Figure 23.3. Pressing the stack of mats and stainless steel plates with a traditional system.

The solutions to these problems are to raise the temperature of the paste, add talc (hydrated calcium-magnesium silicate) to absorb the excess moisture, increase the malaxation time, and reduce the flow of paste into the centrifugal decanter.

Oil Extraction Methods

The next step is extracting the oil from the paste and fruit-water (water of vegetation). The oil can be extracted by pressing, centrifugal decanters, selective filtration, or through a combination of these methods.

Traditional Press. Pressing is the oldest method of oil extraction. This method involves applying pressure to stacked filter mats, covered with about ½ inch (1.3 cm) of paste (color plate 23.7), that alternate with metal disks (color plate 23.8). Pressure is slowly applied up to 400 atmospheres (413 kg/cm²) for approximately 45 minutes (fig. 23.3). A central hollow cylinder allows the expressed oil and water (olive juice) to exit to the interior as well as to the outer surface of the stacked mats. The machinery is cumbersome, the process requires more labor than other extraction methods, the cycle is not continuous, and dirty filter mats can easily contaminate the oil.

Cleanliness of the mats is extremely important. Each time the mats are used, small particles of paste plug the filtration channels and can prevent oil flow out of the paste. The main problem with the use of traditional presses is that fermentation and oxidation defects are

Figure 23.4. Oil dripping from a Sinolea separator.

Figure 23.5. Outside view of a typical centrifugal decanter in a continuous flow system.

absorbed into the oil from the mats. Mats can start to ferment and turn rancid if not handled properly. Solutions to this problem include using presses continuously until harvest is finished and then discarding the mats, storing the mats in a freezer between uses, or thoroughly washing the mats between each use.

The quality of oil produced from traditional presses can fall into two extremes: superior oils when presses are properly operated due to greater flavor and high polyphenol content or very defective oils due to the fermentation of mats. Studies vary in their conclusions for ratings of oils from presses in sensory analysis, with some rating them higher and others lower. Management of the system seems to be the most important variable.

Selective Filtration—Sinolea Process. This process works very differently from the press system since no pressure is applied to the paste. It operates on the principle that in a paste containing oil, solid particles, and water, the oil alone will adhere to metal. The machine has stainless steel blades that dip into the paste; the adhering oil then drips off the blades into a separate container while the solids and water are left behind (fig. 23.4). Extraction is stopped when fruit-water begins to appear in the oil. The lack of pressure produces light, free-run oil with a unique quality and value.

The equipment is complicated and requires frequent cleaning, maintenance of the stainless steel blade mechanisms, and a constant heat source to keep the paste at an even temperature. Very few selective filtration systems are still in operation in the world; most have been replaced by centrifugal decanters. There is one Sinolea-brand machine operating in California.

Three-Phase and Two-Phase Centrifugal Decanters. If olive paste, or olive juice containing both water and oil,

is allowed to sit in containers, the oil, with a lower specific gravity, rises to the top naturally. Historically, with the use of ladles, oil was decanted away from the water and solid material. This natural separation takes considerable time, and the contact with fruit enzymes, breakdown products, and fermenting fruit-water produces defective oil.

Modern decanters are large, horizontal centrifuges (fig. 23.5) that separate the oil from the solids and water in the same process as in a decantation tank, but faster. The savings in time increases the efficiency of the system, but also decreases the time the oil is in contact with the fermenting fruit-water.

The decanters spin at approximately 3,000 rotations per minute. Centrifugal force moves the heavier solid materials to the outside, a water layer is formed in the middle, and the oil is left at the innermost layer. There is no exact line of separation between the three phases of solid, water, and oil, so the oil contains some water. To solve this problem, an additional vertical centrifugation is used later to remove most of the remaining fruit-water from the oil.

The three-phase system decanter separates the paste into a relatively dry solid, fruit-water, and oil. Water is added to this system to get it to flow through the decanter. A minimum quantity of water is added to separate the solid material better and to retain water-soluble polyphenols as much as possible, but the overall effect is to wash away some of the flavor and antioxidant qualities of the oil. Samples should be taken every hour and analyzed daily to determine the status of the separation. Preferably, the solid residue, or pomace, should have an oil content of no more than 6 to 7 percent and 50 percent moisture while the fruit-water should not contain more than 0.3 percent oil and 8 percent solids.

Two-phase system decanters were introduced in the early 1990s. They function under the same principle as three-phase decanters except that the solid and fruit-water exit together. No water needs to be added to the two-phase system.

Experience with the two systems has shown that the two-phase system has some advantages, that is, better retention of polyphenols because no water is added and less loss of oil as long as the system is operated properly. Two-phase system oils are generally more bitter and fruitier in taste test comparisons. One problem with the two-phase system is a greater potential to lose oil when the olives are low in moisture. This is due to a thinner interface between the two phases during centrifugation. Another difficulty is less visual evidence of what is happening with waste characteristics because the solid and fruit-water phases are mixed. See table 23.5 for differences in oil extraction methods.

The two-phase system produces the greatest weight of solid waste because it has the highest moisture content. All the wastewater is mixed in with the solids. The small amount of wash water produced is quite low in biological oxygen demand (BOD). The polyphenol content and bitterness of the oil is lowest in the three-phase system because of the addition of water.

Vertical Centrifuge. Vertical centrifuges spin at two times the velocity of a decanter and provide four times the separation force for the solid, water, and oil phases (figs. 23.6 and 23.7). The additional separation of the three phases further removes solid particles and water from the oil (color plate 23.9).

Fresh, warm water is usually added to clean the oil, creating a greater interface area between the phases. Processors use two centrifuges in three-phase systems: one for the "wet" oil from the decanter and another to separate the small quantity of oil remaining in the wastewater.

Figure 23.6. Outside view of a modern, self-flushing vertical centrifuge.

Figure 23.7. Inside view of an older model vertical centrifuge opened for cleaning.

Table 23.5. Differences between oil extraction methods

	Press	Three-phase	Two-phase
Kg of solid waste per metric t of olives	350	500	800
Solid waste moisture (%)	25	48	55–75
Kg of wastewater per metric t of olives	600	1,200	250
Fruit-water moisture (%)	86	90	99
Biological oxygen demand (BOD) (ppm in water)	100,000	80,000	10,000
Free acidity (%)	0.50–0.86	0.13–0.39	0.17–0.65
Peroxide (meq • O_2/kg)	10.00–12.50	6.70–8.70	6.20–9.40
Oil polyphenol content (ppm caffeic acid)	16,900	10,000	23,000

Sources: Hermoso-Fernandez et al. 1998; Alba 1997.

Processing Waste

There are two predominant waste products produced as a result of processing with the press and three-phase decanter systems, the solid material (pomace) (color plate 23.10), which is relatively dry, and the fruit-water, often referred to as water-of-vegetation. The two-phase system produces one waste product that is a mixture of the water and solid materials. In countries where significant production occurs, the pomace is often sold for further oil extraction with solvents.

The fruit-water (wastewater) (color plate 23.11) can be a significant pollutant because of its organic load. If added to natural waterways, the high biological oxygen demand (BOD) causes damage to aquatic life. Both the solid and liquid portions of the process are composed of the same organic materials as most fruits, leaves, and other organic material left in the field to decompose naturally. Because of the small particle size, however, it is difficult to filter out the pure water from dissolved organic substances.

If these substances decompose anaerobically, methane and disagreeable odors are produced. Incorporation with dry solid materials in order to create aerobic conditions produces compost that can be spread back onto the land. Olive pomace can be composted if mixed with materials high in nitrogen, but even then the pits decompose very slowly. Another option is to run the pomace through a machine that separates out the pit fragments. The pits can be burned as fuel and the pitless pulp can be fed to livestock. Each city or county government regulates the disposal of processing-plant waste products. Compost facilities are regulated to minimize odors and leachate runoff. Municipal discharge to sewage systems is sometimes another option, but it is usually very expensive.

OIL STORAGE, FILTRATION, AND BOTTLING

Storage

Premium quality oils should be stored in stainless steel and maintained at a constant temperature of between 59° and 65°F (15° and 18°C). The headspace in the top of the tank should also be flushed with an inert gas such as nitrogen to prevent oxygen contact with the oil. After processing, oil should be stored in bulk for 1 to 3 months to settle out any particulate matter and excess fruit-water. Bulk storage and decantation can eliminate most problems of sediment in bottles. Storage tanks should be funnel shaped at the bottom (fig. 23.8) and purged periodically, from the bottom, removing the

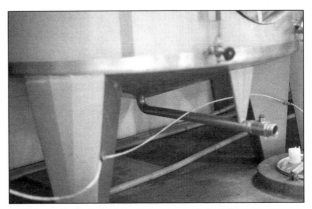

Figure 23.8. Stainless steel storage tank for olive oil with a funnel-shaped tank bottom.

heavier water and solid materials before they ferment and contaminate the oil. Racking oil from the top increases oxidation and loss of volatile aromatics. Storage and decantation is especially important for oils that are not going to be filtered prior to bottling. Oils that are unfiltered, bottled, and sold immediately after processing are termed *new* and must be consumed quickly (within a few weeks) to avoid flavor changes within the bottle.

Filtration

Olive oil is often filtered to make sure that the product, at the time of bottling, remains as consistent as possible during its shelf life. Some producers do not filter their oil prior to bottling because it can remove some of the polyphenols and slightly change the flavor. Unfiltered oils, however, run the risk of developing solid, dark-colored sediments in the bottom of the bottle. If there is excess moisture in the oil, it can also form a gelatinous-looking, cloudy material near the bottom of the bottle, ferment, and cause off flavors.

There are several types of filtration systems for olive oil:

- Cotton Gravity Filter. Oil passes through a thick, fluffy, cotton pad by gravity (usually used only as a prefilter).

- Diatomaceous Earth Filter. Oil is mixed with diatomaceous earth and then pressure-pumped through a plastic filter medium that captures the suspended particulate matter and excess water.

- Paper Filter. Oil is pressure-pumped through a fine paper filtration medium (fig. 23.9).

Bottling

The matching of bottling with sales ("Just-in-Time Bottling") and delivery to customers in an efficient manner allows oil to be kept in bulk tanks under ideal

Figure 23.9. Paper filter pressure pump.

Figure 23.10. Logo of the California Olive Oil Council (COOC) used to certify California olive oil.

storage conditions until a batch is ordered. Since olive oil tends to mellow over time, it also allows for the blend to be modified during the year in order to produce a more consistent product for the consumer. Some producers start the sales season with a blend containing a higher percentage of later-harvested oil or oil from less-pungent varieties. Then they gradually add more early-harvested oil or more oil from stronger-flavored varieties in their later blends because these stronger flavors tend to mellow with time.

A new product recently introduced in Europe is "frozen-new" oil. This product is purchased frozen by the consumer, thawed out for use when needed, and keeps without significant flavor changes for about 2 to 3 weeks. Frozen-new oil takes advantage of a market demand for out-of-season fresh-new oil, which is usually very fruity and spicy in flavor.

OLIVE OIL GRADES AND STANDARDS

An olive oil consists of 98 percent lipids and 2 percent unsaponifiable volatiles, polyphenols, pigments, aromas, and flavenoids. The lipids consist of glycerides and fatty acids such as palmitic, linoleic, and oleic. Linoleic and oleic acids increase with olive maturity while palmitic decreases with maturity. Because palmitic is a saturated fatty acid and oleic and linoleic are unsaturated, oil becomes less viscous (thinner) as fruit ripens. The water-soluble (unsaponifiable) flavor components of oil typically consist of terpenes (300 to 700 mg/kg), chlorophyll (5 to 15 ppm—color and antioxidant), carotenoids (5 to 15 ppm—color), tocopherols (vitamin E and antioxidant), esters (flavor), and phenols and polyphenols (50 to 500 mg/kg—flavor and antioxidant properties).

The International Olive Oil Council (IOOC) has a United Nations charter to develop standards for quality and purity criteria for olive oil based on the above lipid and nonlipid components. Their main focus is the regulation of legal aspects of the olive oil industry and preventing unfair competition. The standards they have developed are recognized by most of the countries of the world. The United States, however, is not a member of the IOOC and is not legally bound by their standards.

A private membership organization of olive oil producers and processors in California called the California Olive Oil Council (fig. 23.10) has adopted the international standards and is promoting the adoption of these standards by the State of California and the U.S. government. Consumers have become familiar with some of the international standards and nomenclature that most labels indicate, such as "Extra Virgin Olive Oil," "Virgin Olive Oil," and "Olive Oil."

In 1997, the California legislature enacted a law for labeling olive oil that specifies truth in labeling as to location of production, processing, and bottling. State Senate Bill 920 makes it a crime to sell imitation olive oil or to sell olive oil labeled as California olive oil that contains oil produced anywhere else. It also specifies that oils labeled according to designated, U.S.-approved, viticultural areas be composed of 75 percent of oil that is derived solely from olives grown in that designated U.S. viticultural area. Viticultural areas or apellations were chosen because of their specific designated geographical boundaries that relate well to specific olive oil production zones.

Nine Grades of Olive Oil

The international standards were revised in 2003 to include nine grades of olive oil. Oils must meet certain criteria for inclusion in specific categories. The olive oils must not be adulterated with any other type of oil, must pass a sensory analysis by a certified panel of tasters, and meet the analytical criteria of the standard. Table 23.6 is a summary of the quality criteria standards.

Olive oil is defined as oil obtained solely from the fruit of olive trees (*Olea europaea sativa*). Furthermore, virgin oils are obtained solely by mechanical means that do not lead to alterations in the oil. All oils must pass the tests for free fatty acid, peroxide, UV absorbency, water and volatiles, insoluble impurities, flash point, metal traces, and halogenated solvents.

Extra-Virgin Olive Oil. This grade contains no defects and has some positive attributes, as evaluated by the mean of a certified taste panel. Extra-virgin oil must also have a free acidity level of less than 1.0 percent and a peroxide value of less than 20 milliequivalents O_2 per kilogram.

Virgin Olive Oil. Oil with a sensory analysis rating of the mean of tasters, having defects from 0 to less than 2.5, a free acidity of less than 2 percent, and a peroxide value of less than 20 is termed virgin. It is of a slightly lower quality than extra-virgin.

Ordinary-Virgin Olive Oil. This is an oil with a slightly lower organoleptic rating (defects from the mean of tasters 2.5 to less than 6.0) and a free acidity of less than 3.3 percent with a peroxide value of less than 20.

Virgin Lamp Oil (Lampante). This oil has many defects, is not fit for human consumption, and is intended for refining. These oils come from bad fruit or improper handling and processing.

Refined Olive Oil. Refining methods are used to obtain this oil from virgin oils. These methods do not alter the glyceridic structure. The refining process usually consists of heating the oil and, under a vacuum, pulling off all the volatile components. Refined olive oil is usually odorless, tasteless, and colorless.

Olive Oil. Blends of refined and virgin oils.

Crude Olive-Pomace Oil. This oil is obtained by treating pomace with solvents and fractional distillation to extract the residual oil. It is a crude product made with the intention of further refining and is not for human consumption.

Refined Olive-Pomace Oil. Oil that is obtained from crude pomace oil by refining methods that do not alter the initial glyceridic structure is termed refined olive-pomace oil. It is not for human consumption.

Table 23.6. International Olive Oil Council quality criteria and standards for olive oil

	Extra virgin	Virgin	Ordinary virgin	Lamp virgin	Refined olive	Olive oil	Crude pomace	Refined pomace	Olive pomace
Organoleptic characteristics									
mean defects	=0	0<2.5	2.5<6.0	>6.0	acceptable	good	not tested	acceptable	good
mean attribute	>0	>0							
Free acidity (%)	<0.8	<2.0	<3.3	>3.3	<0.3	<1.0	—	<0.3	<1.0
Peroxide value (meq/kg)	<20	<20	<20	—	<5	<15	—	<5	<15
UV absorbency									
270 nm	<0.22	<0.25	<0.30	—	<1.10	<0.90	—	<2.00	<1.70
^K	<0.01	<0.01	<0.01	—	<0.16	<0.15	—	<0.20	<0.18
H_2O and volatiles (%)	<0.2	<0.2	<0.2	<0.3	<0.1	<0.1	<1.5	<0.1	<0.1
Insoluble impurities (%)	<0.1	<0.1	<0.1	<0.2	<0.05	<0.05	—	<0.05	<0.05
Flash point (°C)	—	—	—	—	—	—	>120°	—	—
Metal traces (mg/kg)									
iron	<3.0	<3.0	<3.0	<3.0	<3.0	<3.0	—	<3.0	<3.0
copper	<0.1	<0.1	<0.1	<0.1	<0.1	<0.1	—	<0.1	<0.1
Halogenated solvents (mg/kg)									
each solvent	<0.1	<0.1	<0.1		<0.1	<0.1	—	<0.1	<0.1
sum of solvents	<0.2	<0.2	<0.2		<0.2	<0.2	—	<0.2	<0.2

Source: International Olive Oil Council 2003.

Olive-Pomace Oil. This is a blend of refined olive-pomace oil and virgin olive oil and is fit for human consumption. In no case shall this blend be called *olive oil*.

Laboratory analysis of oils is used to measure the presence or absence of seed oils in an olive oil. It also measures free acidity and peroxide values, which indicate the amount of oxidation and fatty-acid chain separation in an oil. Oxidation is the process by which oils break down, turn rancid, and develop spoiled flavors.

SENSORY EVALUATION OF OILS

One of the most important aspects of olive oil classification and value determination is sensory analysis. The first and primary objective in sensory evaluation for olive oil is to determine whether oils contain one or more of the defects that commonly occur from improper fruit storage, handling, pest infestation, oil storage, and processing. For certain characteristics, human sensory evaluation is one hundred times more accurate than laboratory equipment (fig. 23.11). Aroma and taste are very complex and cannot be determined in the laboratory. The tongue can also detect texture differences difficult to measure analytically.

The second objective of oil-sensory evaluation is to describe the positive characteristics of the oil in relation to its intensity of olive-fruity character. Olive oil should have a fruity olive flavor that is characteristic of the variety or blend of varieties making up the oil. There should be no vinegary or fermented odor or flavor. Neither should the oil be rancid or possess any other off flavor that is essentially not of the olive. Bitterness and

pungency are often present in olive oils, especially when newly made. They are not defects and mellow as an oil ages.

The California Olive Oil Council has established a taste panel for olive oil sensory evaluation (fig. 23.12) using the methods outlined by the International Olive Oil Council. The panel meets periodically to evaluate olive oils for their members. The University of California has served to assure an unbiased analysis of oils and suitable training of official tasters.

Marketing

Spain, the world's largest olive oil producer, and Greece, the third largest producer, both export much of their excess production in bulk to other European Union (EU) countries where it is consumed or repackaged and exported. Italy, the second largest producer, actually consumes more olive oil than it produces, but also imports oil for redistribution and marketing to other countries.

Many of the EU countries pay direct subsidies to their olive growers. They also have marketing cam-

Figure 23.12. Olive oil sensory analysis consists of smelling the oil, tasting it, and recording the intensity of both positive and negative attributes.

Figure 23.11. Arrangement test of 12 flavor intensities used to select olive oil taste panel members.

paigns to boost the consumption of olive oil through promotion of the healthful aspects of a Mediterranean diet and regional loyalties. Brand advertising is based on personal taste, confidence in companies, and price aggressiveness.

Price is a very important factor in the world commodity market for olive oil. A limited supply raises prices, which leads to a decrease in demand. In 1997, world production rose by 47 percent, which replenished low stocks, lowered prices, and increased consumption by 27 percent. Production trends are up due to expanded plantings of olives in Europe, Latin America, the United States, and Australia. World consumption trends increased by 3.9 percent from 1994 to 1998. Sales of olive oil in the United States increased by 88 percent from 1994 to 1998 (Information Resources 1999). From 1997 to 1998 olive oil consumption in the United States increased by 6.5 percent in a fairly flat market for all fats and oils.

Recently a gourmet market has developed in the United States for special oils with specific flavor characteristics and a reputation for higher quality. These are condiment oils used to add flavor to foods, particularly Mediterranean dishes. Many of these oils are presented in styled bottles for the gourmet consumer. Labels indicating that the product is produced in California are popular and bring a premium price in the marketplace. Differentiation as to the county where the olives were produced and viticultural appellations can add a further premium to the gourmet oils. It is estimated that there are more than one hundred labels of California-produced olive oils, mostly developed in the last few years. Currently, the U.S. market is underdeveloped for olive oil. If the price is reasonable, there is a great potential here for this popular product, especially for the health-conscious consumer.

ECONOMICS OF OIL PRODUCTION

Although the new gourmet olive oil industry got its recent start in the North Coast counties, the land costs are extremely high and it is not likely that many large-scale olive oil producers will locate there. The Central Valley has flatter land and less expensive water and labor. Flat land makes for easier mechanical harvesting, which may be essential for competitive economic production of olive oil.

The two potential advantages the coastal valleys have is the association with fine wines for symbiotic marketing relationships and the real or perceived difference in oil quality that is generally produced in cooler growing regions. It is likely, however, that the warmer Central Valley will have an agricultural advantage over the cooler coastal valleys when it comes to olive yields.

In 1999 and 2001, cost studies were completed on establishing olive orchards and producing olive oil on both the North and Central coasts of California. According to those studies, first-year establishment costs were about $4,500 per acre (180 trees/acre). A mature, producing orchard, which takes 8 to 10 years to come into full production, produces an average yield of 2.5 tons per acre. The studies found that total approximate costs per acre were $9,500, which included costs for cultural practices (pest control, pruning, irrigation, mowing, etc.); hand harvest and transport ($350/ton); oil processing (custom milling: $350/ton)); marketing (bottling, labeling, storage, promotion, distribution); overhead (office, taxes, insurance); and capitol recovery (land, buildings, equipment).

These mature orchards produced an average yield of 2.5 tons per acre at a production cost of $3,600 per ton and an oil yield of 45 gallons per ton, with per gallon production costs of $84.00. Seventy-one cases of 12,500-ml bottles were produced (112.5 gallons), with costs per bottle of $11.00, making the retail cost at about $22.00 per bottle.

In 2004 another cost study was completed on establishing and production of a super-high-density olive oil orchard in the Central Valley. First-year establishment costs for that system were $5,300 per acre (670 trees/acre). By the fourth year, this orchard produced 5.0 tons per acre. Total costs per acre were $8,400, which included the costs for cultural practices (pest control, pruning, irrigation, mowing, etc.); mechanical harvest and transport ($40/ton); oil processing (custom milling: $200/ton); marketing (bottling, labeling, storage, promotion, distribution); overhead (office, taxes, insurance); and capitol recovery (land, buildings, equipment).

This orchard produced an average yield of 5.0 tons per acre at a production cost of $1,700 per ton and an oil yield of 45 gallons per ton, with per gallon costs of $38.00. One hundred and forty-two cases of 12,500-ml bottles were produced (225 gallons), with costs per bottle below $5.00, making the retail price about $10.00 per bottle.

For producers interested in selling raw olives, which would not include the cost of processing, oil transport, storage, bottling, labeling, or marketing, the study found the production cost for the coastal orchard was approximately $2,000 per ton based on a yield of 2.5 tons per acre. For the super-high-density Central Valley orchard, cultural and harvest costs were approximately $1,000 per ton based on a yield of 5.0 tons per acre.

That is twice the yield and half the expense.

In the last five years, raw olive fruit was commonly sold for $300 to $500 per ton from semi-abandoned orchards in the Sacramento Valley foothills while small quantities of specialty oil varieties (Tuscan Blend) were sold for $1,000 per ton.

REFERENCES

Alba, J. 1997. Caracteristicas de los aceites de oliva y subproductos de los sistemas de elaboracion en España. Grasas y Aceites 48:338–343

Barranco, D., R. Fernandez-Escobar, L. Rallo. 2001. El cultivo del olivo, 4ª edicion. Madrid: Ediciones Mundi-Prensa.

Barranco, D., A. Cimato, P. Fiorino, L. Rallo, A. Touzani, C. Castañeda, F. Serafini, and I. Trujillo. 2000. World catalogue of olive varieties. Madrid: International Olive Oil Council.

California Olive Oil Council. 1997. Olive oil labeling, Senate Bill 920. Sacramento.

Cimato, A., C. Cantini, G. Sani, and M. Marranci. 1997. Il Germoplasma dell' olivo in Toscana, Regione Toscana. Florence: CNR Publishers.

Fantozzi, P. 1994. Introduction to the problem of evaluating olive oil quality, International Symposium on Olive Growing, Jerusalem, Israel, Sept. 6–10, 1993. Acta Horticultura, vol. 356.

Garcia, J. M., J. M. Castellano, A. Morilla, S. Perdiguero, F. Gutierrez, and M. A. Albi. 1994. Controlled atmosphere storage of mill olives. In P. Eccher Zer-Zerbini, M. L. Wolfe, P. Bertolini, K. Haffner, J. Hribar, E. Hohn, and Z. Somogyi, eds., Proceedings of the workshop on controlled atmosphere storage of fruit and vegetables, April 22–23, 1993, Milan, Italy. Commission of the European Communities. 83–87.

Griggs, W. H., H. T. Hartman, M. V. Bradley, B. T. Iwakiri, and J. E. Whisler. 1975. Olive pollination in California. California Agricultural Experiment Station Bulletin 869. Department of Pomology, University of California, Davis.

Gucci, R., and C. Cantini. 2000. Pruning and training systems for modern olive growing. Collingwood, VIC, Australia: CSIRO Publishing.

Harwood, J. L., and R. Aparicio. 2000. Handbook of olive oil: Analysis and properties. Gaitherburg, MD: Aspen Publishers.

Hermoso Fernandez, M., J. Gonzales, M. Uceda, A. Garcia-Ortiz, J. Morales, L. Frias, and A. Fernandez. 1998. Elaboracion de aceite de oliva de calidad— Obtencion por el sistema de dos fases. Manual from the Estacion de Olivicultura y Elaiotecnia. Finca "Venta del Llano" Mengibar, Jaen, Spain. Junta de Andalucia vol. 61/98.

Hermoso Fernandez, M., M. Uceda, A. Garcia-Ortiz, J. Morales, L. Frias, and A. Fernandez. 1991. Elaboracion de aceite de oliva de calidad. Manual from the Estacion de Olivicultura y Elaiotecnia. Finca "Venta del Llano" Mengibar, Jaen, Spain. Junta de Andalucia vol. 5/91.

Information Resources. 1999. INFOSCAN Statistics: Market sales of olive oil by year, 1993–98. Chicago.

International Olive Oil Council. 1995. Olivae 59. December.

———. 1996a. Olivae 61. April

———. 1996b. Olivae 62. June

———. 1996c. Olivae 64. December

———. 1996d. Organoleptic Assessment of Virgin Olive Oil. Coi/T. 20/Doc. no. 15/Rev.

———. 1997a. Olivae 65. February.

———. 1997b. Olivae 67. June.

———. 1997d. World Olive Encyclopaedia. Madrid.

———. 2001. Olivae 87. June.

———. 2003. Trade standard applying to olive oil and olive-pomace oil, revised. CoI/T. 15NC no. 3.

Kiritsakis, A. K., E. B. Lenert, W. C. Willet, and R. J. Hernandez. 1998. Olive oil, from tree to table, 2nd edition. Trumbull, CT: Food and Nutrition Press.

Supermarket Business Magazine. 1999. Consumer expenditures study. September.

Tous, J. M. 1997. El olivo, 2ª edicion. Institut de Recerca i Tecnologia Agroalimentaria Mas Bove, Diputacion de Tarragona. Sant Francesc, Spain: Editors Societat Anonima.

Tous, J. M., A. Romero, D. Barranco. 1993. Variedades del olivo. Barcelona: Fundacion La Caixa.

USDA Economic Research Service. Imports and exports of olive oil by country, 1994–98. 1999. Washington, D.C.

Vossen, P. M., 1992. Italian olive oil production. Technical report on the olive oil production tour (Nov. 24–Dec. 3). Santa Rosa: University of California Cooperative Extension, Sonoma County.

———. 1995. Olive oil production in France. Technical report on the olive oil production tour (May 22–May 30). Santa Rosa: University of California Cooperative Extension, Sonoma County.

————. 1997. Spanish olive oil production. Technical report on the olive oil production tour (Nov. 28–Dec. 8). Santa Rosa: University of California Cooperative Extension, Sonoma County.

————. 2000. Italian olive oil production. Technical report on the olive oil production tour (Nov. 25–Dec. 9). Santa Rosa. University of California Cooperative Extension, Sonoma County.

Vossen, P. M., K. Klonsky, and R. L. DeMoura. 2001. Sample costs to establish an olive orchard and produce olive oil—Central Coast of California. Department of Agricultural and Resource Economics. University of California, Davis. http://coststudies.ucdavis.edu.

Vossen, P.M., J. H. Connell, K. Klonsky, and P. Livingston. 2004. Sample costs to establish a super-high-density olive orchard and produce oil—Sacramento Valley of California. Department of Agricultural and Resource Economics, University of California, Davis. http://coststudies.ucdavis.edu.

Vossen, P. M., G. S. Sibbett, R. Evers, K. Klonsky, and P. Livingston. 1999. Sample costs to establish an olive orchard and produce olive oil, North Coast of California. Department of Agricultural and Resource Economics, University of California, Davis.

Index

Photos and illustrations are indicated with *italic* type. Major discussions are indicated with **bold** type.

A

abscisic acid, 41
abscission processes, 15, 52–53, 54
acidic soils. *See* pH levels, soil
acidulant solution storage, 147
acreage statistics, 5–8, 157–158
Agrinion cultivar, 3
alkali soils. *See* pH levels, soil
Allegra cultivar, **21**, 24, 45, 47, 116
alternate bearing management
    overview, **54**, **59**, 93
    oil-producing olives, 161
    pruning, 54, 59, 103
    thinning, 54, 59, 101–103
American plum borer (*Euzophera semifuneralis*), **114**
ammonium, 80
animal damage, preventing, 33
annual weeds, 123–128
anthocyanins, 145
Aonidiella aurantii (California red scale), *96*, 112
Arbequina cultivar, *2*, 45
Armillaria root rot, *97*, **120–121**
Ascolana Tenera cultivar, 3
Ascolano cultivar
    characteristics, **20–21**
    chemical composition, 145
    chemical thinning, 101
    culling techniques, 141–142
    cutting propagation potential, 22
    density guidelines, 30
    disease/insect susceptibility, 45, 47, 112
    fruit appearance, *98*
    grafting compatibility, 24
    oil production, 9, 159–160
    olive mite susceptibility, 112
    pollination, 52

production areas/levels, 7–8
rootstock considerations, 45, 47
storage guidelines, 146, 147
temperature preferences, 21
Aspidiotus nerii (oleander scale), *96*, **110–111**
available water content (AWC), defined, 65–66

B

bacteria during processing, 148, 150, 151–152, 153
bactericides, 119
Bactrocera oleae (olive fly), *94*, **105–107**
balled trees, planting, 32
bare-root trees, planting, 32
Barouni cultivar, 8, **21**, 22, 52, 150–151
Beresford, Fred G., 4–5
bermudagrass, 123, 124
biennial weeds, 123–128
Bioletti, Frederic, 4, 5
biological control, 107, 109, 110, 112
bird's eye spot, 20, 21, *97*, 119–120
black fruit, 161
black scale (*Saissetia oleae*), 19, 56, *95*, **107–109**
black vine weevil (*Oriorhynchus sulcatus*), *96*, **114**
bloom stages, **16–17**, 49–51, 61, *93*, 102
boron
    overview, 75, **82**, 91
    deficiency problems, 83–90, *93*
    shallow soils, 78
    tolerance levels, 28
botany, overview, **15–17**
bottling process, 167–168
branch and twig borer (*Polycaon confertus*), *96*, **113–114**
brine solution storage, 147–148
Bryant, Edwin, 3

budding propagation, 24–25
bud formation, **15–16**, 49–50, 83–84
buffer systems, soil, 77–78
Butte County, production history, 5–6

C

calcium
    overview, **81**, **91**
    buffer systems, 77–78
    deficiency identification, *85*
    seasonal levels, 84, 86
    sodic soils, 80, 89
California Olive Committee (COC), 12–13
California Olive Oil Council, 168, 170
California red scale (*Aonidiella aurantii*), *96*, **112**
Calkins, John S., 4
Camulos oil mill, 4
canned olives
    consumption levels, 11–12
    development, 4–5
    grades/standards, 153–155
    types, 8–9
    See also processing guidelines
"canned-ripe olives of the tree-ripened type," defined, 141
canned trees, planting, 32
canning process. *See* processing guidelines
canopy-contact harvest method, 139–140
canopy size and evapotranspiration, 62–63
carbohydrate assimilation, **35–37**
carbon dioxide
    photosynthesis, 35–36, 71
    storage considerations, 146–147
carbon storage, 41
cation exchange capacity (CEC), 77, 87–88